Advance Revi

"In *Healing Amelia* Dr. Noricks takes us once again into the consulting room of a master clinician. This time we are witness to the full-length treatment of a multi-troubled young woman. Along the way we are treated not only to further applications of Dr. Noricks' method for healing problematic emotions, but also to the treatment of the intricate interplay of biology and psychology, and the planful use of new understandings on how memory operates and changes. Both intriguing and touching, there is much to be learned here by the interested layperson and the seasoned psychotherapist alike."—**Hugh Marr, PhD, Co-author,** *What Story Are You Living,* **Clinical Psychologist, Alexandria, Virginia.**

"Jay Noricks' approach is pure excellence. All of our Parts serve a purpose and this model has worked wonders for me! Not only have I adopted it within my own practice, but I have introduced it to my clinical interns. *Parts and Memory Therapy* has provided me with deep insight and we can use it with any population. I would highly recommend this approach for all clinicians. Our mind is a powerful tool, and with the right guidance, anything is possible."—**Kelley Johnson, LCSW, Director of Social Work & Clinical Services, Behavioral Health Unit, Valley Hospital, Las Vegas, Nevada.**

"Loved what I read! Fascinating! Dr. Jay Noricks has done an amazing job in bringing together Parts Psychology to bear on healing PMS and PMDD in *Healing Amelia*. I am unaware of any other author who has connected the dots between the physiological state of PMS and its psychological origins. More fascinating is how he describes Parts and their psychology, and the treatment methods to heal the emotional pain, thereby improving the physical symptoms of PMS. Considering that half of the world's population is female, and as many as 40% of them suffer with PMS, this is an invaluable contribution. Highly recommended!"—**Esly Regina Carvalho, PhD, Author,** *Breaking Free; Heal Your Brain: Heal Your Body.* **Clinical & Psychological Coordinator, TraumaClinic do Brazil, Brasilia.**

"Jay Noricks' *Parts Psychology* was one of my first introductions to working psychotherapeutically with an individual's internal 'Parts'—or subpersonalities—of the self and has continued to support my integrative practice with clients. Demonstrated in *Healing Amelia*, is Jay Noricks' innovative conceptualization of the psyche through Parts and Memory Therapy, offering effective and sustainable healing for his patients. It is exciting to see his model applied to specific female issues. It is appropriate for both the lay person as well as professionals in the field."—**Bree Rhodes, Psychotherapist, Brisbane, Australia.**

"This book is a revolutionary and cutting-edge approach to the treatment of PMDD and postpartum depression. Dr. Noricks' *Healing Amelia* breaks new ground for mental health issues in general and gynecologic associated mood disorders more specifically."—**Joseph Urban, MD, Park City, Utah.**

"*Healing Amelia* provides us as therapists with a new lens for working with clients feeling stuck in their PMS and/or postpartum depression. I am relieved and grateful for Jay Noricks' work as I feel like I finally have the tools to help these clients in a deeply meaningful, and long-lasting way."—**Emma Knighton, MA, Unity Within Counseling, PLLC, Seattle, Washington.**

"Amelia's healing journey sketches in detail Parts and Memory Therapy. The extensive and intricate workings of this therapy reach out into all of our parts, extending a hand that pulls them up to the surface where healing can commence. Dr. Noricks' case history with Amelia and other patients points to a radical method that is systematic, clear, and bears powerful results for those seeking a unique and definitive kind of therapy."—**Neda Najmi, MS, MFT, Campinas, Brazil.**

HEALING AMELIA

TAMING YOUR EGO STATES AND INNER VOICES WITH PARTS AND MEMORY THERAPY

One Woman's Narrative of Healing Postpartum Depression, Premenstrual Dysphoric Disorder, and Marital Conflict

Jay Noricks, PhD

New University Press, LLC
Los Angeles

New University Press, LLC
5013 Range View Ave.
Los Angeles, CA 90042

For Permissions write to:
editor@newuniversitypress.com

Copyright © 2018 by Jay Noricks

Cover Illustration by Siena Holland
Cover Formatting by Trescela Samson
Black and White Illustrations by Katrina Goretskaya

ISBN: 978-0-9829219-7-5

Library of Congress Control Number (LCCN): 2018902757

This book is for Dina Noricks, my wife, best friend, lover, and colleague. She has stood with me every step of the way from the day we met, has read my early and later efforts, and has permitted me to introduce her to her own inner world of Parts. I've learned so much by having a colleague with me to share thoughts and issues and new understandings. Dina's support has permitted me to continue in my full-time psycho-therapy practice and book-writing despite ten years of Stage 4 carcinoid cancer. She has kept me alive.

Acknowledgments

I don't think any author writes a book without significant help and support from a crowd of others. My interns over the last three years, my colleagues, and the participants in my Parts and Memory Therapy workshops all had a significant impact on my writing. In addition, the following individuals edited, commented on, or wrote significant critiques of the book during its writing: Andy Cadwell, Belen Caindeck, Elona Culwell, Michael Farmer, Thomas W. Hill, Sydney Ley-Cadwell, Dina Noricks, Jacob Noricks, Don and Brenda Parquet, Jonathan Pishner, Trescela Samson, Jillian Shumway, Diane Standley, James Stokes, and Patrick Tobey. Additionally, four professional editors—Paul Hebner, Linda Carbone, Melissa Kirk and Darcy Noricks—contributed significantly to the final form of the book. Melissa contributed throughout the last year of writing, and Darcy for all four.

Zetta Brown and Jim Brown contributed proofreading and formatting. Siena Holland and Katrina Goretskaya are artists. Siena drew the book's front cover and several color illustrations of individual Parts. Katrina drew most of the color illustrations that appear on my websites and all of the black and white ones that are sprinkled through the book. Trescela Samson formatted the book cover. Thanks to all and apologies to any whom I failed to mention because of my sloppy record-keeping.

Contents

Preface

Amelia originally came to me for help in deciding whether to divorce her husband or have another child with him, quite an extreme set of options. She explained that she loved him but they had such blow-out, scary fights, it might be healthier if they separated. Their last fight had escalated to the point of screaming, pushing and shoving, and the destruction of each other's possessions. They were both given to rages. And Amelia still suffered with postpartum depression following her second child.

We worked on her rage and her depression and in a few months found that in addition to the reduction in those symptoms, her PMS (Premenstrual Syndrome) and PMDD (Premenstrual Dysphoric Disorder) symptoms disappeared, too. That's when I decided to write a book that would include documentation of our discovery of a cure for PMDD and near elimination of all PMS symptoms. I have found no other psychotherapy that can make this claim.

The common belief about premenstrual distress is that it is a physiological condition, a kind of physical ailment that women have little choice about. Either you have PMS/PMDD or you don't, and either you passively accept the monthly distress or you struggle with it through lifestyle adjustments, pharmaceutical products, or—as a final resort—surgical menopause. The success of Parts and Memory Therapy with Amelia and the five other women described in Appendix 2 demonstrates that there is another option. Parts and Memory Therapy is an emotion-focused, trauma-based psychotherapy that can decisively bring remission to PMS and PMDD.

But treatment of PMS or PMDD is not the focus of the book. Instead, because Amelia's symptoms were so intrusive in her life—during ovulation, premenstrually and menstrually—we used the improvement in her symptoms to measure broader progress in her therapy. In particular, her progress with her premenstrual distress signaled progress in fixing her marriage, reducing her rage, healing her postpartum depression, and healing the rupture in what should have been a loving emotional bond between Amelia and her daughter.

THE NARRATIVES

There are two intertwined narratives in this book. The first story is that of Amelia, an educated Latin American woman who fell in love with a vacationing American schoolteacher and eventually followed him to the United States. It is not quite a love story. Rather, it is the story of what happens in a loving relationship after the Disney movie ends, after the prince carries away the princess on his white horse to live happily ever after. It is the story of Amelia's life before and after the great romantic connection faded and after the prince's great white horse had been put to pasture. It describes the healing of both the childhood wounds and post-marital wounds that had to heal in order for Amelia's marriage to work. While it is a personal story, it is also a story of marital therapy. Amelia's story reveals itself—sometimes in current events, sometimes in childhood experiences—over the course of 77 one-hour sessions and one three-hour session during 22 months of psychotherapy.

The second narrative describes how Parts and Memory Therapy works—as it heals Amelia and reveals the fascinating details of her inner world. This world, like the inner worlds of other normal people, contains many selves: angry, sad, lonely, loving and nurturing, young, old, caring and uncaring. As Amelia visualizes her many Parts, or subpersonalities, some appear exactly as she remembers herself at different ages of her life. Others have no resemblance to her at all—in fact they seem to be products of a vivid and sometimes strange imagination. The story of discovery and work with personified Parts of the self forms the core of the book. Accepting this narrative requires a leap of faith, or simply an interest in a good story, as Amelia learns to visualize and then have back-and-forth conversations with her inner selves.

Parts and Memory Therapy

Twenty years in the making, Parts and Memory Therapy is currently the only psychotherapy that focuses on the traumatized Parts of the self as targets for healing while also grounding the healing interventions in the neuroscience of memory reconsolidation. There are perhaps ten therapies that do significant work with internal Parts of the self, and a few with effective interventions for the emotional states of Parts and patients (see Watkins and Watkins, 1997; Schwartz, 1995), and there is one psychotherapy (See Ecker, Ticic and Hulley, 2012) that grounds its work in memory reconsolidation but not Parts. There is no other therapy that does both.

Parts and Memory Therapy is a therapy that views the normal mind as naturally multiple, with divisions in the personality having a life of their own. The idea is an old one—at least a century—but has begun to emerge into mainstream consciousness only in the last few decades. The Disney/Pixar film *Inside Out* is a recent example of the broader awareness of the idea that our unconscious selves (Parts) influence our conscious selves.

ORGANIZATION OF THE BOOK

Three sections organize the book. Part One introduces Amelia, the theory of Parts and Memory Therapy, and our early work with Amelia's postpartum depression, rage, and PMS and PMDD. By the end of our early work we think the therapy might be nearly finished. Amelia even plans to have another child.

In Part Two we discover the presence of a powerful managerial Part that Amelia calls *The Witch*, who foments a rebellion against the successes we had achieved in Part One. Although she is uncooperative and resistant to much of our therapy, her intention is good: she wants to protect Amelia from re-experiencing the emotional devastation of postpartum depression that she experienced with her last child. Throughout these middle chapters we struggle to achieve again the results in personal and marital harmony we thought we had achieved during the first third of therapy.

Part Three chronicles the final resolution of Amelia's issues, from rage to mother-daughter bonding, and from PMS and PMDD to the question of whether to have another child.

Character (Parts) Illustrations

Throughout the book I have sprinkled an artist's depictions of the internal characters that inhabit Amelia's inner world. As we continued our therapy more and more Parts appeared. Some remained the same in appearance as when we met them, but most of them experienced a transformation in their looks as healing happened. The illustrations were drawn two years after we completed the therapy and were based upon their description in the book. Amelia approved the artist's work.

A Note on Grammar

The book tells Amelia's story in her own words. I've used italics to set off quotes of Amelia from my own writing. Quoted passages are reconstructions from my shorthand notes taken during each session. Because I knew early-on that I would be writing about Amelia, I was meticulous in taking careful and exhaustive notes. However, because I reconstructed Amelia's remarks from my shorthand, her grammar in the text is better than it would have been if I had audiotaped her. English is a language she learned only as an adult.

One feature of Amelia's grammar that I've faithfully represented is the lack of contractions in her speech. She would carefully articulate "I am" rather than "I'm," and similarly with "she will" rather than "she'll," and "will not" rather than "won't," etc. I have preserved this quaint way of speaking English throughout the book.

Finally, I have capitalized the word *Part* whenever it appears if it refers to an internal character. The word is so ordinary, but so important. I wanted to emphasize that it has a special meaning in connection with "Parts of self."

Jay Noricks PhD

March 1, 2018

PART ONE

Learning to Work with Parts of Self

Chapter 1

Sobbing on the Floor of the Shower

Amelia had given birth to her second child, her son Nathan, almost three years earlier. A deep postpartum depression had followed and continued, somewhat lessened, into the present. Near the end of our second session, she spoke of a typical day during the early months of tending to her new baby:

> *"I am lying on the couch, maybe watching a movie. The baby would be next to me on the couch. I am feeling I am not a good mother. My husband comes home and the house is a mess. He asks why I have not done the dishes. I feel guilty and sad. Then I feel I am not a good wife. I wish my mother was here to help me. I get angry at him for asking about the dishes. But I know he is right. I am not a good mother or a good wife."*

I wanted to guide Amelia through the next step in doing a special kind of therapy, and so I asked if she was currently experiencing the depressed feelings she had just described. *"Yes, I can feel the depressed self in my body. I want to run away. I miss my family and home. I imagine taking the kids with me, home."* It was a perfect answer and lead-in for me. I asked her to "focus on the body sensation of the *depressed self* and to speak to it, aloud or silently, and ask it for an image of itself in your mind."

Amelia did so, and almost immediately said, *"I can see my-self sobbing, naked, and curled into a ball on the floor of the shower."* Amelia called this image—the first of her Parts we would meet in therapy—*Postpartum Me.*

Amelia later told me that she wasn't aware of any actual occasions of crying while lying on the floor of her shower. The scene, then, is an iconic one, conveying an emotional state that's real, but in a scene that's perhaps only imagined. We would come back to this image of Postpartum Me frequently in Amelia's therapy.

Postpartum Me

WHAT ARE PARTS?

Parts are subpersonalities within us that have formed in response to intense life experiences, most often during the years of growing up, but possibly throughout our lives, for as long as we have new experiences or chronic problems. Some examples include your first crush, your first public embarrassment, your first rejection by friends, or later, your first pregnancy and childbirth. Having Parts of self is a universal human characteristic. Other terms for Parts you might have heard include *sub-personalities*, *ego states*, self-states, *voices*, and *sides*.

All Parts have a unique set of memories, linked by their common elements or themes such as those in the examples. As Postpartum Me's name suggests, her memories relate to childbirth and the depressions that followed the birth of Amelia's two children. The disturbing memories housed by a Part are our targets for healing through neutralizing the negative emotions. When memories are positive, they don't generally require neutralizing, but occasionally they do, too.

PARTS AND MEMORY THERAPY

Parts and Memory Therapy is a psychotherapy that focuses on emotion rather than thinking as a starting point for therapy. It works to heal you by helping you discover the internal Parts of you that carry emotional pain, and then by neutralizing the emotion memories that are the source of the pain. Postpartum Me, Amelia's depressed Part, is an example of the kind of normal division within our larger personality that's common to all of us.

The memories in question are mostly—but not always—disturbing ones. They might range from disappointing your mother or father when you were four years old to the harsh words you exchanged with your husband just last week. And they could include a multitude of memories between then and now of you growing up and becoming you.

In describing how memories and Parts work in all of us, I'll be telling the story of Amelia, who was my patient for almost two years. If her problems were as simple as they first appeared, we might have finished our work in ten to twelve sessions. However, she had other issues—and a troubled childhood and adolescence—that surprised us with their effects on her everyday adult life.

MEETING AMELIA

First Meeting

At our first meeting Amelia wore a conservative navy-blue dress and black pumps. A full head of curly black hair framed her attractive oval face. She wore rimless glasses that accentuated high cheek bones and a light olive complexion. She was of medium height and her body was slim despite the birth of two children. There were vertical tension lines in the space between her eyes but she managed to present a hesitant smile with only a hint of sadness. She understood psychotherapy and was prepared to do the deep work it required.

Originally from Costa Rica, Amelia had come to the United States, eight years prior to our meeting, after marrying her American husband Michael. They met while both were on vacation. He was visiting a Costa Rican resort city during his summer vacation from teaching, and she was on vacation from her position in the human relations department of a large manufacturing company. He stayed on to teach for a year in an international school and then brought Amelia back to the United States as his bride.

Starting Out in America

Amelia and Michael settled in St. George, Utah, just an hour's drive from my office in Las Vegas. In St. George, the school district was literally begging new teachers to settle there because its growth rate was one of the five highest in the United States.

Michael signed on to teach high school mathematics. He was a tall, slim man with thin blond hair and, incongruously, the beginning of a small pot belly. Although he was never physically present during Amelia's therapy, he was always nearby, in Amelia's thoughts and emotions. Later, he did his own individual therapy with me.

Amelia and I met at the end of summer when she attended a training workshop I had given for therapists who wanted to develop new skills. She often visited Las Vegas for the greater training opportunities there. She had already earned a college degree in psychology in Costa Rica. She added a master's degree in school psychology and a second one in marriage and family therapy after arriving in the United States.

Meeting in Las Vegas

By the time I met her, Amelia had two children, aged five and almost three. Utilizing her degree in marriage and family therapy, she was working hard at building a private practice in psychotherapy as she juggled child-care and husband-care. She was a licensed intern, and in the process of completing the three thousand hours of face-to-face therapy with patients that she needed before she could be fully licensed.

In the workshop Amelia attended, I introduced Parts and Memory Therapy and conducted training in its use over the course of eight hours on a Saturday in August. Unsatisfied with standard cognitive therapy, I had developed this model over the previous twenty years for doing deeper work with patients in distress. Amelia had recently begun her career as a psychotherapist and hoped to include Parts and Memory Therapy in her own practice.

She came to me, however, not as a colleague but as a patient. She wanted to do therapy on her own issues. Fortunately, because she had already taken my workshop, she didn't have to be convinced that we all have injured internal Parts that could be healed through direct interaction with them. We were able to begin work with her internal subpersonalities right away. Postpartum Me was just the first of many.

AMELIA'S THERAPEUTIC ISSUES

We began therapy shortly after Amelia's thirty-fifth birthday, an age that was important to her if she were to have another child. Both she and Michael wanted a third child, but both recognized that they needed to work out their relationship issues before they could take that step. Amelia didn't see how that could happen. She felt overwhelmed by life. She had an unsatisfactory marriage, a demanding career, and wanted to be a better mother to her first two children. In addition to better managing her high-stress life and experiencing less conflict with Michael, she hoped to find clarity through our therapy in deciding whether to have a third child.

There are many ways to tell the story of Amelia's healing. I've chosen to emphasize just four of the concerns that demanded our attention. I haven't included marital therapy among these concerns because we never worked together on specific couples' complaints. All of the therapy with Amelia and with Michael was on individual issues. But sometimes that's all it takes to fix a marriage.

The individual issues we worked through all had significant impacts on the couple's marriage. The most important of these therapy targets were her uncontrollable rage, her postpartum depression, her failure to successfully bond with her daughter in a loving relationship, and her destabilizing PMS/PMDD (Premenstrual Syndrome/Premenstrual Dysphoric Disorder).

Amelia's Rage

Anger with the threat of overwhelming rage was an issue throughout the therapy. When we had completed our work with one angry Part, another appeared. The reduction of Amelia's rage through healing the emotional memories that formed the foundation for the rage was a significant measure of how well we were doing in healing her.

Amelia felt alone and abandoned by Michael, especially since the birth of Nathan. She was depressed, and had been for more than two years. And she was angrier than she had ever been in her life. She walked on egg shells at home, anxious to prevent another bitter argument. Sometimes, when her anger overflowed into outright rage, it threatened walls and household objects—and especially Michael's possessions—and sometimes it threatened to destroy her marriage.

At the earliest stage of our therapy, we had not yet connected Amelia's rage to any other mood state except depression, but we would find many triggers for it, especially during Amelia's PMS episodes. Postpartum Me was one source of that rage, and so was a Part we called *Old Woman*, who showed herself as an image of a crippled old woman, barely able to walk. There were several other internal Parts that needed anger softening before our work was done.

Postpartum Depression

Concurrent with our discussion of Amelia's overwhelming rage, we also began work to alleviate her postpartum depression. As we talked about her experiences, Amelia remembered that Michael had become distant from her during her first pregnancy and remained so for a year after the birth of their daughter. It was a grinding, tiresome time. Her depression blocked the joy she had expected to feel for her newborn. Instead, she felt lethargic and neglected as she kept house and tended to her baby in a monotonous daily routine. She had taken a year off from work to be with her baby but found it much less rewarding than she had hoped. Her coworkers from the agency where she worked didn't visit her and Michael rarely talked to her. She was lonely in the extreme.

She became pregnant again when their daughter was 18 months old. Her relationship with Michael continued to be distant. Still, she fought through her depression and continued the professional training in psychotherapy (marriage and family therapy) she had begun before her first pregnancy.

After the birth of her son, her postpartum depression was severe, worse than the first time. Michael was again emotionally absent for her during her struggles. She took antidepressant medication for a year but it provided little relief. She was miserable. She became obsessive in her focus on Nathan, neglecting her daughter Noelle and caring little about Michael's feelings or activities.

Their marital relationship continued to worsen until, roughly six months before starting therapy with me, they had a horrible fight, with each of them screaming, blaming, and destroying possessions of the other. Amelia would have divorced Michael then if she had the money to do so.

The fight was alarming enough to each of them that they agreed to seek therapy. After a couple of false starts with other therapists, they eventually found their way to me.

Failure in Mother-Daughter Bonding

Amelia's third issue was a problem faced by a significant number of new mothers with postpartum depression. It's their inability to forge the expected loving bond with their child. Between fifteen and twenty percent of mothers with postpartum depression experience this problem. Amelia regularly felt only irritation and aversion toward her daughter while maintaining a close and healthy bond with her son. This led to a lopsidedness, a favoritism for her son that threatened the cohesion of the family.

This fixation and love-bond with her son was the experience that eventually made her aware of the lack of such a bond with her daughter. She talked about her different kinds of connections with her two children:

> "My pregnancy was fantastic! I was blissful and happy. After the baby was born I had no problems for four months. Then my milk dried up. With my first child, I nursed for seven months. At four months with my son, I became irritable. I could not feed the baby. I had no energy to get up. Michael had to go back to work after the summer, so I had a baby and a two-year-old and no help. I became attached to the baby at this time. It relaxed me when he took the nipple, even if I had no milk. I just wanted to be with my baby. I did not want to be around my husband or my daughter, just my son. I would snap at and yell at my daughter."

Amelia's alienation from her daughter later became a focus for healing during our second year together. The therapeutic problem became one of how to draw upon the positive bond with Nathan to build up the neglected bond with Noelle.

PMS and PMDD

Amelia's fourth issue was her *Premenstrual Syndrome* (PMS) and *Premenstrual Dysphoric Disorder* (PMDD). I've treated these two categories as a single problem because PMDD seems to be just an extreme form of PMS. I've lumped both together as PMS except when clarity requires me to separate them into two categories

Although her postpartum depression lurked in the background of our early work together, Amelia soon noticed that she was more likely to feel seriously depressed—or more easily triggered into rage—during two occasions every month: for a few days at ovulation and again about three days before menstruation.

Counting the first day of her period as Day 1 of the average 28-day cycle, the hormonal shifts for a few days at ovulation around Day 14, and again during Days 26, 27, and 28 just before her period, were difficult times for Amelia. We began to track her periods, and the symptoms she experienced over the course of each month. We used the information to examine whether our interventions were helpful. Eventually, our progress in reducing PMS symptoms—together with anger reduction—became the touchstone by which we measured our overall progress in the therapy.

PMS AND PMDD BACKGROUND

Although PMS distress came to be a primary focus of our work together, Amelia didn't initially mention it as a therapeutic concern. Yet her greatest hurts and greatest rages appeared during the premenstrual phase of her menstrual cycle. Later, at about the halfway point in therapy, Amelia commented on why she hadn't originally made reducing her PMS a goal of therapy:

"I did not have it as a goal because I did not think it was possible to reduce that physical or emotional stress. I thought it was just my hormones creating the chaos. When I was having my cycle and I would be depressed or anxious, it never occurred to me that it was related to things that happened in my life, like my marriage difficulties or other things in my history."

In another session, she added: *"I thought that my problems with my body were just something I had to accept as part of the rest of my life—or until my body changed with menopause."*

Unfortunately, Amelia's lack of awareness of treatment options for PMS is similar to that of the larger therapeutic community of counselors and psychotherapists. When I shared with an experienced female colleague that I was working on applying psychotherapy to PMS, she replied, "But isn't that just something you get used to or maybe take some pills for?" Additionally, my research of the literature and of websites concerned with PMS or PMDD, rarely found any significant interest in treatment with psychotherapy.

What is PMS?

More than 150 different symptoms have been connected to the Premenstrual Syndrome. But there is no consistent set of diagnostic criteria. In the table below, I've included a sample copy of the PMS Questionnaire I use for my patients (adapted from the work of Guy Abraham [1980]). If you are significantly distressed by the symptoms found in one or more of these sets, you could say that you have PMS. But there is no consensus on how to define it. As a rough measure, if you score more than fifteen points, summed across all twenty-nine symptoms, I would say you have a variety of PMS. Amelia and the patients I include in Appendix 2 all scored more than 30 points across all symptoms, most often more than 40 points.

JAY NORICKS PHD

TABLE 1. PREMENSTRUAL SYNDROME (PMS) QUESTIONNAIRE

Patient Name: _____

Date: _____ Age: _____ Height: _____ Weight: _____

Please rate the following symptoms according to the degree of severity with which you experience them.

0 = None   1 = Mild   2 = Moderate   3 = Severe

PMS – 1 (Cognitive / Emotional)

	Circle One			
Angry/Irritable	0	1	2	3
Anxious	0	1	2	3
Mood Swings	0	1	2	3
Nervous Tension	0	1	2	3
Overwhelmed	0	1	2	3
Suspicious	0	1	2	3

PMS – 2 (Cognitive / Emotional)

	Circle One			
Crying	0	1	2	3
Confused	0	1	2	3
Depressed	0	1	2	3
Forgetful	0	1	2	3
Insomnia/Hypersomnia	0	1	2	3
Less Interest Usual Activities	0	1	2	3

PMS – 3 (Physiological)

Dizzy/Fainting	0	1	2	3
Fatigue	0	1	2	3
Food Cravings	0	1	2	3
Headache	0	1	2	3
Palpitations	0	1	2	3

PMS – 4 (Water Retention)

	Circle One			
Abdominal Bloating	0	1	2	3
Breast Tenderness	0	1	2	3
Fluid Retention	0	1	2	3
Swollen Hands/Feet	0	1	2	3
Weight Gain	0	1	2	3

PMS – 5 (Other Symptoms)

Acne	0	1	2	3
Backache	0	1	2	3
Constipation	0	1	2	3
Diarrhea	0	1	2	3
Hives	0	1	2	3
Oily Skin	0	1	2	3
Radiation Down Thighs	0	1	2	3

Add All Items for Total Score:

Total Score _____

I use the questionnaire, not as a diagnostic tool but as a means of tracking progress in therapy. In the PMDD (Premenstrual Dysphoric Disorder) section below you will find the specifically defined and diagnosable condition recognized as extreme PMS.

PMS that is severe enough to be labeled "Premenstrual Syndrome" affects twenty to forty percent (up to 24 million) of premenopausal American women, while approximately seventy-five percent of women (45 million) experience at least some premenstrual symptoms (American Psychiatric Association 2013).

PMS Patterns

Women can experience PMS in different ways. Counting the first day of menses as Day 1 and the last day before the onset of menses as Day 28 (for the average 28-day cycle), the typical experience is for symptoms to begin between Day 24 and Day 26 of the cycle. Generally, there is an increase in intensity through Day 28 and a rapid cessation of symptoms on Day 1 or Day 2 after a woman's period begins.

Amelia's pattern was atypical. She would have high intensity PMS symptoms for two to three days at ovulation (roughly Days 14, 15, and 16) and, after a relatively calm state, again experience symptoms beginning about Day 25 before her period. Unlike other women with this pattern, Amelia wouldn't find relief at the beginning of menses but would continue to suffer until the end of her period.

A second atypical pattern experienced by some women is the sudden appearance of severe symptoms at ovulation, with these symptoms continuing for all two weeks until the beginning of menses. A third pattern is for symptoms to first appear at about Day 8 of the cycle with a sharp rise in severity until ovulation and then a slower increase in intensity until maximum severity at Day 28. Many women experience slight variations of one or more of these patterns (McCormick, 2003). In my practice, it's common for women to experience PMS symptoms during ovulation, somewhere around Days 13-15.

What Is PMDD?

Unlike PMS, Premenstrual Dysphoric Disorder (PMDD) is an official diagnosis of the American Psychiatric Association's *Diagnostic and Statistical Manual of Mental Disorders* (2013). According to the American Psychiatric Association, between three and eight percent of premenopausal women (roughly five million American women) are significantly incapacitated for a few days each month with PMDD, unable to function socially or professionally. The same statistics also seem to hold for women in other English-speaking countries. At eight percent, that would mean that almost five million American women suffer from the condition. This was one of Amelia's problems—a major one—and the reason our therapy took twice as long as I had expected.

In the PMDD table below, the twenty-nine symptoms I track for PMS have been reduced in the official diagnosis of PMDD to just eleven sets of symptoms. (I prefer the longer list in everyday therapy because it's easier for us to see progress). All of the symptoms listed for the PMDD diagnosis are also included in the PMS table.

A woman who has significant symptoms from five or more of the eleven sets, where at least one of those sets is one of the first four on the list, meets the first part of the PMDD diagnosis. She meets the second part of the diagnosis if her symptoms are severe enough to cause significant difficulty in her work, school or career, or in her interpersonal relationships.

Amelia's PMDD Symptoms

In Amelia's case, her symptoms often required her to cancel three or four days of work appointments while she retreated to bed. If she tried to push through her symptoms, she found it impossible to concentrate on the needs of her own therapy patients. Outside her home or office, her lack of concentration made it difficult to drive even short distances. Her anxiety was like a weight on her chest, so great that sometimes she struggled to breathe. Her anger was easily triggered at these times and might easily lead to rage-filled arguments with Michael—who also was subject to fits of anger. In addition to irritation and anger, her symptoms included fatigue, hopelessness, feeling overwhelmed, and outbursts of crying, as well as such physical symptoms as headaches, breast tenderness, acne and bloating. These are the symptoms she most frequently mentioned, but when Amelia looked at this list, she claimed all eleven symptom groups.

TABLE 2. PREMENSTRUAL DYSPHORIC DISORDER (PMDD) SYMPTOMS

1. Mood swings, sudden sadness, crying, or increased sensitivity to rejection
2. Irritated, angry, or increased conflict
3. Hopeless, depressed or putting yourself down
4. Anxious, tense, or on edge
5. Decreased interest in usual activities
6. Difficulty concentrating
7. Lethargic, lack of energy
8. Appetite change, craving certain foods, or over-eating
9. Insomnia or hypersomnia
10. Overwhelmed or feeling out of control
11. Joint or muscle pain, tender or swollen breasts, or feeling bloated

MORE ABOUT AMELIA

Over the course of the book, Amelia's story will reveal itself in the therapy as we heal her painful memories (and a few positive ones) that punctuated her life from age five to the present. Because the therapy focuses on painful experiences rather than joyful ones, Amelia's story is mostly a story of overcoming life's difficult times. But the background to it all is that she's a successful, very intelligent, ambitious woman, with two master's degrees, a professional career, two engaging children, and a husband she loves a great deal, at least some of the time. There was frequently joy in her life too.

We'll return to Amelia's story after a more complete introduction to Parts and Memory Therapy in the following chapter. If you'd rather continue with Amelia's story without knowing more now about how the therapy works, you can skip to Chapter 3. Then, for more information on the therapy model, you can return to Chapter 2 for reference.

Chapter 2
How Parts and Memory Therapy Works

Parts and Memory Therapy is a framework for healing emotional problems, ranging from mild discomfort to misery. Often such problems resist ordinary talk therapy. While the approach is general enough to be applicable to all psychotherapeutic issues for all genders, this book describes its use in the healing of certain women's issues. In particular, the book describes Parts therapy for postpartum depression and for emotional issues that occur during the ovulation or menstrual cycle. For this reason, I address women as the subject of the therapy. Many individual chapters of my 2011 book, *Parts Psychology*, address work with men.

MORE ABOUT PARTS

The *Parts* that are the main topic of the book are sometimes called *self-states, subpersonalities, ego states, voices, sides,* and several other things. In this book, I will mostly use the terms *Part* and *subpersonality,* with an occasional *self-state* just to avoid repetition. These are the internal, natural segments of the whole self that store our painful memories.

The idea behind working with Parts is a bit scary for some people, fun and exciting for some, and preposterous to others. This idea is that our minds are naturally divided into sub-minds, each of which is installed within subpersonalities of the whole person. Each subpersonality, or Part, influences our emotions, thinking, and behavior. More than that, our Parts are never absent; they influence us constantly. Without them we would be centered, self-aware persons, but without direction, color, or individual character.

Parts begin to form in early childhood, and each collects memories with a common theme. For example, the first time you're wrongly blamed for something, your unconscious mind creates a new Part or subpersonality that helps you deal with the hurt of that experience. As time passes, this new Part of you collects other memories of times when you were unjustly blamed for something you didn't do. Similarly, the first time you were embarrassed in public, your mind creates a Part to help you handle that problem. All later embarrassing memories would add to the content of the Part specializing in such embarrassing moments. The more novelty in your life, then the more discrete Parts you develop.

Having Parts of the self is universal. We recognize this in our everyday language. We have all heard, or expressed in our own stories, something like: "I really like being around my boyfriend, but another part of me is afraid of missing out on someone who might be even better for me." We're also familiar with the sentiment "I really hate my job, but another part of me reminds me I couldn't make so much money anywhere else."

These contradictory feelings and thoughts are the opposing positions held by internal Parts of the self. They're not just metaphors, although the images that stand for them are shaped by symbolic meanings. They are real.

This book describes how we can work with these Parts to bring about permanent healing of even major mental health issues such as clinical depression, extreme anger, and debilitating anxiety.

HAVING ANOTHER CHILD?

The book's cover-to-cover theme is Amelia's struggle with the question of whether to have a third child with a husband who is distant and unavailable during difficult times.

He wasn't emotionally present for her during her previous postpartum trials, and she's afraid he won't be there for her the next time. Against this background theme, I'll describe how Amelia and I worked with her Parts using Parts and Memory Therapy in healing her postpartum depression, PMS (Premenstrual Syndrome), PMDD (Premenstrual Dysphoric Disorder), as well as her frequent rages and her failure to bond with her daughter.

MENSTRUAL CYCLES AND EMOTIONS

Most people view menstrual cycle issues primarily as physical or physiological in nature. Even psychotherapists rarely consider the distress of the menstrual cycle as a focus for therapy.

During the middle phase of writing this book, I spoke to a colleague of mine, a female and an exceptional therapist. I mentioned that my new book would address PMS and PMDD. Her response was: "But aren't those things just hormonal?" I was surprised. While PMS irritability, sadness, anxiety, and many other associated symptoms are experienced during the hormonal changes of a woman's cycle, they're not "just hormonal." Emotional distress is *never* "just" a physiological issue. Emotional distress is *always* partly a function of current stress and a person's history of painful life experiences.

AREN'T VOICES A SIGN OF MENTAL ILLNESS?

There's a common misconception that hearing voices (i.e., the voices of internal Parts), or worse, having conversations with them, is a sign of schizophrenia. This belief is false. Some studies show that up to fifteen percent of the normal population occasionally hear an inner voice.

Schizophrenia is a primary psychotic break with external reality. When this happens, a person can't accurately distinguish between what is real and not real. Like normal people, schizophrenics sometimes hear voices, but hearing voices isn't necessary for the diagnosis of schizophrenia. Non-schizophrenic people who hear voices are generally as accurate in their perceptions about external reality as non-schizophrenic people who don't hear voices.

The schizophrenia misconception entered the popular consciousness in the early twentieth century and continues to be preserved in such casual expressions as: "I'm feeling schizophrenic today about what I want for lunch, so many choices."

Most professional psychotherapists now understand that someone who says they hear or speak to "voices" isn't necessarily schizophrenic or "crazy." Many religious practices involve talking to and hearing voices during prayer or other organized activities. And those of us raised with a critical mother or father may regularly hear the voice of that parent commenting on what we do or say. You're not crazy if you talk to Parts of yourself. And you won't become crazy if you learn to do so.

The second misconception comes from a confusion between normal Parts of the self and what was once labeled *multiple personality disorder*, and renamed *dissociative identity disorder*, nearly four decades ago. The idea of multiple personalities entered the popular consciousness in the second half of the twentieth century through books and films that portrayed the disorder in *Sybil* and *The Three Faces of Eve*. It's now a common motif in television and movies.

Dissociative identity disorder results from chronic childhood abuse or repeated abandonments, primarily before the age of five or six. It's treatable. It differs from having normal Parts because the extreme Parts—called *alters* or *alter personalities*—in dissociative identity disorder have the ability to take executive control of a person's body and mind while acting out their own agendas. When the person returns to normal control, she has amnesia about what transpired when alter personalities were in control.

Normal Parts of the self don't act in this way, and there's no danger of developing dissociative identity disorder from talking with Parts.

LOOKING INSIDE

In introducing you to the experience of talking to Parts, I want to do so in a way that lets you discover the normalcy of having Parts. I also want to avoid too many objections from the *skeptical Part* of you. Skeptical Parts protect you from being gullible. But sometimes they limit your opportunity to learn new things. Throughout the book you'll have many opportunities to learn new things about how the unconscious mind works.

The exercise in the next paragraph is the same one I offer to experienced therapists in my workshops. About 70% of them get it the first time through. I ask the remaining 30%, as professionals, to accept that what their colleagues report as personal truth is worthy of their attention as therapists even when it isn't yet their own personal truth.

I ask the same of you. Even if you're not able to connect to the exercise in a conclusive way, perhaps you can give the benefit of your doubt to the larger majority of women who can relate to having internal Parts. I'm especially hopeful that as you read Amelia's story, you can accept her description of her Parts as *her* truth, and accept that she isn't crazy.

Visiting a Joyful Part

For the workshop experience, imagine you're in a mid-sized room with tables and chairs arranged in a boxlike circle. I'm addressing the group of twenty-five to thirty people with my back to a whiteboard, looking left, right and center to include everyone in the experiment. We're all dressed in comfortable, casual clothing but not the sweats in which we might lie around the house. I usually wear jeans and a navy-blue blazer.

Now, as a member of this audience, please think about a really exciting time in your life and recall the memory of a specific event. It might be a graduation, an award, the pronouncement scene from your wedding, an athletic success or the birth of a child. It could be the reunion moment after a separation from someone you love. It might even be the most exciting sexual experience you have had. Whatever you choose, it should be an event that's personally meaningful to you and a moment of high positive energy.

For the purpose of this discussion, let's say it's your high school or college graduation. For others of you, just follow along in a parallel course as you think about whatever event is high on your list.

For most graduations, the most memorable scene is the one where you walk across the stage to get your degree. Now zoom in on yourself in this memory. Notice the dignitaries on the stage, and the audience looking at you. Perhaps your memory captures the moment when you're shaking hands with the presenter.

Now look at yourself (in whatever memory you've chosen). Most of you will be able to see yourselves from outside yourselves, as if you were above or in front or behind or next to yourselves. Hopefully, you can see yourself from this third-person perspective and not the first-person perspective of looking out of your eyes at the scene but unable to see yourself.

If you can't see yourself as if you were a separate person, try other positive memories until you find one in which you can visualize yourself from outside yourself.

Now comes the leap of faith: focus on the image of yourself in your memory and say hello to her. You can do that aloud or just with your thoughts. Say, "Hello, do you know me?"

For 50-70 percent of you, the image of yourself in your mind will give some indication that she knows of your presence, perhaps with a glance or a smile. She might even nod and say, "Of course." Some of you will notice no discernable response, perhaps because she's focused on the activity in which you found her.

Even if she doesn't respond to you right away, ask her to nod her head up and down for "yes" if she can hear you, or shake her head left to right for "no" if she can't hear you. (If she shakes her head "no," you'll know she's messing with you!)

And now, regardless of whether or how the image responded, say to her: "Congratulations! You did well in life!" Most likely, this Part of you doesn't know how things actually turned out, so if they didn't turn out well, there's no need to rain on her party.

Moving Past Doubt About Parts

Then come back to the book. You just talked to a Part of yourself. As many people do when I first take them through this exercise, you may find yourself doubting that the image of yourself really responded when you talked to her. Or you might wonder if a smile or a glance from the image is enough evidence to show that she can communicate with you as if she were a separate person. But read on; there's more in this introduction. In any case, you can always return to the image of yourself in the positive memory. You can try again to talk to her. The exercise is harmless.

Seeing Yourself from Outside Yourself

There are other techniques to help you visualize yourself from outside yourself rather than seeing the memory through your own eyes, and it's possible to do memory work without this. But the therapy works best when you can imagine you're having a conversation with another person. That outside image of yourself will be your resource for healing; you will guide her in healing herself when healing is necessary.

If you can't yet find an outside view of yourself in your positive memories, you may do so in painful memories. In a car accident, for example, it's common for victims to view the scene from above or beside the scene. But I wanted to introduce the idea of the outside-yourself view in a positive experience. In the next exercise, I'll introduce a method of working with Parts through more difficult memories.

What I suggest to my trainees is, even if they don't have a clear image of a Part in this first exercise, that they accept that most others in the group have Parts that respond to them, and to use that evidence as a basis for moving forward with the training. I'm personally one of those who have difficulty visualizing Parts of myself, yet I can still work with my own Parts, even if in a somewhat fuzzy way.

The key is to interact with Parts *as if* they are actual people. In doing that, a fully animated image of yourself is quite helpful but not entirely necessary for the therapy to be successful.

Visiting a Disturbed Part

WARNING: if you experienced chronic abuse or repeated abandonment in your early childhood and haven't yet worked with a therapist on your issues, don't take the next step of visualizing yourself in a painful memory scene. You should do so only in the presence of a therapist who is comfortable with working with traumatic memories.

I introduced the previous visualization of positive memories to show you how you can find images of yourself in your memories and that these younger versions of you are Parts (subpersonalities) of the external you. I also wanted to show you that by saying hello to these memory pictures you can begin to do Parts work of your own, such as by activating these positive memories when you're feeling the blues.

These are happy memories that don't require the therapeutic touch. In doing psychotherapy, however, most of the memories you'll work with are painful or otherwise disturbing. In the earlier exercise, I wanted to illustrate the technique without causing you distress. For most of us, it's actually much easier to visualize ourselves in painful or traumatic memories than to do so in positive memories.

If you feel that you can access a painful memory without triggering a lot of emotional distress, go ahead and pick one for internal viewing, perhaps one of mild scolding from a parent or teacher. Or maybe an embarrassing moment when you said or did something that caused you to turn red for a moment. I suggest one of middle intensity rather than one of abuse.

You can pick a recent memory or one from childhood. A recent one for me is being mistaken for a shoplifter in the drugstore across my office parking lot. I had noticed a store employee following me as I went from the watch-battery aisle to the artificial-tears aisle, and then a glance and almost-stop at the cookie display, before finally going to checkout. Then, when I paid for my items the clerk looked at me oddly. By the time I walked back to my office, I had figured it out. They suspected I was a thief. The incident was embarrassing. I can easily recall and view myself at the counter feeling uncomfortable with the attitude of the clerk, and wondering about the employee who had followed me around the store. For this exercise, I could say hello to the image of myself at the counter, and even ask him what he's feeling.

Returning now to your own image of yourself in a disturbing memory, say hello to her. You might get a response. If you do, tell her that things will get better, and then come back to the book.

Visiting an Angry Part

For the last exercise, we won't start directly with an autobiographical memory, but, instead, hopefully, with a current-time Part that carries relevant memories in its personal memory bank. **DO NOT** do this exercise if you're a survivor of chronic abuse or abandonment. This exercise suggests that you can develop at least a nodding acquaintance with the angry Part of you. Everybody has an angry Part. This is the Part of you that protects you from feeling more vulnerable emotions, such as fear, grief, or shame.

Think about the person who angers or irritates you more than anyone else in the world. To make that irritation or anger stronger, think about the things this person has said or done. You might feel a body sensation along with the anger, perhaps in your chest, your throat, or your face or head.

Now, speak to that body sensation silently or aloud, and say something like this: "Let me see you, please. Please give me a picture of you in my mind." In your first effort, you might find an image of your angry Part right away, but about 40% of you will not. So don't be concerned if you can't easily visualize your angry Part. If you do see your angry Part, the image might look like you as you are at this moment, but perhaps with a frown or a grimace. The image might look like you as a teenager, if you were an angry teenager. But it might not look like you at all. It might look like an angry parent. It might be a bright red ball, or the sun, a fire, or just the color red.

My own angry Part looks like *The Thing*, the cartoon image of comic-book fame. Some of you may see a picture of the person who angers you, rather than a picture of yourself. In that case, you can usually get the image to switch to a picture of yourself simply by asking it to change places with you, so that you're standing over there where it stands now. Yes, I know the thought of doing this may feel weird, but if you accomplish it, you're doing Parts work.

Say hello to the angry Part of you and thank her or him (women often have male angry Parts) for appearing. Then say, "See you later." In the future, when you feel an uncomfortable irritation, you might want to find this image and ask it (silently or aloud) to "step back" so you can remain calm in the face of whatever is disturbing you.

Those three exercises represent the way I begin many workshops. From there I usually ask for a volunteer to come forward and sit with me in facing chairs as we demonstrate how to work with the early memories of an angry Part. I emphasize that the earliest disturbing memories carried in the memory bank of an angry Part aren't going to be about anger, but about emotions the angry Part protects us from feeling, such as fear, grief, and shame.

AN EXAMPLE OF WORKING WITH PARTS

I can't ask you to step forward and be a volunteer for a shared audience of readers, but I can still provide you with an example of how the healing of a disturbing memory can work. The example is actually from an individual session rather than a workshop. I chose it because it shows how Parts and Memory Therapy can work with PMS (Premenstrual Syndrome) symptoms, one of the topics of the book.

In this example, my patient is a thirty-eight-year-old mother of four, a stay-at-home mom who originally came to me for help with depression. I'll call her Jane. In the course of working together, we found that during the last five days before her period each month she experienced a range of disturbing emotions, including sadness, anger, and the belief that others were critical of her. On this particular PMS-day she was angry with her ninety-five-year-old grandmother. She sensed that her grandmother was upset with her for not getting up earlier to fix their coffee. Jane was angry with her grandmother "for making me feel guilty."

Find the Angry Part

In this illustration, we first locate Jane's angry Part and then heal a relevant disturbing memory from the Part's personal set of autobiographical memories. (Each Part has a different set of memories.)

Jane described awakening that morning and coming down the stairs at about 8:00 AM and fixing coffee. She described her grandmother's response to her poured coffee: "Grandma slurps her coffee and says, 'Better than a million dollars!'" As she normally did, Grandma then launched into an unbroken verbal description of all the things that were on her mind, including the plots of her favorite TV shows and what advice she had for parenting Jane's children. Jane was irritated by Grandma's slurping and angered by her exclamation that the coffee was "better than a million dollars!" She was also bothered by Grandma's endless stream of talk.

Jane experienced a strong, uncomfortable pressure in her upper chest. She believed that Grandma was being critical of her, interpreting Grandma's words as implying that she should have been down much earlier to fix the coffee, since Grandma got up at 5:00 AM and was physically unable to fix the coffee on her own.

PMS Emotion Overwhelms Logic

Jane could not accept my suggestion that Grandma was actually complimenting her and emphasizing her appreciation of her. (During a PMS episode, it isn't unusual for some women to be suspicious of others' actions.)

I asked Jane to maintain her connection to the pressure she felt in her upper chest, and then to speak to that sensation and ask it to give her a picture of itself in her mind. The result was that Jane could now visualize an image of herself "pretty much as I am now but younger and with a frown." This was Jane's angry Part.

The Earliest Disturbing Memory

After an introductory exchange between Jane and her angry Part, I coached her to ask the Part to focus on her irritation or anger while letting her mind float back to the earliest disturbing memory that came up.

The memory that surfaced was an interaction between Jane and her mother thirty years earlier when, as an "eight-year-old chatterbox," Jane kept trying to keep her mother's attention through a constant flow of talk. "My mother was frustrated and she told me to be quiet for a while. That hurt my feelings. I felt she was rejecting me."

Jane could see the parallel between her memory of feeling her mother's rejection thirty years ago and her feeling that Grandma was rejecting her now (by criticizing her for not fixing the coffee earlier).

Neutralizing the Part's Emotions

I asked Jane if she was ready to neutralize the memory of her mother's **rejection**, and she agreed. She chose a fantasy wind intervention (more below) in which she visualized a powerful wind blowing over, around and through the eight-year-old chatterbox. The wind ground the child Part's **hurt feelings** into dust and blew them away forever. The healing took less than a minute. The memory was then no longer disturbing to the eight-year-old.

The angry Part now similarly felt neutral for her mother's rejection and, in turn, so did Jane. She now recognized that she had been angry because she felt guilty for making Grandma wait for her coffee. But once she had healed the memory of her eight-year-old's experience, she was also relieved of her guilt and anger for her grandmother. She was no longer angry with Grandma. She accepted that Grandma's comment, "Better than a million dollars!" was an expression of gratitude. And she was no longer irritated by Grandma's slurping of her coffee. Her current response to Grandma had been colored by the PMS-triggered memory of an event from childhood. And we found that childhood memory by asking the angry Part to find the memory that was causing the problem.

The sequence of events I described in treating the eight-year-old-chatterbox, the adult angry Part, and Jane may seem too simple to you. You might ask, "If it's that simple, why can't I do it myself?" Actually, you could if you pulled all of the elements together, but that's not easy to do when you're trying to do your own therapy.

Neutralizing Has a Firm Basis in Neuroscience

The key element is the *activation* of the problem memory (e.g., rejection by a mother) and the Part (e.g., the eight-year-old chatterbox) that continues to experience it, trapped in time in the "implicit emotional memory"—the technical term for the emotional part of the memory as opposed to the factual story of events.

There's a sound basis in neuroscience for explaining the process of neutralizing memories. Unless the implicit emotional memory is activated, it can't be edited or erased as we did in the example. For this reason, simply recalling a distant memory and then imagining wind blowing through you wouldn't neutralize the memory. You have to first activate it by connecting to the Part of you that experienced it at the time. Some of my patients learn to do their own healing. Near the end of the book, Amelia does so dramatically, and brings about a major change in her internal world of Parts as well as her external experience of life. Most people, however, do best when guided by a therapist.

Memory Reconsolidation

Neutralizing memories is accomplished in accordance of what we now know as *memory reconsolidation*, the process by which old—seemingly permanent—implicit emotional memories can be destabilized and then edited through overwriting their existing neural pathways with new information. Thus, as in the section above, the targeted emotional memory is first reactivated, which destabilizes the existing emotional memory circuit. Then, using a visualization of discarding or otherwise dispensing with the targeted negative emotion, the neural pathway is overwritten with this new information of emotional neutrality. (See Dahlitz & Hall, 2015, and Ecker et.al., 2012, in Appendix 1 for in-depth explanations of memory reconsolidation.) The result is permanent neutrality in place of sadness, fear, anger, etc. while leaving intact the original explicit (factual) nonemotional memories.

FREESTANDING AND STUCK-IN-TIME PARTS

It's important to understand both types of Parts because I'll be talking about them throughout the book. *Stuck-in-Time Parts* are like those in the first two exercises, where you located images of yourself in both positive and negative memories.

The "eight-year-old chatterbox" in Jane's memory is also a Stuck-in-Time Part. These Parts are stuck in the time the memories were formed. Surprisingly, you can have conversations with them and they can probably tell you all about the events in which you found them, and all about their associated experiences and emotions. But they'll likely have no knowledge of your present-time life nor of life before the memory event where you found them. More on this later.

Freestanding Parts are different. The angry Part you located is a Freestanding Part. So too is the Part that Amelia found curled into a ball on the floor of the shower in the previous chapter. Jane's image of herself as a younger and frowning version of herself is also a Freestanding Part. Parts of this kind aren't limited in their memories or knowledge to a single life-history event. They're aware of your current life-situation and have memories that cover a significant portion of your life.

A Freestanding Part may be more difficult for you to accept as real because it can't be as easily explained away as "just a memory." These Parts generally claim many—sometimes dozens—of memories as their own.

The primary content of a Freestanding Part is a set of memories related to each other through one or two themes, such as memories of loss, memories of shame, or memories of injustice. Each of these individual memories contains its own Stuck-in-Time Part. Since Stuck-in-Time Parts appear in the memory banks of Freestanding Parts they can be considered to be subparts of the Freestanding Parts.

Memories Linked to Themes

Here's an example of themed memories from a different patient. The Freestanding Part showed herself as a twelve-year-old girl with a collection of memories connected by the theme of *not doing anything right*. Although she presented herself as a pre-teen, she was a full participant in the adult patient's conscious life.

Throughout childhood her father criticized her chores (dishes, cleaning, vacuuming) as poorly done. In her sports activities, he never praised, only criticized her performances. For school report cards, anything less than a grade of "A" was unacceptable.

Each of these linked memories and other similar ones constituted the primary contents of the twelve-year-old subpersonality. Not surprisingly, the adult patient was quite sensitive to criticism. The twelve-year-old Freestanding Part was co-conscious (meaning aware of and experiencing events as they happened) with her and regularly found fault when the adult did or said something imperfectly. Unfortunately, while positive memories are much nicer to contemplate, painful memories like these are the ones that truly shape us.

Freestanding Parts have—or quickly create—a visual image of themselves, usually resembling the outside person (the *conscious self*) in various modes of dress, body attitude, or age. However, sometimes a Part will show itself as an entirely unrelated image, such as a cloud, a blob, a cartoon character, a sinister onlooker, a monster or a Wicked Witch of the West. An angry Part, as you saw above, might present itself in an angry picture of you or as a ball of fire or some other symbolic image.

The most important characteristic of a Freestanding Part is a sense of self and a sense that she's real, even if your skeptical Part insists that she can't be real. The Part will display an ability to think and communicate, and a desire to continue to exist. For many readers these ideas are completely new or even strange. But they have been known and described in the psychological literature for almost a century. In Appendix 1 at the end of the book I provide a short historical overview of other scholars' work with Parts.

In the next section, I introduce two of my former patients and describe the Parts that operate within their systems. This will help you to understand the variety of ways Parts organize themselves and play active roles in our external lives.

MADELINE: A SIMPLE PARTS SYSTEM

Every internal system of Parts is different. There are many ways of organizing subpersonalities. One way to do so is with a small set of Freestanding Parts and few if any Stuck-in-Time Parts. (If you can't locate a Stuck-in-Time Part in an autobiographical memory, that means you're viewing the scene through your own eyes as you re-experience the event. In healing the memory, you work directly with the Freestanding Part in the same way you would with a Stuck-in-time Part.)

Madeline, a district sales manager for her company, has just seven internal Parts of which we're aware. They are Freestanding Parts and each one specializes in being experientially present for matters that are of particular interest to her. Each is fully co-conscious with Madeline, meaning that each Part is capable of being present in at least observer status in whatever conscious activity Madeline might be engaged. As the result of her therapy, Madeline can easily communicate with any of them. However, most of my patients choose not to maintain such links to their internal self-states once they graduate themselves from therapy.

In Madeline's system, there are three adults, two adolescents, a six-year-old and a two-year-old. Originally, Madeline and I knew of only five of them, but through occasional meetings over many years, we discovered the other two. Each of them has a name of her own, but they chose those names spontaneously during the course of therapy. *Baby,* the name of the two-year-old, was actually bestowed upon her by the other Parts.

The three adults specialize in different functions in Madeline's life. One is the internal manager of all the other Parts. She's also the angry Part and the primary sexual Part, although each of the adults can be sexual at times. Another adult Part is a worrier, bringing to Madeline's attention anything that might need attention in the near or middle-distant future. The third adult is the taskmaster and external manager of everyday home and work life. She makes life orderly and ensures that everything operates properly and on time. One of the adolescents is the romantic Part, while the other keeps track of Madeline's health needs. (For many women, the falling-in-love Part is an adolescent.) The six-year-old is playful, loves small animals, and is bonded to Madeline's husband as a child to a protector. It's unclear how Baby affects Madeline.

DAVID: A COMPLEX PARTS SYSTEM

David is a patient with a much larger set of internal Parts. And none of them chose names for themselves different from his own. He is a thirty-eight-year-old physician with a number of Stuck-in-Time Parts separately representing his experiences during college, medical school, medical residency, and additional training periods. There is perhaps a dozen of these Stuck-in-Time Parts. Although each Part holds a set of memories stretching over several years, they have little or no awareness of David's current activities or his childhood. They're similar in this way to many of Amelia's Parts that we'll soon meet. Although not conscious of events in David's current life, the Parts can nevertheless be triggered by such events, which David experiences as an intensification of a current emotional state.

David also has a few Freestanding Parts with longer memory spans and full awareness of current life. They're co-conscious with him. They present themselves as age 38, 36, 19, 13, and 8.

David 19 is the sexual Part, primarily interested in sex or sports activities. *David 38* is the system's internal manager, the Part with the most complete understanding of David's inner and outer worlds. David calls the 36-year-old Part *The San Francisco Part*. He is the optimistic achiever, interested in accomplishing things and reaping the benefits of success. *David 13* is contentious and pushes back when David's wife seems to him to be acting selfishly. *David 8* is needy, and much like the six-year-old in Madeline's system, serves as a kind of marital glue. He misses David's wife when she's away. These five self-states, along with a father Part and a husband Part, are the Freestanding Parts most similar to Madeline's organization of subpersonalities. Although four of David's Freestanding Parts are younger than David's actual age, all were co-conscious with David's conscious self—the Part of us we usually consider the *I* and *me* of us—who manages everyday life and interaction with others. We might say that Madeline had a more fully integrated system than David, but that doesn't imply that hers was in any way a better system than his. Just a different kind of system. David's system is in many ways more similar to Amelia's system, which I'll describe throughout the book.

USING PARTS AND MEMORY THERAPY

The standard treatment approach for Parts and Memory Therapy looks fairly simple on paper, although it's often more complicated in real life. You'll see this as you follow Amelia's story. Here are the steps we typically take when working with a patient.

TABLE 3. THE PARTS AND MEMORY THERAPY PROTOCOL
1. Define the problem (i.e., help the patient to describe the problem in specific—especially emotional—rather than general terms).
2. Find the Part that carries the problem (e.g., find the angry Part, the depressed Part, etc.).
3. Collect the autobiographical memories that are the foundation for the problem.
4. Neutralize the problem memories (through visualizing the Part releasing the negative emotions and sensations attached to the memories).

HEALING THROUGH NEUTRALIZING MEMORIES

Parts and Memory Therapy's most important healing intervention is that of *neutralizing memories*. By making neutral a Part's painful memories, the therapy makes the Part more flexible and more open to alternative, healthier actions. (See H. Watkins [1980] and Schwartz [1995] in Appendix 1 for earlier versions of this concept.)

All people acquire Parts as the result of normal development from childhood on. Parts help us handle difficult or novel experiences. Over time the original challenging experience and others like it provide a foundation for the kind of solution a new Part provides to a person. For example, observing your father beating your mother could provide a model (a solution) for how to treat your own significant others. Or, the same abusive observations might cause you to develop the solution of immediately exiting any situation that hints at conflict. In cases like this, the solution itself may become a problem.

In either case, healing the problem (or "solution") requires neutralizing the emotional memories that serve as the foundation of the problem. Once these memories are neutralized, the person is free to find a different solution—one that isn't driven by emotional pain. When a Part is healed, so too is the patient—at least for that aspect of her life.

Parts in Adulthood

Although most Parts develop in childhood and adolescence, they can appear at any age. Painful or challenging experiences in adulthood can also bring into existence new Parts. There's no age limit. Often, new adult Parts require no healing work. Good examples of this are the professional Parts we develop to carry out the demands of our jobs. No need to fix Parts that don't cause problems.

Dissociation

A Part carries the emotional pain on behalf of the person and, over time, partially dissociates it from the person's awareness. To dissociate something is to move it partially or fully out of awareness. That's what happens to most of our memories of emotional pain. They're dissociated out of the awareness of our conscious self. The conscious self only becomes aware of the full amount of pain when the memory is reactivated by some sort of trigger.

Although dissociated and apparently lessoned, the emotional pain never goes away on its own. It's always there, lurking in the unconscious background awaiting a relevant trigger. When we find the Part and the memories it stores, we neutralize the dissociated pain forever.

HEALING INTERVENTIONS

Neutralizing memories works by visualizing the emotions being released from the explicit memories after identifying what kinds of emotions are involved. For example, the therapist might guide you in visualizing rainfall washing away your grief from the painful experience of rejection by someone you love. You might be able to neutralize your painful memories by simply imagining that you are throwing them into the trash or shredding them in a paper shredder or dissolving them in acid. You might also benefit, however, from a more elaborate ritual, as illustrated below.

Once relieved of your painful emotions or body sensations, you retain all of the factual aspects of your original autobiographical memories, including the factual knowledge that those memories were once painful to you. However, you're no longer disturbed by the memories in any way. *That* is what I'm calling *healing*.

The healing interventions are deliberate fantasies that edit or erase the painful emotions or body sensations of your explicit, factual memories. For your emotional mind, available to you when you work with Parts, imagined experiences are just as real as external ones in your physical world.

Here are three narratives I sometimes use to neutralize the painful emotions of Parts stuck in difficult memories. My patient is free to close her eyes or keep them open as I narrate the intervention.

A Flowing Waterfall

Visualize the Part standing in a waterfall and notice how sometimes there are drops of water and sometimes mist and sometimes a powerful pouring of water. Let the water flow over, around and through her. Notice how the Part's hair is plastered to her head and her clothes are stuck to her skin. Ask her to locate where it is within her that she stores the problem memory and then ask her to feel the water dissolving the pain and negative emotions connected to the memory. Notice how the negative emotions dissolve in the water and the water washes them out of her. You may even notice how the water around her is discolored as the dissolved emotions are washed away. As the water continues to wash away her fear [or sad-ness, shame, etc.] you may notice how it gradually becomes clear again as the memory is washed clean.

The Flames of a Bonfire

Visualize a bonfire for the Part, with the Part standing in front of it. Then ask her to locate where it is within her that she stores the painful memories. Now ask her to reach inside of herself and lift out the negative emotions [or negative energy] and throw them into the fire. As the fire touches them, you can see them burst into flame and be totally incinerated. Ask her to go back for more and keep repeating the action until all of the negative emotions and sensations that were attached to the memories are entirely burnt up.

Wind in an Open Field

Visualize the Part standing in an open field and bring up a powerful wind to blow over, around, and through her. Ask her to locate where it is within her that she stores the memory and ask her to feel the wind scouring the memory and washing it clean of fear [or sadness, shame, etc.]. As the wind breaks up the fear into tiny particles, you may notice that when the wind blows away from her it's darker because it's carrying away the particles of those emotions as dust or sand. Let the wind continue to blow until the memory is just a neutral memory with no emotion attached to it.

RESCUES AND INTROJECTS

There are two additional techniques that are important in the work with Amelia. They are *rescuing* a Part and *unmasking* an *introject*.

Rescues

The *rescue* is common to many therapies that work with difficult or traumatic memories, and probably originates in the work of nineteenth century French psychiatrists. With this intervention, the therapist helps you to locate a Stuck-in-Time Part in a problem memory and then guides you in rescuing that Part in using your imagination to move her to a safe place in the past, present or imagined future.

For Amelia, the safe place was usually her internal picture of her children's playroom. She would recall a painful scene and then rescue the version of herself that she found in that scene by taking the Part's hand and stepping from the traumatic scene to the calm scene of the playroom. The rescue contributes to neutralizing the painful memory, although it's generally not enough by itself to accomplish complete healing. The rescue is necessary when there's too much commotion in the scene for the Stuck-in-Time Part to focus on the intervention.

Introjects

An *introject* is an internal Part your mind has created to represent certain of the influences an important person has had (and continues to have) in your life. Most often these Parts are images of parents, stepparents, abusers or other demanding people. The image is a costume; underneath the costume is a version of you playing the role of being the introjected person. The introject only downloads certain of the significant person's personal characteristics, usually negative ones. One type of introject can bring nurturing images of parents that comfort us in times of stress. This type of introject doesn't need therapeutic attention. The other type of introject, the negative introject, requires therapy if we are to end its harmful effects on us.

Introjects are especially common in patients who grew up in homes with strict, demanding parents. When an introject is the kind of Part that's both emotionally toxic and unshakeable in its belief that it *is* the person it represents (e.g., that it actually *is* your mother), then it should be unmasked. Otherwise, the confusion among Parts hinders the therapy.

All Parts within the patient's internal world are *self-states,* not *other-states.* I emphasize this because in our vulnerable moments, we're sometimes tempted to think otherwise, especially when internal images *seem* so real. But our minds are entirely ours. Nothing in our minds can be anything but a part of us. This means that images or voices of mothers, fathers, abusers, demons, spirits, and every other imaginable thing can by the nature of the physical brain only be our own creations. Most of us think this is obvious. But in the worlds of our Parts or subpersonalities, there's sometimes confusion about this. Our internal Parts can sometimes be convinced that an encounter with an internal parent is an encounter with the real parent.

Unmasking Introjects

The *unmasking* of introjects was important in Amelia's therapy. Introjects show themselves in "costumes" or "masks" that make them seem to be the outside person they represent. Beneath the costume is a Part of the patient, usually a child Part. The problem introject needs to take off its costume and be the child underneath.

Unmasking refers to the removal of the costume. Unmasking an introject is usually accomplished by convincing the Part wearing the costume to "unzip" it and step out of it or pull it over her head and just be the girl underneath. The "convincing" takes the following form: 1) thank the introject for its service; 2) congratulate the child under the costume for an acting role well done; and 3) ask the Part to come out from under the costume. We then work to heal the child Part who played the introject role, often for many painful years. This intervention will become clearer in a later chapter when we first unmask an Amelia introject.

SUD AND SUE SCALES

The SUD (for "Subjective Units of Distress") scale (Wolpe, 1969) is an important element in gauging our progress in healing. It measures a Part's level of distress when it focuses upon the painful memories we process. A zero on the scale indicates complete emotional neutrality for a given memory, meaning that the memory is merely factual, like the text of a history book.

Our goal is to reduce every disturbing memory with which we work to a SUD value of zero. A ten on the SUD scale represents the greatest distress that you or your internal Part can imagine. There's nothing worse than a ten.

If I ask you what your SUD score is for a painful memory, and then ask the Stuck-in-time Part what her score is for the same memory, the Part's distress is always greater than (or equal to) yours. That's because a major function of a Part is to tuck away painful memories so that the conscious self can function without being constantly overwhelmed by trauma. When your SUD rating of a painful memory is at zero, then your memory has been permanently healed.

The SUE Scale

The SUE (for "Subjective Units of Energy") scale measures emotional energy that isn't *negative* (Noricks, 2011). I developed this scale for measuring work with problem memories my patients experienced as positive or not clearly negative. A ten means that a memory is so powerful as to be almost overwhelming. A zero means that the memory is simply a flat, black-and-white record of a historical moment, one without an emotional response of any kind.

The SUE Scale for Love

Even positive memories may interfere with everyday life. For example, continuing to feel romantic love for a former sweetheart can negatively impact a current relationship. Neutralizing that love can be easily accomplished. You'll see the use of this scale when we process Amelia's memories of old loves.

The SUE Scale for Pornography

Another example that calls for the use of the SUE scale is the treatment of a pornography addiction. A patient who retreats too often into the sexual ecstasy of pornographic images can damage an ongoing relationship. In addition to treating the underlying painful experiences (measured with the SUD scale) that cause a person to escape into pornography, I also want to reduce to a SUE rating of zero the positive energy in memories of previous pornographic experiences.

Interestingly, after healing a porn addiction, the patient remains capable of responding to new pornographic images, but is no longer compelled to pursue them. Pornography use becomes a choice rather than a compulsion. Amelia didn't have a problem with porn, but her husband Michael did. My eventual work with Michael's addiction was an important background element to Amelia's story.

In the following chapters I'll focus upon Amelia's story as it's revealed in the therapy. Whenever there seems to be a new little twist in the workings of internal Parts, I'll take the time to explain what's going on. I'll also make a note here and there as to how well the therapy seems to be working in reducing Amelia's symptoms.

Chapter 3

Postpartum Me, a Head-Banging Little Girl, and a Lost Boy

At our third session, I asked Amelia to return to the image of her sobbing self, curled into a ball on the floor of the shower. This is the Part we found at the end of our second session. She was the primary Part that carried the postpartum depression that followed Amelia's second child.

POSTPARTUM ME

Amelia found the Part easily. The next step was to develop ease of communication with her. I coached Amelia to ask her sobbing self a series of questions aimed at assessing her awareness of Amelia in current time. This was important because many Parts are unaware of a person's current life. Although their emotions may be triggered by current-time events, they may have no specific knowledge beyond the point in time of the memory where they're located.

The conversations worked like this: I would pose a question and Amelia would then ask the question of the Part. She would listen to the response and report that to me. With some patients, Parts respond by delivering a completed thought to the patient, and sometimes it seems they're responding with articulated speech, much like the speech of everyday conversation. With others, it seems that the patient knows or discovers the answers at the moment when she asks the question; she then shares that information with me. Amelia generally experienced her interactions with her Parts like conversations with another person, as if her Parts were actually moving their lips and talking to her.

Amelia Talks with Her Postpartum Part

When asked her age, the Part didn't respond. Amelia added, however, that the Part felt old. We then asked questions that would let us know how much the Part knew about Amelia's family life. *Postpartum Me,* as we came to call her, thought that Amelia's youngest child was still a baby, when actually he was almost three. She thought that Amelia's oldest child, her daughter, was two years old, when she was actually five. Evidently Postpartum Me was stuck in the throes of Amelia's postpartum depression three years previously. We thought of her as about thirty-two years old.

Further questions revealed that the Part didn't like Amelia's husband Michael. In particular, she was angry because *"he left her alone"* following the birth of their second child. It's significant that Amelia quotes Postpartum Me in the third person and not the first person, i.e., rather than *"he ignored me,"* Amelia said, *"he ignored her."* Throughout the therapy Amelia would switch between the first person and the third person when quoting or summarizing information from an internal Part of her. This is normal when we work with our Parts.

Depression Comes from Memories

At this point, we began asking about the Part's earliest memories so that we could begin the process of healing the depression. My assumption is always that depression results from life experiences, captured in autobiographical memories. Amelia and I always tried to start with a Part's earliest painful memory. In this way we make use of a generalization effect where the healing of earlier memories generalizes to later memories and reduces the negative energy attached to the later memories before we actually work with them. For some reason, this generalization effect doesn't happen in the opposite direction, from more recent to earlier memories.

Although I asked for the Part's earliest memory, the first memories that came to Amelia's mind were the repeated experiences of being left alone by her parents after their final separation. Those experiences occurred when Amelia was thirteen, almost fourteen. They were disturbing to Postpartum Me at a level 10 on the 0-10 SUD ("Subjective Units of Disturbance") scale. Other early memories soon appeared, however, predating these. The common theme of Postpartum Me's memories was clearly relationship loss: from threatened or actual loss— as with Amelia's experience of her parent's divorce—to her felt sense of loss when Michael ignored her after the birth of their second child.

Fear of Separation

One set of memories that continued to distress Postpartum Me involved her parents talking about permanently separating. These memories dated to when Amelia had just turned thirteen and were disturbing at a level 9. Earlier than these memories, were the multiple occasions of her parents' fierce arguments, beginning when Amelia was eight years old. Perhaps because the arguments happened often enough to seem somewhat normal, Postpartum Me was disturbed by them only to a level 6 or 7.

We didn't yet know whether Postpartum Me had even earlier memories. When Amelia asked the Part to share her earliest memories, she saw memories before age eight, but they may have come from a different Part of her. It's characteristic of the memory sets of subpersonalities that their experiences only cover a particular time period. Only a few Parts claim to have access to the patient's very earliest memories.

HEALING BEGINS

As described in the last chapter, neutralizing memories is the process by which we help an internal Part (i.e., a self-state or subpersonality) overcome its painful emotions or body sensations. I like *healing* as the general term for what we're doing. *Neutralizing* refers to reducing to zero the amount of negative energy attached to painful memories. It's the process by which healing occurs. Neutralizing means healing.

Over time, I've learned that it's best to begin the neutralizing process in a session before too many memories have accumulated in that session. Otherwise, when you leave the office, incompletely healed but newly conscious memories may cause you emotional distress for a few days or even a week. For this reason, before our session ended, I guided Amelia in healing the memories we had so far discovered. We began with the earliest: her parents' frequent verbal fights Amelia remembered from the age of eight and later.

Healing Postpartum Me

Since Postpartum Me was already in a shower stall, it seemed reasonable to use a water intervention to neutralize the memories we had uncovered. I asked Amelia to visualize water from the shower-head flowing over, around and through Postpartum Me as she lay on the shower floor. As I pointed out in the previous chapter, fantasy visualizations are just as real in the emotional world of Parts as are actual events in the external world are to patients.

A few moments after beginning the visualization, Amelia observed: *"It is like she is bleeding out; the water is running red."* I assured Amelia that it would soon run clear. Within a minute Amelia said, *"She is sitting up now, looking at the wa-*

ter coming out of her. It is clear now." The Part's 0-10 SUD score for the first set of memories had been reduced to 1.

While a 1 on the SUD scale is a dramatic improvement, the only sure indication that the memory is healed is a score of zero. If we can't achieve that, it means either that another Part is blocking the complete healing, or that negative emotion from an earlier memory has somehow been projected onto the scene we're working with. For this reason, we didn't stop our work at a score of 1.

I coached Amelia to ask Postpartum Me if she knew what was still bothering her. With a SUD of 1, a Part frequently can't identify what continues to bother her but we ask anyway because doing so helps to focus attention inward. Amelia said that the reason the score wasn't zero was because *"she still has bad memories"*—which, of course, we already knew. We repeated the intervention but added to Amelia's visualization that the water from the shower would now blast Postpartum Me with "triple strength." Within fifteen seconds, the SUD score moved to zero.

Healing Teenage Memories

We then turned our attention to Amelia's early-teen memories of her parents talking about divorce. Amelia began the visualization with Postpartum Me sitting in the shower, with the water flowing over and through her. Very soon, however, Amelia said of the Part's bundle of negative emotions: *"It is like a black coal lump in her chest. She needs something stronger than water, like acid."* I agreed with her wish to add a vial of sulfuric acid to the water.

Shortly after she began to repeat the visualization, Amelia said, *"It is breaking up into little pieces."* Then, *"It is clear."* The SUD level had reached zero. I was pleased that Amelia had become proactive—adding acid to the intervention—in increasing the strength of the healing ritual. Too often, I haven't made it clear to patients that it's okay to join me in creating fantasies that work.

It's worth repeating here that fantasies work because once we've activated the previously dissociated memories—and the Part can again experience the original emotions—we can edit these memories, and the edited memories are just as real to these subpersonalities as external events are to the rest of us in the objective world.

Memories of Being Alone

We still had time in our session to return to Postpartum Me's first-listed emotional memories, those of being alone (and feeling alone) following her parents' final separation. These memories had already spontaneously reduced from a SUD level of 10 to an 8 as a result of our work on the two previous sets of memories. I expected some reduction because of the generalization effect I mentioned earlier. Neutralizing earlier events partially desensitizes later events.

Amelia visualized Postpartum Me being inundated by the water in the shower as she tried to imagine the negative emotion of **aloneness** being dissolved and washed out of her. Amelia soon said, *"The feeling goes from her throat to her stomach like an oil, and the water is having trouble dissolving it."*

Using Story-Telling to Help the Healing

Because we were temporarily stumped on how to proceed with a neutralizing metaphor strong enough to dissolve the emotion of aloneness, I suggested that Amelia coach Postpartum Me to describe in detail the story of her being alone after her parents' final separation. Uncovering the story of the problem memory is often helpful to the process of healing a Part of its pain and distress:

"It was Christmas after my graduation and I had just turned sixteen. My mother was going on a trip and taking my sister. My dad was going somewhere else. Taking me was an inconvenience for them. They were not taking into consideration her feelings. She felt unloved. She was at her aunt's house and she cried all night—to the point that she got sick with a fever and a throat infection." (The switching of "she" for "I" and "her" for "my" in this quote is normal.)

Hoping that the Part's telling of her story would now enable neutralizing this painful memory, we focused on Postpartum Me's feelings of **abandonment** and of **being unloved**. The water visualization now quickly reduced the Part's SUD level to a 2, but the Part couldn't identify the source of the remaining distress. We tried the water metaphor again, using an increased water flow to try to heal the Part's distress, but it didn't seem to help. Amelia said, *"She is feeling sticky because of the oil."*

In order to move the healing forward, I again asked Amelia to invite the Part to tell us what was troubling her:

"She does not understand because this was supposed to be a special year. She graduated high school. She remembers being in total darkness at her aunt's house, crying. She felt like a piece of garbage, discarded."

Following this sharing, Amelia again visualized Postpartum Me in the flowing water. Within ten seconds, she laughed and said, *"She grabbed dishwashing soap and a brush and washed it out."* The SUD level was now zero. The Part acted spontaneously in grabbing the soap and brush without Amelia suggesting that she do so. Sometimes Parts act independently of the conscious self.

Relaxing after Deep Work

Amelia added: *"She feels comfortable now on the floor of the shower. She is sitting up now enjoying the flow of water on her. She is saying, 'Goodbye. See you later.'"* We could see that the Part felt better because her posture changed; she was no longer curled into a ball on the floor of the shower, but was sitting up and cheerful. We'll see more of these symbolic changes—such as body-type changes, increased youthfulness, and ragged clothing changing to new—as we heal other Parts.

As we scheduled our next session, Amelia interrupted to say, *"That was weird. The thoughts she had about the memories—the colors she washed out of her body—were different for each memory. And there was a difference in texture: blood, coal, oil."* The symbolism here of color and texture would be interesting to explore, but it wouldn't immediately further the therapy in the sense that insight into these rich meanings would produce healing. I chose instead to aim for efficiency and the reduction of Amelia's expense of time and money. However, if she had expressed a desire to do that exploration, I would have agreed. We planned to return to Postpartum Me in our next session.

POSTPARTUM ME

A week later, on a Thursday, we met again. At the outset Amelia reported that she had experienced *"a rough couple of days with my PMS."* She had been angry and short with her children and Michael, but stopped short of a full blowout with him. From Sunday through Tuesday, she had experienced *"lack of concentration, not thinking well, cramping, impatience, frustration. Then I was fine yesterday* [Wednesday]— *like someone took something out of my brain. In church on Sunday I visualized God taking Postpartum Me out and hugging her and saying He will take care of her. Maybe that helped."*

As Amelia's comments show here, she was beginning to connect her PMS to her inner Parts and her ongoing moods. These connections would continue to characterize the therapy for as long as we worked together. She was also learning to make use of her new knowledge of Parts to help her cope with everyday stresses. I was pleased with her progress. Many patients leave their Parts in the therapy room and don't return to them until the next meeting.

Following Amelia's update, I asked her to find Postpartum Me. Immediately, she said, *"She has been waiting for us. She feels pinned to the floor of the shower. She feels stuck."* Apparently, Amelia's PMS symptoms affected our ongoing work with the Part. Being "stuck", though, was something we could use. We took Postpartum Me's feeling of being stuck and bridged to memories associated with that feeling. Bridging means connecting between two things that have something in common. We did that here by asking Postpartum Me to focus on the feeling of "stuckness" while letting her mind float back in time to the earliest memory that she could recall. (This is called an *affect bridge* because we used affect (feelings or emotions) to connect stuckness to an early memory.)

Amelia Blames Her Mother

The bridge brought up memories of contentious conversations Amelia had had with her mother following the divorce from her father. *"She* [Postpartum Me] *blamed her mother a lot and she was rebellious. She did not feel connected to her mother because there was so much conflict. She felt alone and almost lost, missing both her father and her mother."* I coached Amelia to visualize Postpartum Me under the flow of the water again and to let the water neutralize the feelings of being **alone** and **lost** by dissolving them and washing them away.

Amelia soon reported: *"Those emotions are located in her back and the water brought out a sticky black something. Her back is covered with stickiness, and the bottoms of her feet, too."* Amelia continued visualizing the water intervention and a few moments later said, *"She is still stuck a little bit by her feet to the floor. She is not sure why."*

I suggested blasting her feet with very strong spray, but after trying that, she responded that the spray was painful to Postpartum Me. Pain or increased pain during a neutralizing ritual is a sure sign that some other Part is blocking the intervention. We needed to find that blocking Part.

Blocking by a Child Part

I asked Amelia to look around Postpartum Me's environment for the blocking Part. She soon identified the blocker, saying, *"It is a child, six or seven years old."* We called her Amelia 7. (To keep track of the Parts we worked with, I decided to give them an age label, unless they provided a name of their own.) Amelia 7 is a subpart of Postpartum Me, which means that she's a Stuck-in-Time Part with a small set of memories and no awareness of Amelia's current life.

She looked like Amelia looked at the same age. When asked, the little-girl Part indicated that she knew Amelia as an older her. Because this Part seemed to be amplifying her own pain onto Postpartum Me rather than intentionally blocking the work, I thought the best approach would be to work with the child Part's painful memories and heal them before trying to continue with Postpartum Me. If the blocking had come from a manager—a Part that controls or tries to control other Parts—I would instead have focused on negotiating with it for permission to continue.

Healing the Child Part

Amelia 7 indicated that her earliest memory was that of *"seeing her dad drunk at Christmas and fighting with her mom."* Another memory was that of the hurt she felt when her father brought presents at Christmas for everybody but her. She had several other memories that, like these first two, suggested to her that her father didn't love her. Amelia chose a fire intervention for healing the Christmas disappointments. She visualized a large bonfire with the little girl standing in front of it. Then she coached her to reach inside of herself and throw her **painful emotions** into the fire, watch them ignite and then burn up in the fire. Shortly after beginning this visualization, Amelia said, *"Now she is throwing things into the fire in anger, like she is having a tantrum and crying. She is crying because she is sad."*

Amelia next asked her to throw the **sadness** into the fire as well. I didn't ask Amelia to work with the child's anger tantrum because anger is always a response to more vulnerable emotions. If we succeeded in neutralizing the anger, we would still have to deal with the vulnerable emotion—in this case sadness—that generates the anger. When we heal the vulnerable emotion first, the anger dissipates on its own without further attention.

"She is better," Amelia said, *"but there is a lot to burn."* In aid of the healing, I asked Amelia to tell the little girl's story for her. Amelia said, *"Her dad is never around, even on important days like First Communion. She was never important to him. He was never there."*

Often a Part is reluctant to release emotional memories because of a false belief that factual memories would also disappear. For this reason, I suggested that Amelia assure the little girl that she would help her to remember how her father had treated her and that she would always be there for her. Then Amelia continued the visualization. Soon, she said, *"She is tired after all that crying."* I asked her to direct the child Part to focus on the feeling of being **tired** and to burn that up too.

The new pass of the intervention produced a smile from Amelia as she said, *"That is weird! It is like she is taking off her skin and hair and finding new skin and hair underneath. She feels prettier. And happier. She is not sad anymore. It is like there is a new her. When she was throwing things into the fire, she ripped off her clothes and threw them into the fire. So when she did the fire again, she peeled off her skin and threw that into the fire. She is happy now."*

The Child Comforts the Adult

I asked if the child Part knew Postpartum Me. *"Yes, she knows her. I took her to her and she is comforting her* [i.e., Amelia 7 is comforting Postpartum Me]. *Now she is guiding Postpartum Me in peeling off her skin and throwing it into the fire. She is guiding her in peeling off the black stuff. She comes out of the shower now. She is sitting next to the little girl now. She has no other painful memories."*

Although Amelia 7 was no longer bothered by her father's drunkenness or forgetfulness, in later sessions other Parts appear who will revisit the father's hurtful actions.

For our next session I thought we might be able to work with Postpartum Me to bridge to other Freestanding Parts who similarly carried painful memories. This sort of internal bridging allows us to shortcut the longer process of beginning with the negative emotion, finding the body sensation, and inviting the patient to present us with an image of the Part that carries the emotion.

HEALING DISTRESS OF THE MENSTRUAL CYCLE

At the outset of our next session, our fifth, Amelia said that she was *"feeling a lot better. I had a period and I was not feeling cranky at all! I was not unhappy with my husband and I was patient with the kids."* She added: *"During my period, I felt tired but not emotionally upset. I am still upset at my ovulation time but not now at my period time. The period used to be worse than the ovulation."*

Technically, distress during a period isn't PMS. However, Amelia perceived no difference between her emotional discomfort prior to her period and during it. In this case she had also experienced no distress during the five days before her period.

This was very good news and suggested that Amelia's emotional upset during her menstrual cycle was, as we had hypothesized PMS to be, partly the result of her earlier painful life experiences. By extension, similar negative emotions of other premenstrual women might also be at least partially due to earlier painful life experiences.

While this book is about therapy for *premenstrual* distress, collateral healing of the *menstrual* distress that may accompany a woman's period seems intuitively related. This was the first time during the therapy that I began to think about writing a book about psychotherapy for PMS. Like the vast majority of people, I previously had no inkling that psychotherapy might be helpful.

A PART NAMED FATTY

In our next session we returned as planned to Postpartum Me and Amelia 7. We wanted to try to connect internally to other distressed Parts known to them. Checking with these two Parts, Amelia said, *"They feel there is a male Part, dark and full of anger. But they don't know him."* Since it appeared that the Parts couldn't directly link Amelia to this angry male Part, she focused on the angry feeling and connected to the male by following the path of anger; i.e., she sat patiently with her anger until she could visualize the angry Part.

When she found him, she described him as *"fat, sitting on a couch in a basement. He is really grumpy. The room is dark. He is older than me. He does not want to be bothered."* Amelia calmed the Part by thanking him for being a part of her life and for helping her to survive to adulthood. Additionally, she praised him for being so good at what he did (although it was unclear at this point just what his function might be). This flattery led him to agree to help in the therapy.

The Value of Praise

Praising a reluctant Part, including an angry Part, is often the best way to gain cooperation. Most Parts have had little direct experience with your more skeptical outside world and are generally literal in their communication, meaning that if you tell them they're doing a good job, they'll feel they're getting the praise they deserve. Despite their presentation of sometimes ferocious images of themselves, they tend to be hungry for attention in the form of praise, recognition, and attentive listening.

The appearance of a male subpersonality within a female patient isn't unusual—especially angry male Parts. Many women have angry Parts they experience as male, perhaps because males express anger more readily and strongly than females do from an early age.

Fatty Picks a Nicer Name

This male said his name was *Fatty,* but he didn't like the name. He liked the idea of having a different name, and with Amelia's encouragement, he chose the name *Brave* for himself. Amelia said that Brave was somewhere in his fifties in age. She explained to him that he could help her now by letting us heal his painful memories.

When asked about his earliest painful memory, he wasn't sure what came first. *"He feels that he was angry all the time."* Because he couldn't identify an earliest experience, and also because he presented as a large angry male, I suspected that he was an internal manager and protector of other Parts rather than a Part that directly experienced Amelia's external life.

Managers are Parts that influence, protect, and control other Parts. When Amelia checked with Brave as to whether he protected other Parts, he said that he did. *"He showed me quickly a baby he protects."* The baby's earliest painful memory was of *"being left alone."*

Healing the Baby Amelia

Initially, Brave was reluctant to permit Amelia to heal the baby he protected. However, after she explained that she would merely guide *him* in the process and that *he* would be in charge, Brave agreed. Amelia visualized a gentle wind blowing over the baby, neutralizing the emotions attached to **being left alone**. After about twenty seconds, she said of Brave: *"He is letting the wind blow over the baby. Okay, the baby is warm. It is like the baby was dead. She was blue. Now she has life back. She is moving and happy. Brave is happy, too."*

Of course, the baby Brave protected was Amelia in her infancy. While some might say that a baby's brain hasn't yet matured enough to remember being alone, that isn't an issue we have to deal with. We don't have to decide whether the memory is a real one in the same way that you might clearly remember last night's quarrel with someone. Nor do we need to look for corroboration that Amelia was indeed left alone. What is real in Amelia's emotional brain is that there was a baby who felt alone, and there was another Part whose job it was to protect the baby. Parts and Memory Therapy works with what you experience as true regardless of whether we have independent evidence that what you remember as happening really happened.

Once we've healed a disturbing memory, we've accomplished our goal. We no longer need to be concerned with it. After Amelia finished her wind intervention to neutralize the baby's **aloneness**, she confirmed that the baby no longer felt alone, and Brave the protector was no longer angry.

Healing Brave

After healing a Part of its negative emotions, I like to ask if it's comfortable where it is or would it prefer to go to a safer or more pleasing place? Amelia said, *"He wants to but he is afraid."* Finding out that Brave was afraid, made it clear that he had his own disturbing memories after all. Any strong emotion felt by a Part means that there are disturbing memories that serve as a foundation for that emotion. He shared with Amelia that *"he got lost when he was little, about four or five."* Amelia again used a wind intervention for the healing. As she visualized the process, she said, *"There is a lot coming out of him, like he is deflating. There is a lot. He is getting younger. A lot is still coming out."* Then, after a full minute of the visualization, she said, *"Okay, it is zero* [on the SUD scale]." He no longer experienced fear when he thought of being lost.

Brave was unsure if he had other disturbing memories but Amelia observed: *"He is comfortable now to go out to a sunny place. He takes the baby to a garden. He is walking around with the baby. He is younger now, in his twenties and he has hair now—he was bald before—and he is wearing different clothes. He looks like my dad when he was younger."*

Brave was a *father introject,* a kind of Part that wears a costume in the image of a significant person in your life. I'll say more about introjects later in the book, especially about *negative* introjects that seem to delight in causing pain for other Parts. Brave, however, is a *positive* introject in a supportive, protective role. There was no need to make any further changes with him. And he was a good counterpoint to the largely negative memories Amelia held of her father.

Before ending the session, we asked Brave if he knew of other Parts that might need healing. He indicated that he didn't know of any others directly, but he could sense them. In our next session, we planned to try to bridge from Brave's "sense" to those Parts.

A Lost Boy

Because none of Amelia's other issues demanded attention, we began the next session as planned, by locating Brave and attempting to bridge to another hurt Part in need of healing. Amelia asked him if he could bring over another Part who needed our help. *"He is confused. He is not sure what he is looking for."* I wasn't actually sure if Brave could do what I was asking. I was really just doing an experiment without a downside. If it didn't work, we would go back to Amelia's direct feelings and look for their sources. If it worked, then we could continue inner-world exploration without starting over.

I coached Amelia to guide Brave by asking him to simply allow himself to *feel* the connection he told us about and to "sit with it." Without forcing anything, he should just experience the connection and eventually let his thoughts and feelings carry him to the source of the connection he felt. To my relief, the experiment was successful. Brave soon showed Amelia an image of *"a boy in the forest, shivering and scared. He is scared and does not answer to my hello."* He was lost in the forest.

The boy soon shared with us that he was ten years old and didn't have a name. He knew Brave but not Amelia. She explained that she was his adult self and that she had come to heal him of his distress. He wanted relief from his pain, but couldn't recall any specific memories.

In the absence of specific memories, we can direct the intervention at the negative emotion anyway. Previous therapy work had shown me that focusing just on the problem emotion while visualizing an intervention will usually flood the Part (and thus the patient) with the underlying memories. We can then proceed with the healing. Amelia began a wind visualization, asking the ten- year-old to feel the wind blowing over and through him as it broke up his fear into tiny particles of dust and blew them away.

Right away, memories from Amelia's childhood filled her mind. *"He remembers hitting his head against the wall, pulling his hair, and feeling desperate when he was six or seven."* These or similar memories will come up again when we work with Parts that appear as female. Interestingly, the boy visualized himself as a girl when he recalled the head-banging, although he continued to present himself as a male.

Sometimes the symbolic form in which memories present themselves can obscure the actual content of autobiographical events. For example, the lost-in-a-forest theme and the self-presentation of the Part as a male in Amelia's female body are clearly loaded with symbolism. Amelia had never been lost in a forest and had always been female. Nor could she recall any time in her life when she wanted to be male.

While we would treat the memories as real for the purpose of healing, I still hoped that we could establish that the boy's memories were historically accurate when we explored the symbolism. In this way we might be able to maintain a clean narrative of Amelia's story.

Amelia Has Male Parts

Here and elsewhere some of Amelia's Parts show up as male. I've learned to ignore a Part's gender in the interest of therapeutic efficiency. It's common for both female and male patients to have opposite-sex Parts. Because gender identity wasn't an issue in this case, a side journey to explore why the Part presented itself as male might be of some academic interest but it wouldn't likely be helpful in healing Amelia's painful childhood experiences. Amelia thought that the ten-year-old probably showed himself as a male because she was a *tomboy* at that time in her life. That's probably the best explanation for why the lost boy presented himself as male.

Amelia acknowledged that head-banging was indeed something she had done as a child. She thus assured me that we were on target and not following an irrelevant fantasy tangent; that is, the boy's memory was accurate. When asked, the boy claimed Amelia's parents as his own but he felt no connection to them. This was further confirmation that the boy's memories were also Amelia's memories. (Sometimes a Part will disavow having the same parents as the patient.)

Lost in the Forest

Assured that aside from presenting himself as a male, the ten-year-old seemed to accurately remember Amelia's childhood, we resumed the wind intervention. This time Amelia asked the boy to focus on his feeling of **desperation** and to allow the wind to break it up and blow it away. Within seconds, Amelia could see a change. *"He is shivering less,"* she said. And then: *"He is not shivering now. But he s feeling more lost. He does not know why he is in the forest—that is why he is feeling lost."*

Shifting focus again, Amelia asked the boy to concentrate on **feeling lost** as the wind blew through him. This brought other recollections: *"He remembers that his mom and dad worked a lot and were rarely around. He is mostly at his grandmother's house, just by himself, ignored because everybody is busy. He is only noticed if he breaks something or does something wrong. He feels alone, lost, unimportant."*

Amelia then asked the boy to focus on feeling **alone**, **lost**, **unimportant** as she continued to visualize blowing a wind through him. *"He keeps bringing me to my grandmother's house, with lots of people around, but he does things by himself* [i.e., the people don't interact with him]." I later learned that while there were lots of uncles and aunts and other visitors in the house, none were children. Amelia's grandmother discouraged her from having friends at the house. She was left to fend for herself.

Our progress with the little boy seemed to be slow, and I thought we might benefit from a more powerful healing metaphor. I suggested that Amelia imagine a roaring tornado setting down directly over and around the house, sucking out all of the **loneliness** from the scene. Amelia reported, *"After the tornado, there are still some people around but now he is interacting with them. His body is in the forest but his mind is in the house. He does not want to be in the forest."*

Trying the Rescue Intervention

It was time for the simple *rescue* intervention, in which we visualize moving an internal Part from an uncomfortable place to a safer place. Amelia imagined taking the little boy by the hand and stepping with him out of the forest and into grandmother's house. This helped him but he was still bothered by something he couldn't articulate.

Amelia renewed the gentler wind intervention and then said, *"He is thinking about how much he misses being physically touched, being held. He was around three or four or five and there was a memory of being held, and then not held. That makes sense, because my mom went to work about that time. Okay, he is confused for some reason. Like why is he there at his grandmother's house? And he does not know where he should be."*

Amelia repeated the wind intervention once more, asking the boy to focus on his **confusion** as the wind's target. Then, *"He is okay being there. He wants to go play."* Finally, a positive result! The most common indication I've found that a child Part's painful memories have been neutralized is when the child wants to go play. It appeared that we had finally healed the distress Amelia felt as a child when she began living with her grandmother. It was all about losing her (his) attachment to her (his) mother and feeling lost in the new environment of grandma's house.

We had spent most of the session working with the ten-year-old boy Part and it seemed a good time for a quick assessment of how Amelia was feeling. She said that she wasn't irritable, although she felt anxious and stressed about *"making everything work, be organized. Like having to leave work early to pick up the kids, check finances, prepare for the next day."* Basically, a hectic life was normal for Amelia. She managed everything for the family except Michael. But she was doing well in the therapy.

HEALING PMS IRRITABILITY WITH PARTS WORK

I wasn't too concerned with Amelia's anxiety about her current daily life. It seemed appropriate to me, given her demanding multiple responsibilities. We could probably bring some relief for that fairly quickly. I was more concerned with the deeper issues for which she came to therapy. "Not feeling irritable" was a good sign because **being irritable** was a mood state that had visited Amelia on a monthly basis since she first began to menstruate. If this change maintained itself, it would mean we had succeeded in neutralizing one of Amelia's major PMS symptoms. That would be exciting!

Amelia expected to ovulate in two or three days, right about Day 14 of her cycle. That meant we would get a test as to whether the therapy was helping with her ovulation-PMS before our next session. Amelia regularly experienced PMS symptoms at ovulation in addition to the PMS that other women experienced in just the week before menses.

SUMMARY OF PARTS

As Amelia's story continues, many new subpersonalities appear. They are significant in understanding how Amelia came to be who she is. Some are minor characters and some are major characters. Of those whose memories we had so far processed, only Postpartum Me continued to be significant in Amelia's story. Amelia 7, Fatty/Brave, and the ten-year-old-boy are important in the early part of the story because each carried different aspects of Amelia's loneliness and neglect. But we didn't hear from them again during our work together.

> **Postpartum Me**. Age about thirty-two. She presented as a sobbing, naked adult curled into a ball on the floor of a shower. She functioned to hold memories that underlay Amelia's postpartum depression following her second child.

Amelia 7. A subpart of Postpartum Me. She carried memories of the absence of her father when she needed him.

Fatty/Brave. This Part originally said his name was Fatty but preferred to be called Brave. His function within Amelia's inner world was to protect a very young Amelia from the feeling of being alone. Amelia's first image of him was as an obese man in his fifties. The therapy transformed his image into one resembling her father in his twenties. As a positive father introject, he needed no further therapy.

Ten-Year-Old Boy. When discovered, this subpersonality was overcome with fear. He felt lost in a symbolic forest. His primary function was that of carrying the memories of feeling alone and lacking safe attachments within his family. He was the Part that developed to carry the confusion that Amelia felt when her mother began to leave her in the care of her paternal grandmother at about the age of four or five. Overall, the boy was only a minor actor in Amelia's life play.

Chapter 4
Healing with Magical Thinking

In Chapter 2 I presented an overview of Parts and Memory Therapy. Now that you've seen the therapy in action, I want to take a few more paragraphs to respond to frequent questions about the reality of internal Parts and why working with them provides major healing that working with the external patient's fully conscious self doesn't. Common questions often go something like this: "Since a distressed Part is a part of the self, isn't it the self that gives up the distress? And if that's true, why is it necessary to engage a Part in order to relieve the distress? Why not just work directly with the self?"

THE CONSCIOUS SELF AND PARTS

The answers have to do with the organization of the whole personality. The mind works quite differently than the popular view we acquire as we grow up, and quite differently as well from what many experts tell us. Rather than the mind having one set of characteristics all the time, the conscious self is made up of different sets of memories, experiences, and expectations, which I call Parts. The conscious self displays its characteristic personality traits only as different Parts blend with it. The traits are actually the traits of the underlying Parts. From this point of view, the self is pretty much neutral and dependent upon what Parts bring to it for motivation, beliefs, emotions and agendas. When an angry or anxious Part blends with the conscious self, the person shows herself to the world as angry or anxious, but other Parts are present, too.

We See Parts Vaguely

When you and I observe a person, we see the blended Parts of her only vaguely as we interpret her expression, her tone of voice, or her body language, and then understand that she's feeling angry or anxious. She and her angry and anxious Parts are one as the conscious self at a given moment. But at another time, we might see the same woman as happy and carefree, when different things happening in her life encourage happier Parts to be at the forefront.

In therapy, because we don't see her Parts clearly, we have to work with them indirectly, through the conscious self. We guide the conscious self (the patient) in visualizing her Parts. Only then can we work with them, and only through her. It's true that a Part is a part of the conscious self, but so are other Parts. If we work only with the conscious self, we don't know which of the blended Parts is dominant in the conscious self at any given moment. We don't know *who* is speaking to us through the conscious self.

Parts Store Memories

Individual Parts are the structures that house memories. Parts and Memory Therapy edits the memories where they're stored in the content of Parts. Memories aren't stored directly in the conscious self. If the conscious self is like a house near a creek and a Part is the creek, then when the creek overflows into the house, we can clean up the overflow for temporary relief. But it does nothing to fix the problem of living next to a creek that sometimes overflows. We have to somehow fix the creek so that it doesn't overflow. We might need to dredge the creek or build up the banks so it runs true. With people, fixing the creek means healing the emotional memories that drive the Parts to overflow into the house of the conscious self. Once the Parts are healed the conscious self can think and behave in ways that are appropriate to our life situations.

HEALING EMOTIONAL MEMORIES

In order to heal the *implicit emotional memories* (the stored emotional memories connected to specific life events) that are the sources of our pain, we have to activate them. That activation comes from locating the Parts that hold the memories and then directing the Parts to focus on the stored memories. We'll know the Part has activated the memories when we ask the Part to share how disturbing a given memory is on a 0-10 scale (the SUD scale), and the Part tells us something like "7 or 8." Now we can edit the emotional memories. We can't do that with a conscious self who tells us that the remembered event "happened long ago and doesn't bother me anymore."

Sometimes, when a memory is activated, both the patient and the Part feel the emotions of the remembered event. It depends upon how closely blended the Part is with the conscious self. I've found that while we can achieve temporary relief for someone by directing an intervention at the conscious self (the house near the creek) rather than the Part (the creek), but the relief from the symptoms lasts for a few days at most. The Part (the creek) still needs to be fixed.

Parts Give Meaning to Actions

Another way to think about the conscious self in relation to Parts is to say that the self perceives reality through a set of lenses that are Parts or subpersonalities. When a Part blends with the conscious self, that subpersonality determines the meaning of what the self perceives in the external world. If a different subpersonality blends with the self at another time, the meaning of the external perception is different. For example, a woman may look at her husband, fresh out of the shower, through the lens provided by her sexual or romantic Part. She responds accordingly. But if the same woman views her husband through the lens of the haggard, overworked mother of two demanding, sick children, she isn't likely to respond amorously to her husband. She's more likely to be concerned with the mess he's making, or with how he could be helping with the children rather than taking a shower in the first place.

Magical Thinking

Another question that sometimes comes up has to do with the visualizations that neutralize emotional memories, such as: "I'm still having difficulty understanding how one can release the negative emotions of a memory through visualization. It sounds suspiciously like *magical thinking*. How can an exercise of the imagination heal the memory of a painful experience that happened in the real world?"

Many patients, when relieved of the heavy emotional burden of a traumatic memory, actually say, "It feels like magic!" Many of them ask how can something that caused pain for so long be neutralized in a just few minutes. And then they worry that the pain will return, and they check and recheck over the next couple of weeks to be sure the pain is really gone. Eventually they accept that the therapy works. So, yes, for many people it feels like magic. But it isn't magic. It's neuroscience in action.

Memory Reconsolidation

The references in Appendix 1 at the end of the book provide more information, but the process is called "memory reconsolidation." The short version is that reactivating the memory through interviewing the Part that carries it opens a five-hour window during which the emotional memory can be edited where it's stored in the brain. A wind, water, or fire fantasy that eliminates the implicit emotions attached to the explicit memory is real at the level of the brain's memory circuits. And once the five-hour window is closed, the changes are permanent (see the reference to the Dahlitz and Hall's [2015] edited book).

As for "healing real-world experience," that experience obviously isn't changed. The work focuses on memories of real-world experience, not the real world itself. But the perception of the real world and of the experience does change. Real-world experience is no longer just real-world experience once it's coded into memory. The organization of memory is subject to different processes than the organization of real-world events as they happen. Memory reconsolidation lets us change stored implicit emotions, which changes the way we emotionally perceive our memories of real-world experience. The changes are so profound and quickly achieved that for many it feels like magic

AMELIA'S PARTS IN ACTION

Returning now to our work with seemingly magical experiences, we last talked to Amelia as we completed our work with her lost ten-year-old-boy Part. I was ready to wrap up that session and continue in the following week, but Amelia had been waiting for a chance to mention the anxiety that had been building in her chest throughout the hour.

We didn't have enough time to explore this anxiety in depth, but I hoped to find a way to limit it between sessions. Maybe we could find an image of the anxious Part and convince it to wait for attention until our next meeting.

To help Amelia develop a strong connection to the sus-pected Part, I suggested that she speak (silently) to the sensation in her chest and request an increase in that sensation. When the sensation increased in intensity, I knew we were communicating with the Part—how else to explain the response to this simple request? Then I asked Amelia to address that sensation and ask for an image of it in her mind.

An Old Woman Part Appears

Old Woman

Immediately, Amelia could see *"an old woman with white hair, wearing a long skirt and a shawl. She can barely walk. She is crippled, weak."* The image was a simple black-and-white one, no color at all. When asked, the old woman acknowledged that she knew Amelia and that she was always involved when Amelia experienced her monthly distress at ovulation. (Remember that ovulation distress is linked to premenstrual distress as an atypical pattern of PMS.) She said it was okay just to call her *Old Woman*. Symbolically, the Part's physical image reflected how Amelia felt during her PMS at ovulation and later. Old Woman said she looked forward to talking with us again.

As we ended this, our sixth session, yet another Part intruded, this time as a sensation in Amelia's head, which she believed was also connected to her anxiety and stress. We lacked the time to explore it, and it returned at the end of the next session as well. It wasn't until our eighth session that we had a chance to interview the Part. It showed itself as a big man, a giant who seemed to amplify anger as his role in Amelia's life.

PMS As the Old Woman's Symptoms

Meeting in the following week, we first checked Amelia's PMS symptoms. Her usual ovulation-distress appeared five days before our session, on a Sunday. We now knew that her symptoms were Old Woman's symptoms, produced by the Part's blending with Amelia.

Although she was calm for our session, Amelia had felt bloated and irritated during some of those five days, and tired for three or four days, but she managed to drag herself to work. At home she was lethargic and irritable and had yelled at the kids. Michael ignored her. She had already been feeling stressed about finances, and with having to move her office to a new location (a dispute with her landlord led her to break her lease). She thought these stresses may have made her symptoms worse than they had to be. Her symptoms suggested that we hadn't neutralized her irritability as we had hoped, although we had eliminated one source of it.

There was also good news: *"Normally, I would be subject to rages for two days. And sometimes I would have to cancel a [psychotherapy] client and go home to bed."* But she hadn't raged this time, and she missed no days at work. She was irritated, but less so. Another difference from the usual was that her fatigue lasted longer than normal. Amelia viewed this as a positive: *"The lingering of tiredness is new, but it is better than being angry."* Overall, the results were positive.

OLD WOMAN

We returned to Old Woman from our previous session. Amelia readily talked about her new Part: *"I kept seeing her all week. She was present all of this week. I felt her tiredness, the sensation she had of wanting to give up. I wished I could have two or three days just to do nothing."* When asked about her earliest painful memory, Old Woman first revealed a feeling of being extremely tired and having difficulty concentrating. *"The feeling was almost paralysis. She has a walker to help her move around but she is frozen holding it. She cannot go forward or sit down."* Amelia spoke inwardly and silently to her image of Old Woman and asked that the Part's fatigue and paralysis *step back*. For me, stepping back means inward separation from the body; I don't really know what it means to Parts. But it works. After Amelia made the request, she quickly observed: *"She sat down; her paralysis was unfrozen."*

Old Woman's Memories

Amelia could then examine the memories that were triggered in Old Woman; *"It was my second job after college. I was in HR [Human Relations] and we worked 12-hour days for four or five months. Then, in another factory, I worked 60 days straight without a day off. Constant trainings. From the mornings to late at night."* Amelia said of Old Woman's participation in the heavy workload: *"She feels stressed. Like she cannot stop. She is not allowed to rest."* The memories were disturbing to Old Woman at a level 9 on the SUD scale. The emotions and body feelings Amelia identified as the source of this rating were **tired, stressed, and pressured**.

What this conversation with Old Woman seems to be showing is that the emotions connected to those past experiences are reactivated in the present during the hormonal changes of Amelia's monthly cycle. For this reason, we expected that healing Old Woman's emotional memories from the past would lessen her negative emotional experiences in the present during Amelia's ovulation.

Old Woman readily agreed to permit Amelia to help her let go of her painful emotions and body sensations. She agreed also to the use of a wind intervention to do so. I coached Amelia as she asked Old Woman to notice where in her body she stored the memories of being **tired, stressed, and pressured** during work in the factories and then to bring a wind to blow through her and break up the feelings into tiny particles of dust and blow them away. Shortly after beginning the visualization, Amelia noted that she was having problems concentrating. We tried to overcome that by increasing the power of the intervention and substituting a tornado for simple breezes of wind. This reduced the SUD score to 7 from 9, but it was stuck there. In an effort to help Old Woman release her remaining distress, we suggested that she tell us more about her memories—encouraging a Part to give voice to her story through the patient often reduces the resistance to healing.

Telling Her Story

"I was on autopilot. There were pressures from my bosses, from the owners, lots of conflict—it was a new company—and confusion. Some workers were getting hurt. She felt responsible. People would come to her and ask her to do something about it—training and implementation, safety measures. She felt guilt and also that she was being used and abused. She was unable to stop the people. She didn't know how to stop people from pushing her so hard. In both factories it was the same."

Following this short narrative, I suggested that Amelia again ask Old Woman to think about the pain she had just described and to visualize rainwater flowing over and through her while dissolving that **pain**. As Amelia visualized the intervention, she described a transformation in Old Woman: *"She has white hair and parts of her hair are getting darker now. And her clothes are starting to get some color—before, they had no color."*

Amelia then returned to the narrative of work at her first jobs: *"I just remember being miserable. In the first job, there was lots of humiliation for not speaking English well, a lot of people abusing her and looking down on her, treating her as if she were stupid. Before, she was the head of a department and now she was just a secretary. She felt she had to take it for the income. She got pregnant and had to keep at it in spite of being tired. She was pushed to her limits, helpless and hopeless. People pushed her and didn't care about her, just used her. She was so frustrated."*

Neutralizing Emotions Makes Old Woman Younger

Again, I asked Amelia to help Old Woman focus on the **negative emotions** and **sensations** that Amelia had just described for her. I tried to boost the power of the intervention by suggesting Amelia now visualize a flood of rainwater flowing through Old Woman, dissolving the negative feelings into muddy or discolored water as it ran out of her. Soon Amelia said of Old Woman: *"She is not white anymore. She is still looking down but her colors are changing. Her face is still old but her hair is dark and her clothes are different colors. She still feels old but maybe doesn't need her walker."* Such positive physical changes in the image of a subpersonality tell us that healing is taking place. They signal that therapy is on the right track.

End of Session Calming

We were near the end of the session. Old Woman had made significant improvements but had more to do. Hoping that

Amelia wouldn't be negatively influenced by Old Woman between sessions, I suggested a *rescue* intervention in which Amelia would visualize moving Old Woman to a more comfortable place. However, Old Woman was comfortable where she was: *"She likes where she is sitting. There are trees all around her in a forest. She is still too tired to move."* Amelia informed Old Woman that we would return to the healing work in our next session.

For the last few minutes of the session, I wanted to concentrate on helping Amelia become centered again before she left my office. She was *"so tired."* I viewed her fatigue as a residual from our work with Old Woman and hoped we could reduce it. I guided her in the *step-back* technique by asking her to notice where in her body the **tired** feeling was greatest and then to speak to that feeling and ask it to step back. We repeated this exercise three times before Amelia could say, *"It is better, a little bit."* And then she added, *"I feel pressure in my head."* Still not wanting to release Amelia while she was distressed, I asked her to speak to that pressure and ask it for a picture of itself.

Amelia said, *"I see a big man. He is a monster in his physique, like a giant."* She coached him to step back for now and we would talk to him next session. The pressure eased. She commented, *"He is in the same forest as Old Woman. He went away."* We planned to work in our next session with both Old Woman and the giant.

A PART NAMED DISTRACTION

It was two weeks before we met again. During this time, Amelia had experienced *"non-stop anxiety."* She was exhausted but also fidgety and unable to relax. Her period had begun the previous day. She was feeling again the usual physical discomfort but, unlike most women with PMS, her emotional symptoms didn't lessen with the beginning of menses.

Fighting with Michael

Amelia talked about a fight she had had with Michael a few days earlier, before her period: *"Postpartum Me was activated again and she hated him. I asked Michael to take care of something because I was not feeling well, and he got angry. I was enraged, so very angry. I cursed him. He still does not get it that when I am weak or sick, I need help. I feel trapped."* In this case, both Postpartum Me and Old Woman seem to have worked together to make Amelia's marital complaints during her PMS vulnerability. The complaints seem to have angered Michael. With both parties to a couple angry, their blow-up is inevitable.

Getting Acquainted with the Giant

With this as the setting for our session we followed our plan of returning to the giant we had met at the end of the previous session. Amelia easily located him and allowed me to guide her in asking a series of questions aimed at learning about his role in her internal world of Parts. Her eyes were closed as she silently conveyed my questions to the giant and then verbally relayed his answers back to me:

> Say hello and ask him if he knows who you are.
> *"Yes, he knows me. He says I am Amelia."*
> Ask if he has a name.
> *"His name is Distraction."*
> Ask if he's blocking our work with Old Woman.
> *"He does not know if he is blocking Old Woman."*
> Does he know your husband?
> *"Yes."*
> Does he like him?
> *"He is indifferent to him. He does not like him or dislike him."*
> Does he know your children?
> *"Yes."*

Does he like them?

"He is indifferent to them."

Does he like you?

"He does not care."

Ask him to share his earliest significant memory.

"He does not know what it is."

Ask for any memory.

"He says he does not have any."

Was he the Part enraged with your husband during your fight with him?

"Yes."

Does he know Postpartum Me from the shower?

"He does not know her."

Does he know you went to college?

"He knows."

Does he know you live in the United States now?

"He does not know if he knows that. He does not care. He seems irritated when I speak to him, bothered."

Is there anyone he likes?

"He does not know."

Does he know any child Parts? Does he protect them?

"He seems to like the baby Part. But he does not watch over her."

Does he know that he lives within your mind?

"He does not know that. Now he does not care."

I included this extended question-and-answer passage to illustrate the sorts of questions we often use to learn something about a newly exposed internal Part. It also illustrates that Parts therapy isn't always as productive as it might seem as I describe it for you.

In this case, the name *Distraction* seems to convey the giant's function—at least during this part of our session when he distracted us from deeper work. More likely, however, the distraction he normally provided allowed Amelia to temporarily escape from the unmanageable emotions she carried from childhood into her rage with Michael. Unfortunately, the distress of childhood memories and her troubled relationship with Michael were unchanged after her rage was spent. We would have to see what developed over time in order to further assess Distraction's role. He seemed to be one of those uncommon managing Parts that claimed no autobiographical memories of their own but instead amplified the emotional extremes of other Parts.

He did finally provide a minimal amount of information when we pointed out the conflict between his stated indifference to Michael and the rage he claimed in the verbal fight with him. His answer was that he had just now become angry. And that was because *"nobody cares for him or about him. He will fight when someone pushes him around."* This suggested that in fact he did identify with Amelia since she was the external person who felt pushed around by Michael.

MOVING ON FROM DISTRACTION

With seemingly little benefit from interviewing Distraction, we moved on. We learned at least that he was probably not a major player in Amelia's internal world. I asked Amelia if she could find Postpartum Me. She easily visualized her. The Part verified that she was involved in Amelia's fight with Michael. Her own anger was more strongly triggered when Michael was also angry.

More Therapy with Old Woman

Amelia also quickly located Old Woman. She, too, was involved in the fight. In fact, she was the Part of Amelia that motivated her to ask Michael for help. It appeared that big man Distraction was triggered when Old Woman was hurt by Michael's refusal to help, although he seemed unaware of the trigger. We can speculate that his great size and strength symbolized his power and that, when activated, he provided

Amelia with the power of rage to deal with Old Woman's (and thus her own) sense of being threatened. It was likely not a coincidence that he lived in the same area of the forest as Old Woman.

At my suggestion, Amelia attempted to neutralize Old Woman's **hurt** caused by Michael's anger with Amelia. She chose rainfall for the intervention and visualized the rain soaking Old Woman from head to foot. She asked her to feel the water dissolving the hurt of Michael's harsh language in the fight. With little success in the first pass of the intervention, Amelia tried again. But again the visualization produced no healing. This meant to me that there had to be another Part blocking the healing—because of the simple truth that anyone, given a free choice, would choose no-pain over pain. She would give up the pain if she could. This is a primary principle when there seems to be resistance to healing.

I've found just two reasons for why a Part is unable to release its pain. The first is because a younger Part from an earlier memory is somehow amplifying its own pain onto the Part we're trying to heal. The second is that there's a blocking Part, a manager of some sort, preventing the healing.

Looking for the Blocking Part

Unfortunately, I first guided us in the wrong direction, as we looked for a blocker among managerial Parts. We turned to Distraction and asked his permission to do the healing. He readily gave it, but another pass of the intervention didn't help Old Woman. Amelia said, *"She has a big hole in her chest and the rain is not healing it."*

We then tried a variety of techniques to find a way to do the healing. First, I coached Amelia to ask all of the Parts involved in the session's work to look around to try to find another Part that might be blocking the healing work. That was Distraction, Postpartum Me, and Old Woman. Amelia soon reported that *"nobody knows."*

Stuck-In-Time Amelia

Next I asked if Amelia could see the image of herself in her fight with Michael. Such an image would be a Stuck-in-Time Part, as described in Chapter 2, even though the memory of the fight was a quite recent one. Such Parts are frequently able to release their distress when the Freestanding Part holding the full set of memories cannot. Old Woman appeared to be the Freestanding Part who held the memory of the recent fight.

Although Amelia couldn't initially view herself from outside herself in this scene, she was eventually able to produce a third-person view (as opposed to the first-person view of looking out at the scene through her own eyes) by asking the angry Amelia in the memory to *"take two steps away from me."*

This may sound complicated but Amelia was now expert in visualizing Parts. She imagined where her eyes would be as she viewed the memory scene and then spoke to the spot behind her eyes, requesting the Part to show herself. Amelia could then see the angry Stuck-in-Time Part as a separate image of herself in the same way that she could see angry Michael in the memory.

She said, *"I am my current age and wearing sweatpants and the shirt I was wearing then. She is angry."* Ignoring Amelia's switching between a first person and third person reference to the Part, we asked this angry Amelia's permission to carry out the healing ritual but she refused: *"She cannot. She has too much anger."*

Finally, having exhausted other means of breaking through the resistance to healing, I decided to look for its source of resistance where I should have looked in the first place—in an earlier memory and a Stuck-in-Time Part whose amplified emotions prevented Old Woman from healing. We located the memory through an *affect bridge,* in which we asked the angry Amelia Part to focus on her anger as she let her mind float back to the earliest memories that come up. These were occasions when Amelia was angry as a child.

Childhood Anger

Amelia described a childhood scene: *"She is angry because she has to hide her feelings when she is upset. She is not permitted to cry. When she gets angry she bangs her head against the wall but she hides this from others."* Amelia explained to the child Part that it was okay for her to cry now, that she didn't have to hold it in anymore. Then she visualized rainfall soaking the little girl and washing away the **bottled-up emotions**.

Shortly after beginning the intervention, Amelia observed, *"She is crying now."* Amelia reassured the child Part that crying was okay, and that she, Amelia, would always take care of her. Then, *"She is crying desperately now."* And then, *"She seems okay now."* To complete the healing of the child Part, Amelia rescued her from her current location to a safe place: *"I took her to the playroom. She is calm now."*

Checking back with the other Parts, Amelia added, *"The angry one in sweatpants is calm now. The Old Woman, too. Distraction is a little calmer. He's talking to the little girl. She looks like my daughter and I'm feeling guilt that sometimes I don't let her express herself."*

This complex session with a variety of different interventions and different kinds of Parts finally ended, seemingly successfully. I thought that in our next session we should return to the head-banging little-girl Part to assess whether she needed additional healing. We should also continue our work with Old Woman and Distraction.

SUMMARY OF PARTS

Old Woman. She shows herself as very old and decrepit, symbolizing the debilitating nature of PMS. She carried the memories of Amelia's work stress from her earliest jobs as well as her current overwhelm with respect to her career demands, parenting duties, and lack of appreciation by Michael. She's an important Freestanding Part both in the next chapter and much later in the book.

Distraction. This giant male seems to have no internal function except as an amplifier of anger and a distraction from emotional pain. He has no continuing presence in the narrative.

Angry Amelia. This recent Stuck-in-Time Part represents an angry Amelia as she recalls herself in a current-time argument with Michael. She was important here only as a vehicle for locating an angry, head-banging child Part.

Head-Banging Little Girl. She represents Amelia's overwhelming anger as a child who dealt with her feelings by banging her head against the wall. She appears again much later in the story but has healed most of the pain that caused her anger.

Chapter 5
Amelia Triumphs

When we met again, Amelia divulged that she had continued to feel overwhelmed since our last session. Although an acupuncture treatment helped somewhat, she was anxious throughout the week. It was also the week of her period, a time that was normally difficult for her. It was too early to know whether the therapy might also reduce the emotional or physical aspects of menses.

RETURN TO THE HEAD-BANGING LITTLE GIRL

We began our deep work by returning to the little-girl Part that Amelia had moved to the playroom, her safe place. She quickly located the little-girl and asked her if she wanted to give up the pain of her head-banging experiences. As expected, she was eager to heal.

Amelia's gentle questioning of the child Part revealed that the source of her head-banging was the anger she felt in response to *"loneliness and the pressure to be perfect."* Amelia explained to the child that it was time to retire from her job as pressure handler, because grown-up Amelia would now take on that duty. She then visualized a light rain falling on the little-girl to wash away her **pressure**. Surprisingly, Amelia explained, rather than being passive during the visualization, the

Head Banging Little Girl

little girl spontaneously chose her own means of healing: *"She feels the pressure like a rock in her head. She takes it and throws it away. She is happy now and not lonely. She is playing with Postpartum Me and the other little girl* [i.e. Amelia 7, the Stuck-in-Time Part from Chapter 3]. *She is being silly now."* As Amelia, eyes closed, described the smiling little girl, she too smiled. The feeling states of the little girl were also *her* feeling states. They were one in that moment.

HEALING OLD WOMAN

We also had unfinished business with Old Woman. We had detoured to work on the angry fight with Michael but didn't check on Old Woman's wound before closing the previous session. Amelia found her internally, sitting on a bench in her forest. She still had the hole in her chest. This time, however, when Amelia repeated her visualization of falling rain, she noticed right away: *"It is healing. The hole was more in her stomach than her chest and it is healing. But it is getting there with wind, not with rain."* A full minute later, she said, *"Okay, it is healed."* The difference in Old Woman's response to the healing ritual this time seems pretty clearly to be that we first healed the head-banging little girl. We did most of it during the previous session and completed it today. The little girl no longer amplified her pain onto Old Woman. And that allowed Old Woman to heal too.

Because it's common for aged or disfigured Parts to appear differently at different stages of the process of healing, I asked whether Old Woman had changed her appearance. Positive changes in physical appearance symbolically tell us that we're making progress in the therapy. Amelia said, *"The Old Woman is tired, and she has the same colors. Last week her hair had become half black and half white from being all white. It is still that way."*

Alone and Depressed in Utah

We moved on to Old Woman's next disturbing memory. It was the experience of *"being alone and depressed after I moved to Utah."* Actually, a set of memories, the experiences were disturbing at a SUD level 6 for Old Woman but only a 2 for Amelia. This common difference between the conscious self and the Part in the amount of distress a memory holds for them illustrates how Parts allow us to move forward with tomorrow's activities without being held hostage by yesterday's pain. The Part holds the distress away from the conscious self, although unconsciously the distressing memory continues in full force.

Amelia, in consultation with Old Woman, chose wind as the healing intervention. She asked Old Woman to focus on her negative emotions as the wind scoured the memories and neutralized the feelings of **loneliness** and **depression**. Within a few moments, Amelia smiled and said, *"She looks younger. The wind blew the feelings out of her. Her hair is now curly and black. She looks like a gypsy, with colorful clothing. She does not look like me, not at all. She has big hair, curly hair and it is long."*

When asked about her next disturbing memory, Old Woman had no more to say. It appeared that we had healed all of her significantly painful memories.

The Gypsy in Amelia

Gypsy

I was curious about Old Woman's continuing role in Amelia's life, and curious as well about whether there would be changes now that Amelia had renamed her *Gypsy*. She summarized the Part's response to my question: *"She is the gypsy in me that moves from place to place. Her job is to learn new things, to help me change, to find adventure and to change. When I was a child, I liked to dress as a gypsy. That was cool. I loved adventure."* Amelia smiled broadly at her summary and then added, *"That was weird. I never thought of that as a Part of me. For Halloween, I would dress up as a gypsy. I have not thought of that in years* [smiling]."

Postpartum Me's Anger

With Old Woman's memories now healed, and with just a little time left in the session, I suggested that Amelia find Postpartum Me to check whether she was still angry about the fight with Michael. *"She still hates him sometimes. She does not like him. But the incident does not make her angry anymore. It makes her resentful and makes her want to be away from him. She wants to reject him. She does not want to be close with him."*

The day's therapy seemed to have softened the Part's anger over Michael's angry attack, but she continued to retain a level of displeasure with him. It was unclear whether this was because the incident wasn't yet neutral for Postpartum Me or because of other painful memories we had yet to treat. We planned to explore this at our next meeting. Amelia then visualized returning Postpartum Me to the children's playroom until our next session. *"She likes it there."*

As Amelia gathered her things to leave the office, she commented on the work we had done on her gypsy Part: *"That was an interesting thing—what just happened, the gypsy thing. I always wanted to travel the world. I knew I was going to leave my country. That is what I liked about Michael. He had been to Europe, all over."*

Amelia's observation corroborates that our Parts appear in our unconscious lives in response to perceived needs and desires, often from experiences we've had at early ages. Gypsy will return in a powerful way later in the book.

Taking a Break from Deep Work

At our next session, our tenth, we didn't do any deep work with Parts. Amelia wanted a more relaxed session. The deep work of Parts and Memory Therapy can be exhausting. It's important to pace the work so that the therapy continues to be something you look forward to. We took time to talk about Amelia's general concerns with her own therapy practice, raising her children, and her husband.

POSTPARTUM ME AND JUSTICE

At the following session, it was time to reconnect to the deep therapy we had begun. I asked if Amelia could locate Postpartum Me: *"She is in the playroom. She still hates my husband a little. She thinks he is selfish."*

Amelia quickly produced three of Postpartum Me's memories. The first was a set of recollections of Michael *"playing video games and not helping her with the kids"* during her postpartum depression.

The second was a set of memories of Michael watching pornography on his computer: *"It was the same as for his video games. He would act upset for being bothered to help her. She felt she wasn't allowed to ask for him to help because if he helped her, it was angrily. So she tried to do everything by herself."*

The third set of memories related to *"traveling to Pennsylvania* [to visit Michael's family] *with two kids, three-and-a-half and one. The one-year-old could not go to sleep in the motel room. Michael could not handle it. He said, 'I am going to bed!' I sat there with one baby in one arm and the other baby in the other arm, crying—and I was crying and thinking what a mistake I made. What was I thinking to pick this kind of man—who was not going to be there for me or for the kids?"*

Amelia visualized Postpartum Me in the shower, with the water flowing over and through her, dissolving and washing her **anger** and **hopelessness** down the drain: *"It is coming out like blood in the shower. It is a hard one to get rid of. She keeps on thinking 'I made a mistake. Why did I pick him?'"* With the healing stalled, I coached Amelia to look for a blocking Part—a subpersonality that was somehow preventing Postpartum Me from releasing her pain. Amelia soon discovered another little girl nearby and asked her permission to continue our work. *"She says she is not interfering. She is just there to hang out."*

Amelia added: *"There is a boy here, too... Yes, he knows me. He says I am the owner of them—of all the Parts."* He refused to give his permission to continue healing Postpartum Me: *"He does not want to. He does not want her to get hurt again. He does not trust my husband."* The little boy held the false belief nearly universal among protective Parts that neutralizing the hurt caused by someone else will make you vulnerable to be hurt like that again. Fortunately, it's not true. If fact, you're better protected when you heal the pain. You have the wisdom of your experiences and you're wiser in the choices you make.

Amelia went on: *"I have been thinking a lot about whether I made a mistake. I used to think a lot about this in the early days of my marriage. I do not know why I am thinking about this. It is when I am not feeling intimate or close to Michael... Yes, it is the boy giving me these thoughts. And I think also about returning to my country. And then I think that I do not want to leave him. I love him!"* (Note the intrusion here of an unidentified loving Part. Whenever a person feels directly opposing thoughts or inclinations, there are always at least two different Parts providing the different perspectives.)

Working with Justice

Any internal Part that's powerful enough to block a healing intervention is by definition a manager, no matter how old it appears to be. In this case, the Part showed itself as a child, between eight and ten years old, but he was still powerful. If we wanted to continue our healing work with Postpartum Me, we had to first work through him.

When asked, he said his name was *Justice*. But when asked the standard question about his earliest painful memories, his response was simply: *"I do not know."* Eventually, after Amelia pressed him about any memories at all, she said, *"He just has a feeling—of being hurt—but it is not a specific memory."* We wanted to know about his painful memories because, lacking direct permission from him to continue our work with Postpartum Me, the next strategy would be to heal *him* enough to give that permission. This is the standard next step when working with recalcitrant managers.

The boy agreed to let us help him neutralize his **hurt**. Amelia then visualized him in a shower of his own and asked him to feel the water wash it away. Then: *"This is an odd Part. He does not have as clear a body as the others. He is kind of cartoonish, so I cannot see his body as clearly. It is kind of shifting."* I reminded Amelia that she didn't necessarily need a clear picture of the Part as long as she could somehow imagine the healing process. She added, *"He does not let the water touch his body."*

Since we had his permission to heal him, the fact that the water didn't reach his body was a sure sign that there was still another blocking Part. I suggested that Amelia ask to speak to his boss. Asking for a Part's boss sometimes works and sometimes doesn't. It makes the implicit assumption that the manager has a manager. She responded, *"He is sneaky; he is jumping around."* Another manager didn't appear.

We were near the end of the session and there wasn't time to continue the search for the new blocking Part, if there was one. For this reason, I suggested that Amelia move Postpartum Me to a safe place, and check with the boy for a suitable place for him. She visualized moving Postpartum Me to the children's playroom and said of the boy, *"He wants to hide in the closet."* We planned to work with both of them in the next session.

Deep Work Interrupted

Current issues in Amelia's life prevented us from returning immediately to work with Justice and Postpartum Me. Amelia had felt overwhelming depression during the week between sessions. Several problems from different sources combined to overwhelm her. Her business landlord had placed restrictions on her use of her office that significantly interfered with the patients she wanted to see. Her daughter was having difficulty concentrating at school. And she and Michael had several arguments during the week.

I couldn't easily pin down the primary source of her depressed mood. It might simply have been stress overload from all she had to do. Based upon the date of her last period, she should have been between her period and ovulation, generally a comfortable time for her. The daily-life difficulties she had described might have been primary, but her physician had also changed her medication for the treatment of her hyperthyroidism—and changes in thyroid hormones can produce emotional difficulties. It might also have been the therapy, and I was concerned about that possibility. I knew that deep work can sometimes cause distress when it's unfinished or incompletely contained. We had left our deep work in a place where we had opened up old wounds but had been unable to heal them. Sometimes, temporary depression can just be about what's happening now; it doesn't always have to be about re-experiencing childhood wounds.

Checking on Justice

Another problem was that Amelia had left our last session with a headache that lasted for two more days. She believed that it was caused by Justice, the new little-boy Part. With just ten minutes left in our session, we decided to do a quick check on Justice to see if he was indeed the source of her headache.

Amelia turned her attention inward and located the little boy in the closet where she had left him. He was anxious and acknowledged that it was *"hard for him to let go of anything."* Previously, when we were unable to help him with a water intervention, I thought there might have been another manager blocking our work. Despite this possibility, I decided to try again to get to know him. We tried to connect with him with simple, get-acquainted questions.

After Amelia asked about Justice's earliest painful memory, she reported, *"He cannot think of anything."* He could, however, answer other questions. He knew Michael but didn't like him because *"he hurts me* [Amelia]*."* He knew her children and didn't like them either, because *"they irritate me... Yes, he had a headache at our last session but he always has a headache. His head is overwhelmed. He has too much stuff in his head."* Some of that stuff had to do with Amelia's postpartum depression following her second child. *"Thinking of it makes him angry."*

Helping Justice with His Irritation

Our session was at an end and we had done no deep work. But I hoped to give Amelia some relief from the pain she felt from Justice. I asked if the boy was still irritated with her kids. She said he was, and when she asked, he agreed to allow her to help him release his current-time **irritation** with the children (i.e., without exploring earlier memories). She used a wind intervention and visualized wind blowing over and through Justice as he focused on letting go of that irritation. He was successful. He also temporarily gave up his irritation with Michael.

I was pleased that we had been able to do a small amount of inner work after all. And it was significant that Justice had fully participated in the intervention without interference from any other Part. My hope was that he would now soften up and permit the healing of Postpartum Me.

Before we parted, Amelia noted that she again had a headache. Fortunately, when she visualized giving the headache back to Justice, she felt much better. Finally, she also visualized giving him an icepack to help him cope with his pain.

Headaches are often caused by a blending Part. In this case Amelia knew which Part it was. Working with other patients, I've found that they're often surprised to get immediate relief for headaches simply by speaking to the headache sensation as if it were a person and asking it to "step back." They might have to repeat the request two or three times. Try it!

DEPRESSION-FREE OVULATION

The week between sessions had been hectic for Amelia. This was our thirteenth session. She had decided to solve the problem with her business landlord by relocating to another office about three miles away. Office-hunting and planning a move is always stressful, and she had spent all of her available time seeking out a suitable office. She planned to move her furniture there during the coming weekend.

The best news, however, was that although she had just ovulated, she wasn't depressed or otherwise oppressed during this phase of her cycle: *"I am not depressed like previously, or irritable. I had some tears from arguments with Michael and some concern about my children, so I probably had some sensitivity. But not as much as before* [during ovulation]." This was indeed good news. I felt optimistic again that the therapy was aiding the relief of her menstrual cycle distress—getting through ovulation without emotional distress was rare for Amelia.

JUSTICE AND THE FATHER INTROJECT

When we met again, we returned to our unfinished work with Justice, the little-boy Part with a continuous headache. When Amelia located him, she smiled and said, *"He still has an ice-pack in his hand."* When asked about his earliest painful memory, Justice still couldn't identify specific memories, but was able to communicate that he was *"nervous all the time."*

This sort of no-response to the earliest-memory question isn't usually a barrier to continued memory processing. Although I prefer to do the healing by directly processing autobiographical memories, we could also work with Justice's free-floating distress. We would direct the fantasy intervention at his emotion and expect this to trigger specific memories to flash through his (and thus the Amelia's) consciousness as the intervention moved forward.

Amelia chose a wind intervention to neutralize the boy's anxiety. She asked him to notice where in his body he felt his **nervousness** and then to experience the wind blowing over, around and through him, breaking up his **nervousness** into tiny particles and blowing it away. The process took longer than usual, but after about forty seconds of silence (I kept a tiny watch attached to my clipboard), Amelia said, *"He remembers being yelled at, being punished, being expected to be perfect."*

The flood of memories provided a new focus for the intervention. Amelia asked Justice to let the wind blow over these memories as they appeared and to notice how the wind stripped his **negative emotions** from the memories. After another minute of silence as Amelia visualized this process, she said, *"The anxiety doesn't come out easy. It is coming but it feels like it's hard to."* She renewed her visualization and after another seventy seconds, she said, *"It is partially out."* And then, *"Now it is stopped."*

As always, when a subpersonality is unable to complete the process of releasing the negative emotions, we look for a blocking Part. I asked Amelia to look around the internal environment where she worked with Justice and to look for another, intrusive Part in the scene. We had previously suspected the presence of such a blocker.

A Father Introject Shows Himself

She quickly reported the presence of an adult Part, an internal image she hadn't seen before. Then she clarified, *"He looks like my father."* We approached the Part as we did nearly every Part, by asking it whether it knew Amelia. *"He knows me. He says he is my father."* He was a *Father Introject*, a Part created in Amelia's unconscious mind to represent certain of her actual father's traits.

I prefer to introduce as few changes as possible in a patient's inner world while still getting the healing done. But my experience with parent introjects is that they often make the healing difficult because of other Parts' delusion that the introject is the actual parent and not a Part.

My immediate thought was to somehow remove it from the scene. Still, I wanted to give it a chance to be cooperative with our work. We asked him why he was blocking the intervention, but he had no explanation. We asked for his permission to continue neutralizing. He agreed. That is, Amelia, still with her eyes closed, responded with a positive *"Uh huh"* to my request for permission. Unfortunately, there was still no further progress when Amelia resumed her visualization of the wind blowing through Justice.

I always feel under pressure in a session to accomplish as much healing as possible during the short amount of time available. For this reason, rather than attempt to learn more about the meaning of interference by the Father Introject, I chose to disable its blocking function. Knowingly or not, he seemed to be blocking our work.

It's tempting to take a side journey and explore unconscious meanings. It's easier on the therapist to do this rather than stick strictly to the task at hand. Basically, it can be fun for both therapist and patient to explore unconscious meanings. Other psychodynamic therapists might want to explore the psychosocial function of an introject that's so powerful that the patient has unconsciously constructed its image among her set of subpersonalities. Many years of experience of working with inner Parts have taught me, however, that no matter how great the insights that follow from taking these tempting byways, insight doesn't directly heal a patient. The end of a session always looms and we may have made little progress in permanently healing the problem on which we worked.

UNMASKING THE INTROJECT

I described the unmasking process in Chapter 2, but it's worth repeating here. We accomplish it by converting the image of the introjected person to an image of the patient. Because everything in a patient's head belongs to the patient—and is a Part of the patient—so too is the introject. It follows that the image of the introject must be a costume worn by an internal actor. So we need to remove the costume. Unmasking removes the introject costume and reveals the image of the patient underneath, generally looking like the patient as she looked at the age when her unconscious mind created the introject.

Several straightforward steps are normally sufficient to accomplish the unmasking. I guided Amelia in the process. First, she praised the Father Introject for helping her to grow up. She congratulated him in being successful in completing his task. In this case, the Father Introject seems to have functioned (because most introjects function this way) to remind the child Amelia of how she needed to behave around her actual father to avoid trouble with him.

Next, she pointed out that he wasn't really her father. Rather he was another version of her, wearing a father costume. She then praised the hidden Part under the costume for being an outstanding actor, *"perhaps the greatest actor of all time."*

Finally, Amelia addressed the actor-Part and asked her to unzip the costume and step out of it, or pull it over her head, and *"just be the Amelia beneath the costume."*

An Eight-Year-Old Part

This formula produced—in place of the father introject—an image of Amelia at about the age of eight, the first of many eight-year-olds we would meet. Amelia quickly introduced herself and established that this child Part also had painful memories: *"She is showing me good times she missed, like birthday parties she missed—because they stopped happening. And she misses those good times. There were fights, conflicts. My dad shows up drunk or not at all. If he comes, he will fight with my mom or other people."*

Amelia healed the little-girl Part fairly quickly. She asked her to notice where it was in her body that she kept the **pain** of her father's spoiled and missed celebrations and then used the wind to break up and blow away that pain. A single pass of the intervention reduced the SUD level to *"a little bit"* and a second pass reduced it to zero. Touchingly, the child Part expressed concern about Amelia: *"She is worried about me, that I am hurt."*

Frequently, Parts are not aware that the external person talking to them is now grown up. That seems to be true here as the little girl expressed concern for Amelia. Amelia explained that she was a grownup now and that her job was to take care of little girls and not the reverse. She visualized rescuing the little girl to her favorite safe place and all was fine.

NEUTRALIZING ANGER

With the blocking introject now out of the way, Amelia quickly completed her neutralizing of Justice's **hurt feelings** about being yelled at and otherwise punished for not being perfect. But when we checked for other painful memories, Amelia found: *"He is still angry with Michael. That has not changed. He does not understand why Michael acts the way he acts— like his screaming, being upset, fighting with me, or being stubborn."* Justice's anger was at a level 10 on the SUD scale.

In general, I don't directly attempt to neutralize a Part's anger. That's because anger is always a secondary, protective emotion and strongly resistant to change. I try instead to help a person find the more vulnerable emotions that anger protects against. Anger dissipates when we heal the underlying emotion.

In this case, however, we had just healed a lot of hurt and Justice was still angry. I agreed when Amelia wanted to direct a wind intervention at the boy's **anger**. While I doubted that we could heal the anger in this way, I wanted Amelia to feel comfortable in directing her own therapy when she could. We could always take the usual route of seeking the more vulnerable emotion after we had failed at the direct path.

Amelia visualized a scene of wind blowing through Justice and soon observed, *"Uh huh, it is coming out like flies."* I was surprised but pleased at Amelia's success. The SUD level was down to a 2 or 3. It was stuck there *"because Michael still acts stupid."* I suggested that Amelia coach Justice to focus upon the likely occasions when Michael will again act stupidly and to then neutralize this expected anger "of today, tomorrow, and next week." Soon Amelia said, *"Uh huh, okay. It is zero. He does not care much about him."* Justice was no longer angry.

We were out of time and so I assured Amelia that we would return to Justice the following week if the boy had more healing to do. She responded by adding, *"I think there is another Part angry with Michael. Not the boy. I think it is someone else."* We planned to follow up on this at our next session.

A GRANDMA PART APPEARS

During the week prior to our next session, Amelia was stressed by her limited financial resources as she bought furniture and other supplies—such as children's toys—for her new office. Her previous office had come with furnishings as well as a child therapy room. Otherwise, she had no complaints of emotional issues. She had just finished her period and had been free of the most challenging aspects of her previous premenstrual and menstrual distress.

Returning to our work with Justice, he wasn't currently angry with Michael. He indicated, however, that he knew of another Part that *was*. He agreed to bridge to that Part, and quickly gave Amelia a picture of it. Evidently, this was the Part she had sensed at the end of our last session.

In meeting a new Part, I almost always ask if it knows who Amelia is. I want to know how well the Part is oriented to her in current time. Often a Part is unaware of Amelia's day, month, or even year. It might even be unaware that it's a Part of Amelia.

Amelia described the new Part as *"an older woman."* We quickly learned that she was co-conscious with Amelia, meaning that she shared Amelia's time and space orientation. She also knew that she was a Part of Amelia and not a separate person from her. *"She is like the mother in me,"* Amelia said of her. Her name was *Grandma* and she claimed an age of sixty. It's not surprising that Amelia's *"mother in me"* was her grandmother, since she was the one who raised and nurtured her during her crucial childhood years.

Grandma's Anger

Grandma acknowledged her anger with Michael, especially *"when he yells at the kids."* She believed that her anger with Michael protected the children. However, Amelia's priority was to reduce her anger with Michael, so she wanted to reduce

Grandma's anger, too. Because if Grandma was angry, so was Amelia. Parts express their emotions through the conscious self. Like nearly all angry Parts, Grandma was reluctant to give up her anger. Amelia proposed an experiment. Grandma was to temporarily place her anger in a container and then check whether she could still protect the children from Michael. If so, Amelia wanted to neutralize her anger. If not, then Grandma could take the anger back. I call this intervention "the *two-step*."

Grandma agreed. Once her **anger** was in the container she found that she could still protect the children: *"Yes, she can take them away or stand between him and them."* Grandma gave up the contents of the container, but her SUD score was still *"a little bit."* She wasn't willing to give up *all* of her anger *"because she does not think he will stop unless she gets angry with him. He does not listen, so she has to be angry to get him to stop. When she shows her anger, he will stop and leave the room or get quiet or turn his anger on her. So she is a buffer between him and the kids."*

Hoping to reduce the anger further, I suggested that Grandma could place the remainder of her anger in a zipped pocket. It would be there if she needed it but she should first try a calmer approach. Reluctantly, according to Amelia, Grandma agreed to put away her remaining anger. But she was skeptical and untrusting. She didn't like Michael and some-times thought Amelia would be better off without him.

LOVE AND ATTACHMENT

Because the Grandma Part seemed to be the current source of Amelia's anger toward Michael, I wondered if the healing and the zipped-pocket arrangement with Grandma had had a posi-tive effect on the way Amelia viewed Michael—separately from the feelings shared by Grandma. She responded, *"I have not felt that much love for him lately. I feel numb. I know I love him. It is knowledge in my head, not a feeling inside. I have not felt that connection for a while. I know I chose to be with him and he is the father of my kids and I know he is a good man. I just do not have back that emotion. When he is being nice, I want to feel that emotion again but I do not feel it. I wonder if it is part of my postpartum. I tell him about not feeling the romantic feelings and it hurts him. When it is not good, I have to push myself to think about all the reasons to stay together—money, co-parenting, logistics. And maybe we can do couples therapy."*

Happily Ever After?

Amelia was confused by her lack of romantic feelings toward Michael while continuing to feel an attachment sufficiently strong to want to be with him in the future. We talked then about the process of fading romantic love in all relationships. It's what happens after the prince and princess ride away on the white horse to live happily ever after. Unfortunately, intense romantic love lasts for most people only twelve to eighteen months. But the attachment love she now felt for Michael could last a lifetime. I pointed out to Amelia that she was now working on the "happily ever after" part of love. It always requires work. The attachment she still felt was the foundation and motivation to continue that work.

Romantic love doesn't actually go away. But it largely fades into the background sooner than we wish. Ideally, it's replaced by a calmer, steadily-fulfilling "attachment love." The memories of the high-energy, being-in-love experiences are contained within a specialized romantic Part of the self. Romantic love doesn't easily die because Parts don't die. But romantic love of the intense, walking-on-air sort can't continue indefinitely. The couple would die of exhaustion. What usually happens is that the romantic Part gets pushed back from the forefront of consciousness as other Parts step forward to manage the everyday business of family life, including the creation and raising of children. And because the romantic Part hasn't disappeared but is only pushed back, it can still be accessed and made a part of everyday life through internal Parts work. This was an option Amelia might choose later in the therapy.

Looking Ahead

As we ended the session, Amelia shared another of her concerns: *"I am not attached to my daughter. I get more irritated with her than my son. I detached from my daughter when I bonded with my newborn son. It happened with my postpartum."* We would work on this issue in our next session.

SUMMARY OF PARTS

Head-Banging Little Girl. She makes a brief appearance for healing of her anger. A different head-banging little-girl Part appears much later in the book, but this one doesn't require additional therapy.

Old Woman/Gypsy. Old Woman completes her therapy in this chapter and no longer appears in her original form. She transforms into a young, curly-haired woman, dressed in colorful clothes. Her change symbolizes the healing of some PMS symptoms. Amelia changes her name to Gypsy. Much later in the book Gypsy is an important participant in Amelia's final healing.

Postpartum Me. She continues to be a primary target of therapy, still carrying significant anger for husband Michael.

Justice. He appeared as a manager, blocking our work with Postpartum Me. Between eight and ten years old, he had chronic headaches. He brought thoughts of returning to Costa Rica when Michael was distant and uncaring with Amelia.

Father Introject. This Part appeared in the form of Amelia's father. He was another blocking manager.

When unmasked, his image changed to that of an eight-year-old girl.

Grandma. Another introject, she functioned to protect Amelia's children from Michael's anger with her own anger. Because she understood that she was a Part of Amelia, and because she worked with rather than resisted the therapy, there was no need to unmask her.

Chapter 6
The Guilt of Motherhood

Amelia used an iPhone app to track her progress through her menstrual cycle. That and her own sensitivity to her moods shifts permitted her to know where she was in her cycle at any given time. At our next meeting, Amelia was again ovulating, which placed her in the midst of the three to four days each month that were usually the worst for her. This time, however, she wasn't angry and hadn't been angry for a noticeable number of days. This seemed to confirm that we were making progress in reducing menstrual cycle distress.

While this was a good sign, Amelia also hesitantly described feeling mildly depressed. She reported *"self-defeating thoughts,"* and a sense that her distress *"was never going to end, feeling really hopeless."* Despite her depressive thinking, she continued to see her own psychotherapy patients. Previously she might have taken a day or two off, retreating to her bed. *"Depression is better than anger,"* she said. *"Like this, I am hurting and this is better than hurting others. When I am doing therapy with others, I focus on them and so I put away my issues. But if a client is emotional, I have to work hard at holding back my emotions."*

With a reduction in Amelia's symptoms at ovulation, and having made progress in reducing Amelia's anger with Michael, we didn't immediately return to her depression. Instead, Amelia wanted to work on an issue that had dismayed her for several years, an issue she had been unable to resolve on her own. This was the troubled relationship she had with her five-year-old daughter, Noelle. In particular, she didn't feel the love for Noelle that she felt for her son. Noelle could tell that her mother favored her brother over her and showed it in her neediness. She even asked Amelia what she had done wrong.

BIG TWIN AND LITTLE TWIN

Big & Little Twin

When I asked Amelia what she felt when she thought of Noelle, she responded, *"Irritation!"* When I asked her where in her body she experienced that irritation, she indicated tightness in her jaw. When she focused upon the sensation in her jaw and asked it to give her mind an image of itself, she saw herself in her living room, wearing black sweatpants and a gray T-shirt, *"angry and screaming at my daughter during my postpartum."*

Immediately after visualizing this Part of her, she said, *"Oh! I feel pressure in my chest."* It was a different Part of her awaiting discovery. She bridged to this new Part by asking the chest pressure to provide an image of itself. The result was an image of Amelia, *"crying, feeling guilty for being a bad mother."* Like the angry Part, this new version of Amelia also wore black sweatpants and a gray T-shirt, but she was in a corner of the room in a fetal position. *"The angry one looks bigger; otherwise they are the same."* Because the two Parts dressed and looked the same except for a difference in size, we thought of them as twins.

Both of them claimed an age of thirty-two (Amelia was thirty-five), which placed them at Amelia's age following the birth of her second child, her son. Significantly, thirty-two was also the age of her major postpartum depression. We settled upon *Big Twin* for the bigger, angry one and *Little Twin* for the smaller, tearful twin in the fetal position. We asked Little Twin to stand by as we got further acquainted with the angry one. We assured her that we would soon return to get to know her as well.

GETTING TO KNOW BIG TWIN

Big Twin knew Amelia and shared her name, and she knew that she was a Part of her. She reported her earliest painful memory as dating to age seven, a memory of her mother yelling at her. It continued to disturb her decades later at a level 6 on the SUD scale. She also remembered her anger with her mother during her teenage years, and this also continued to bother her.

I asked Amelia if this was the Part of her that lacked the maternal attachment to Noelle. She responded, *"She is angry with Noelle. She does not stop crying. She is not a calm girl. Big Twin never felt love for her. If Noelle is calm, not crying, then Big Twin feels nothing.*" Big Twin had no memories of breast feeding baby Noelle. She didn't even recall her birth. Farther back, she also had no memories of being pregnant with her.

The obvious conclusion here is that the angry twin wasn't present, meaning not aware, during any part of the pregnancy and birth process for Noelle. I had seen this phenomenon before. Other mothers sometimes experience a lack of attachment to one of their children and may even refuse to accept the child as their own. With therapy, the problem can be fixed.

Big Twin's Memories

A series of questions revealed more about Big Twin's relationship with Noelle. Her earliest memory of Noelle was when she was two-and-a-half. She was angry with the child at a level 10 on the SUD scale for her nonstop crying.

Big Twin had no memory of meeting Michael in Costa Rica and, in fact, didn't like him. She didn't consider him to be her own husband; he was Amelia's husband only. The earliest memory she had of Michael was of being angry with him when he was unhelpful to her during Amelia's postpartum depression three years previously. While Big Twin denied that Michael was her husband, she claimed Amelia's parents as her own. *"She is kind of indifferent to my father; feels closer to my mother."* (It isn't unusual for Parts—especially angry Parts—to deny family relationship with you, even fathers or mothers.)

Big Twin had no memory of ever being angry with Amelia's son, only with her daughter. *"She loves my son."* Because Big Twin had presented as so angry, I wondered if she carried any positive memories at all. Amelia summarized her response: *"Her grandmother always took care of her. She took her to buy things, bought her dresses, cooked for her, took her to the movies. She always made her feel loved and protected—but not emotionally close. She was a little bit afraid of her grandmother. She had a strong personality and Big Twin didn't want to get in trouble with her."*

Different Parts Have Different Sets of Memories

As you can see from what we learned about Big Twin, her memories were spotty for many periods of Amelia's life. She's a good example of the truth that different Parts of the self have different memories. In fact, if all Parts had the same memories, they wouldn't be Parts. There would be just a single, unitary self. This is the problem behind misguided experts' efforts to heal the extreme form of Parts that we see in dissociative identity disorder. These experts try to get all Parts to share all memories and then fuse them into a single entity. But as we've seen throughout Amelia's story, it's normal to have Parts of the self, and each Part has a different set of memories. Some memories may overlap between Parts but each Part's full set of memories is unique.

GETTING TO KNOW LITTLE TWIN

Because we wanted to get to know both of the twins, we moved the angry one to a visualized safe place—the son's playroom— while we acquainted ourselves with her smaller twin. She had remained as we left her, curled into a ball against the wall of the living room. She, too, knew Amelia and understood that she was a Part of her.

Little Twin's Memories

Little Twin's earliest memory was of moving to Utah from Costa Rica, which, like most transplantations from one culture to another, required that Amelia make significant adjustments in her lifestyle.

Little Twin could recall nothing of Amelia's school-age history. She didn't recall going to college. She had a general awareness that she had met Michael in Costa Rica, but had no specific memory of the meeting.

With additional probing, we found that she could recall Amelia's marriage in Costa Rica, but *"she was not involved much in it."* This suggested to me that Little Twin didn't participate in the wedding as the bride. Most brides would rate their weddings as high-energy, positive memories. Instead, she was mostly an observer. Or, perhaps she wasn't an observer at all but merely reporting on knowledge acquired from other Parts.

Little Twin considered Amelia's parents to be her own, and so were her grandmother, aunts, and uncles. Unlike Big Twin, she also considered Amelia's husband to be her own husband.

Little Twin's Guilt

Amelia described what she learned from Little Twin: *"She feels guilty and sad about her daughter. Because she feels she has hurt her, that she has not been a good mother. She feels the anger she showed for her daughter has damaged her. She remembers her pregnancy, birth, and breast feeding. She enjoyed that. She loves her. She feels powerless when the other one is angry. She says nothing when that one shows her anger. She does nothing to protect her daughter.*

"Little Twin feels she could have done better during the first pregnancy. There was lots of stress that she did not control well. And she felt lonely after the birth. She wishes she could have been with her family. She was all alone. She didn't know how to be a mother. She made mistakes. Her mother was not there to help her. Also, she was not working, so she had no one to talk to. The people from her job were mostly single and did not call her to check on her. She wanted to at least be a good breast-feeding mother—and she did seven months—that was good. She wishes she could have bonded more with her daughter, enjoyed her more during that time."

Understanding the Twins

Summarizing what we know about the twins, they are two linked Parts with opposing attitudes and feelings about both Noelle and Michael. They present themselves visually to Amelia as identical, except that the subordinate one is smaller than the dominant angry one. They have different sets of memories, beginning at different points in time. It's unclear why they're so linked. More often, Parts that are emotionally polarized with each other occupy different positions in the internal landscape, and their relative power is closer to being equal. Here they're always near each other, and their strength is unequal.

We decided to work first with Big Twin. Her lack of attachment to Noelle, as well as her constant anger with her, portended serious adult consequences for the child. Unless Amelia healed the Big Twin Part of herself, Noelle would grow up with serious mother-issues. A mother's lack of maternal attachment to a child always leads to problems later for the child.

Meanwhile, Amelia visualized moving Little Twin to Noelle's room, preserved in memory from when she was a baby. Here she could enjoy her baby daughter's company.

THERAPY WITH BIG TWIN

Our next session was in the middle of December, our sixteenth meeting. Time had flown. We had begun in late summer, worked quickly through the Fall, and were now in the middle of Winter, on the cusp of a new year. After this session, we would break for the Christmas and New Year holidays.

We returned to our work with angry Big Twin. Amelia easily located her when she turned her attention inward. She was a veteran now at navigating her inner world. We had left the Part situated in the memory of her son's room, when he was a baby. Amelia said, *"She is okay, because she has been with her son. He calms her down."* We wanted to heal whatever it was that caused her to lack a sense of kinship with Noelle. I thought the best place to begin that work was with Big Twin's anger, often directed at five-year-old Noelle, but toward others also. We began to look for the sources of anger in Amelia's childhood.

The Pain of a Mother's Anger

Big Twin's earliest painful memory was the incident at age seven, mentioned previously. It was an unembellished recollection of Amelia's mother scolding her for something she had done, although she couldn't remember her offense. At that time, she lived with her grandmother during the workweek but joined her parents on the weekend. The memory came from one of those weekends. It bothered Big Twin at a level 8 on the SUD scale.

Previously, when Amelia reported her own SUD score, it was a 6. Usually, a memory is more disturbing to a Part than a person. That's because one aspect of a Part's job is to sequester the pain of a memory away from the person, so that the person feels less emotion than does the Part.

Big Twin felt sad and afraid as she re-experienced the age-seven memory of misbehaving: *"Her mother would get enraged. One time her mother spanked her really hard just for spilling nail polish on a comforter."*

Surprisingly, because angry Parts often resist reducing their anger, Big Twin readily agreed to healing this memory. Perhaps it was because we intended to focus on the sadness rather than the anger. Amelia visualized a compact rain cloud that hovered over Big Twin, drenching her with water that dissolved and washed away the **sadness**. Within twenty seconds Big Twin was no longer disturbed by the memory. The SUD level was zero.

Burning the Food on the Stove

The next painful incident happened when Amelia was twelve or thirteen. By this time, she was living with her mother fulltime but her parents were divorced. Her mother had gone to the store and had asked Amelia to tend to the food on the stove. At the same time, Amelia was babysitting her much younger sister, who somehow distracted her. She suddenly discovered that the house was full of smoke and a neighbor was banging on the door. The food on the stove had burned.

"My mother came home and screamed at me, telling me what a bad daughter I was. I ran away to my grandmother. That day my grandmother asked to adopt me. My mother said, 'No, never!' She said we would have to work it out. I felt a lot of fear when she took me home from my grandmother. It was a period of a lot of fighting. She expected me to know lots of things I did not know because I was not raised with her. I wanted to leave but she would not let me. I felt no love for her until my twenties. I had more anger than love for her when she divorced. I blamed her because she was angry and mean."

Big Twin agreed to heal the memories related to the stove fire, and Amelia guided her in doing so with a visualization of rain washing the **negative emotions** out of her. The first pass of the intervention lowered Big Twin's distress from a 7 to a 2 on the SUD scale. Her guilt *"for saying hurtful things to her mother"* prevented the memory from being fully neutralized. *"She was a really defiant child,"* Amelia said. Repeating the rain visualization, with a focus on the **guilt** Big Twin felt as a child, brought the memory to zero distress.

Mother's Miscarriage

The next event that continued to distress Big Twin was her mother's miscarriage, soon after her separation from Amelia's father. Her father was angry because he didn't want another child. *"They had a big fight and my mom kicked him out. My mom said that he came close to being physical with her, and she had to threaten him with a knife. Then she had a miscarriage and that made her depressed. She cried all the time. She was grieving."* Two passes of the rain intervention, focusing first on **sadness** for her mother's pain, and then on **guilt** for not helping more, fully neutralized the memory.

Teenaged Rebellion

The final set of Big Twin's memories ranged over four years, from ages thirteen to seventeen, the years between her parents' divorce and college. After the divorce: *"I was really rebellious. I did not feel connected to my mom. Lots of power struggles, long years of struggles—until I started college. Big Twin does not feel angry. More a numbness and emptiness. She was not close with her mom or dad or anybody else."*

Amelia guided Big Twin in neutralizing the painful load of emotions connected to her teen years with her mom. She chose a rain intervention, but this time she specified that it was a warm, tropical rain. Within a minute she was done, and the entire set of memories was neutral. The ease with which these memories healed isn't unusual in the context of our previous work. Once a Part's earlier foundation memories heal, the later memories offer much less resistance, and can often be bundled into sets of memories across multiple years for rapid healing. That's why Parts and Memory Therapy usually begins with the earliest disturbing memories rather than more recent ones. Unfortunately, the healing of later memories seems to have no generalizing effect on earlier memories when we try to do the most recent memories first.

We had evidently completed our work with Big Twin's relationship with her mother. *"After I started college, I had counseling with my mother. So there are no more disturbing memories."*

THERAPY IN THE NEW YEAR

We had not yet worked on Big Twin's anger with Noelle because I first wanted to heal the anger that preceded the problems with Noelle. For our next session, we planned to turn our attention to Noelle. Amelia observed before leaving the session: *"My son is more difficult to deal with than my daughter. Yet I'm calmer with him. My daughter asked me why I am more loving with my son than with her. I did not notice this difference before, but I do not want that."*

After a three-week pause because of the Christmas holidays, Amelia returned to therapy. She reported that she had continued to feel significant distress for a few days just before her period, and also during her period. (The usual pattern is for PMS symptoms to cease with the beginning of menses.) The good news was that her distress was much less than what she felt prior to therapy. I would have preferred to hear that she had no symptoms at all.

On her return to therapy, Amelia said, *"I am happier now in the New Year. It is nice to be happy for no reason."* She was in that state between her period and her ovulation when she felt best. This was progress, but we were also looking for her to feel positively at ovulation and just before her period. In another week, she would be ovulating again and we would have a chance to check whether her happy feelings continued through that time. Overall, I was feeling very pleased and confident about finishing the therapy soon.

THE PROBLEM DAUGHTER, CONTINUED

We again took up the problem of Amelia's frustration with her five-year-old daughter. She turned her attention inward and soon located the angry Big Twin, to whom Noelle wasn't a daughter. Our aim was to begin healing her of her negative experiences with Noelle. It was she who caused Amelia to be excessively frustrated with Noelle.

When asked to think about her feelings for Noelle, Big Twin expressed frustration and anger. We used these feelings to bridge to her earliest negative experiences with the daughter—by focusing on her feelings while letting her mind float back in time.

The set of memories that came up dated to three years previously, when Noelle was two and Amelia's son had just been born: *"Noelle became very sensitive and easily irritated by things she wore, like her socks and shoes. She would have tantrums. And she could not stand anything being done to her, like putting her hair in a ponytail. She was difficult to manage."* Amelia added that *"the other thirty-two-year-old* [i.e., Little Twin] *began the postpartum depression at this time. Big Twin also got angry with God for giving her such a difficult daughter."* The memories disturbed Big Twin to a level 9 or 10 on the SUD scale. Parenthetically, it's reasonable to speculate here that Noelle was having difficulty adjusting to the new baby's replacement of her as the center of attention, and with Amelia's reduced affection for her.

Neutralizing Big Twin's Painful Memories

Big Twin agreed to help Amelia by healing herself of her **frustration** and **anger**. To bring this about, Amelia visualized a strong wind blowing through the Part, breaking up those emotions and blowing them away. Then, opening her eyes again after about thirty seconds, she said, *"Better, but now she feels guilty."* This was a good initial response and one that was consistent with our general strategy of working first with the more vulnerable emotions before working with anger.

I suggested to Amelia that she let Big Twin know that guilt was scarcely more helpful than frustration and anger and she could help now by also letting go of her **guilt**. Another pass of the wind intervention brought the SUD score to a level 1. It wasn't zero *"because she is sorry for that time she missed with her daughter."* This newfound recognition of what she had missed was significant, and exactly the sort of thing I had hoped for as we worked to heal the estrangement of Big Twin from Noelle. She now seemed to be viewing Amelia's daughter as *her* daughter too.

In the next pass of the intervention Amelia asked Big Twin to focus on letting go of her **grief** and **loss**. Then she said, *"It is hard for her to let go of that sorrow. She is holding my daughter in her lap and crying."* As we earlier learned, when a Part can't reach zero on the SUD scale despite repeated passes of the intervention, we always look for a blocking manager or an amplifying Part.

Little Twin's Guilt

I thought that Little Twin, whom we had briefly interviewed, might be the amplifying Part—that is, she might be amplifying her distress onto her closely related Big Twin. I asked Amelia whether this Part might also be present in her internal scene. She responded, *"Yes, and she is crying too. She has so much guilt."* Because we had heard little from her, and because she might inadvertently be preventing further healing, I suggested that Amelia offer Little Twin an opportunity now to tell us her story:

"She feels like she did not connect with her daughter when she was a baby. It was a difficult birth, lots of pain. My daughter was in the hospital for three days—the baby was born with a fever—and she tore both sides of me to come out. I stayed home a lot during the first three days. It was too painful to walk. It took me two weeks to be able to walk well."

I suggested here that Amelia thank Little Twin for carrying her guilt for her. And to suggest also that five years of self-punishment was enough—Noelle was now five years old. Pointing out the length of time that a Part has carried a given burden is a useful way to add perspective to the problem. Even when a Part can't easily comprehend the passage of time—a frequent condition—the conscious self's comprehension of it seems to provide additional energy to the intervention.

Amelia then visualized another wind intervention and asked Little Twin to release her **guilt** for failing to connect to the newborn. Amelia soon shared that, *"She is showing other memories for when she did not do a good job."* After thanking the Part for carrying the guilt and reminding her that it was time to let it go, Amelia again visualized the wind blowing through her. And again, the Part had more to share. *"She feels sad for the last time* [i.e., the second baby] *as well."* As Amelia once more visualized the intervention, she spoke aloud, *"A lot of sadness."* I added a final suggestion that Amelia ask the Part to continue to focus on the **sadness** and to allow the wind to rapidly neutralize the memories as they popped up into her consciousness. Finally, Amelia said, *"Okay, she let them go. Now she is tired."*

We were at the end of the session and for this reason I didn't ask Amelia to probe the tiredness, which might or not be caused by additional negative emotions. I thought we could sort it out in our next session if there was still an issue. The good news was that in addition to healing Little Twin, the work also completed the healing of Big Twin, whose grief was now at zero. The hypothesis that Little Twin's distress had been preventing the healing of Big Twin was correct.

Unfortunately, while the original issues of Big Twin and Little Twin were neutralized, new issues would arise later in the therapy. We had a lot more work to do with these two Parts.

CALM DURING OVULATION

We began our second session of the New Year with more good news. Amelia was again ovulating but the days were not nearly as troublesome as they had been: *"I have been having such good days that I notice when it is different. Yesterday, I was irritated with my husband, and with my daughter who was not getting her homework done. Today, I feel tired, otherwise fine. Previously, on a day like yesterday, I would probably have had to go home to bed. I would have been sick in addition to irritable. And I would have been much more tired. I could not have functioned. Also, it would have lasted three or four days instead of just two."*

I was quite pleased. I did another check with a questionnaire that measures depression, and that also showed improvement. I thought we might be approaching the end of the therapy and that I could soon say that Parts and Memory Therapy heals PMS and related issues. Amelia similarly felt confident. She intended to talk soon with Michael about having a third child. It seemed that, with her own healing going well, she was less troubled by Michael's failings. She had begun to think positively about Michael's wish to have another child.

HEALING DAUGHTER NOELLE

When we returned to her concerns for Noelle, Amelia spoke about a headache she had as she left our last session. She had traced the origin of the headache to *"the Part who felt guilty,"* that is, to Little Twin. *"I rescued her to be with the other Part with my daughter."* The rescue to which she referred was her visualization of moving the guilty Little Twin to be with Noelle and Big Twin. In doing so Amelia relieved herself of her headache. I was happy to find that Amelia had now developed her own stress-relief skill without direction from me.

"This week I have been more affectionate with my daughter and she has responded, wanting to be with me all the time. She butted in on an argument with Michael and said, 'Do not talk to my mommy like that!' It surprised him."

This change in Amelia's feelings and attitude toward her daughter—her letting go of anger and a lack of connection— meant to me that women who fail to bond with a given child are not doomed to continue in that state forever. With appropriate therapy, they can make a fresh start with the affected child.

Commenting on her changed relationship with Noelle, Amelia said, *"Yes, I still feel a little differently for my daughter than my son, but I am much better. I think the guilty one and the angry one* [i.e., Little and Big Twin] *are grieving the loss of time with her. I also think she is oversensitive and it is my fault. Plus, she will be affected all her life because of me."* We ended the session by drawing up a plan for doing therapy with Noelle.

Therapy for Noelle

I met with Noelle and Amelia during the following week, separately from Amelia's regular session. With her mother's encouragement, five-year-old Noelle easily joined in doing her own Parts work. The wounds caused by her mother's neglect of her in favor of her brother seemed to be completely healed in two sessions, one week apart.

It appeared that therapy might be nearly completed for Amelia. She was almost ready to graduate herself. She had experienced a number of partial cycles and one full menstrual cycle without the great distress she normally felt during ovulation and before and during her period. She had a better relationship with both Noelle and Michael, and she was optimistic enough about the future to begin planning a third child. Unfortunately, I was going to hear bad news in the next session.

SUMMARY OF PART 1

Originally, Amelia had come to therapy for relief from long-lasting depression, anxiety about her marriage, and anger with Michael. She chose to focus on her anger with Michael as her first priority. It soon became evident, however, that all of her emotional symptoms were intermixed, requiring that we treat certain symptoms in some sessions but other symptoms in other sessions. Much of her anger with Michael had its beginning during her postpartum depression following the birth of her son three years previously.

As therapy continued we came to recognize that many of Amelia's symptoms were not continuous throughout the month, but linked to the phases of her menstrual cycle. Within a few weeks, Amelia began keeping detailed records of her emotional and physical symptoms over the course of her menstrual cycle. These notes, examined during our regular psychotherapy sessions, allowed us to track the changes in the type and intensity of her symptoms over time. We treated those and other symptoms as they arose.

We had begun therapy at the end of summer and met for sixteen sessions before the end of the year. Two additional sessions in the New Year, for a total of eighteen sessions over five months, concluded the first phase of treatment. Amelia had made tremendous progress over this time and it appeared that we would complete our work within a few more sessions. PMS/PMDD symptoms had significantly reduced. She wasn't depressed. She was no longer taking a day or two off to manage the emotional pain of ovulation, and her PMS symptoms were minimal or absent. Marital life was positive overall. With Amelia's anger episodes reduced, Michael reduced his angry responses to her. They were talking seriously about having a third child.

SUMMARY OF PARTS

Postpartum Me. Age, about thirty-two. She presented as a sobbing, naked adult curled into a ball in a shower stall. She functioned to hold memories that underlay Amelia's postpartum depression following her second child.

Amelia 7. A subpart of Postpartum Me. She carried memories of the absence of her father when she needed him.

Fatty/Brave. This Part originally said his name was Fatty but preferred to be called Brave. His function within Amelia's inner world was to protect a very young Amelia from the feeling of being alone. Originally presenting himself as an obese man in his fifties, the therapy transformed his image into one resembling her father in his twenties. As a positive father introject, he needed no further therapy.

Ten-Year-Old Boy. When discovered this self-state presented with fear. He felt lost in a symbolic forest. His primary function was that of carrying the memories of feeling alone and lacking secure attachments within his family. Overall, the boy was only a minor actor in Amelia's life play.

Old Woman/Gypsy. Over the course of therapy Old Woman transformed from a decrepit, white-haired old woman to a lively and colorful young woman that Amelia identified as the adventuresome gypsy within her. She functioned to help Amelia adjust to new places and also to handle the stress and anger at work and home when she couldn't safely express herself. As Gypsy, this Part was crucial in transforming negative self-blame into optimism for the future.

Distraction. This Part presented as a giant of a man and functioned primarily to amplify Amelia's anger when she felt she was being treated with disrespect.

Justice. A little-boy Part, he functioned as a system manager in influencing other Parts to be angry rather than hurt. He also utilized anger as a defense against the anxiety of having to be perfect.

Father Introject/Little Girl. During the healing process a Part representing Amelia's conception of her father transformed into the image of a little girl of about age seven. She had originally functioned as a young manager with the responsibility for protecting more vulnerable Parts.

Grandma. She was a protective internal Part with a lot of anger for Amelia's husband Michael.

Big Twin and Little Twin. These two Parts carried Amelia's lack of attachment to her daughter Noelle. Big Twin carried the anger toward Noelle and Little Twin carried the guilt and sadness for being a bad mother to her.

PART TWO

The Witch Says Stop!

Chapter 7

Struggles and Setbacks

When Amelia had gone a full month without PMS—both at ovulation and the few days directly before her period, she was optimistic that the difficulties of her menstrual cycle might be a thing of the past. I, too, was optimistic. Her depression had receded; her anger with Michael was minimal; she had healed the breach with Noelle; and she now believed she was safe to have another child. Amelia had convinced me as well. I thought we would conclude the therapy soon. I was wrong.

HINTS OF THE WITCH

Overnight, a large set of new Parts appeared, all experiencing attention-demanding, painful distress. I later learned that most of them were activated by a behind-the-scenes, very powerful manager Amelia called *The Witch*. She or the Parts she controlled required our therapeutic attention for a year more of therapy. Her story unfolds during Part 2 of the book. Her story is also Amelia's story. She's the Part of Amelia that brings to Amelia's conscious awareness all the reasons to distrust Michael, all the reasons she had ignored in favor of hope when she thought of adding a new child to her family. If Amelia is our heroine, then The Witch is our villain (but with good intentions).

131

When we met for our last session of January, we had not yet met The Witch. But her influence was clear. Amelia began by reporting, *"I just had my period. It was horrible! Both before and during it. I was very tired, very irritable. It has been a long time since it was so bad. I had two days of my period. It stopped and then started again. It was as bad as it has ever been in the past!"* With Amelia's atypical pattern of PMS, her symptoms didn't end with the beginning of her period. Her distress began premenstrually but continued throughout her period. Consequently, her menstrual symptoms were just as important to our work as her premenstrual ones.

I was dismayed at the news. She had made such great strides in her therapy. I was vicariously joyful with her as she conquered her problems and happily contemplated her future. What had gone wrong, I wondered? Was it my fault? Did I miss something? Was this just an anomaly? Would her next cycle be back to the new normal that we thought she had achieved? We soon learned that her painful PMS symptoms were not temporary.

SUCCESS BRINGS NEW PROBLEMS

Paradoxically, the setback was the result of Amelia's success in therapy. Taming her cyclical eruptions of anger with Michael, and letting go of the remnants of her depression, had helped her to find a new connection with Michael. Her marriage was strong again. Both she and Michael felt positive about their future together. They decided to have a third child: *"I started taking prenatal vitamins. We are going to try to get pregnant again!"*

Amelia was smiling and excited as she recalled their plans and preparations. But then she sobered as she also shared her doubts: *"I started becoming fearful of all the problems I had with him before, and with postpartum depression. And now that I took out my IUD and started the vitamins, I started worrying. How will I take care of the children if I am de-*

pressed?" Amelia's misgivings would be echoed by The Witch and her minions in the weeks to come.

It was soon clear that major complications had appeared in our pursuit of healing Amelia. An entirely new set of internal Parts appeared, most of them intent upon convincing Amelia *not* to have another child. It would be many months before we again approached the level of success we had in the first five months.

BLOCKS TO HEALING

We began the next phase of the therapy by turning to Amelia's worry about the care of her children should she again be overwhelmed with postpartum depression. By focusing upon that worry, Amelia found it was linked to tension in her chest. When she spoke inwardly to that sensation and asked for an image of it, she discovered a new Part, a thinner version of herself, but claiming the same age as Amelia's thirty-five. She was a *"very scared"* version of Amelia. When asked, the Part confirmed that they had not previously spoken with each other. I later came to view *Thin Amelia* as largely a pawn of The Witch, whom we would shortly meet. We would meet several other pawns before The Witch showed herself. I remain unclear as to whether these Parts had a previous independent existence or whether The Witch somehow carved them out of existing sets of memories, as I had seen powerful managers do in my work with other patients.

Following our standard approach with new Parts, we asked Thin Amelia to share her earliest painful memory. Her memory set seemed to be shallow in time depth. What came up were memories of the anxiety Amelia had felt just three years previously, during her postpartum depression. The Part felt overwhelmed with anxiety, but readily agreed to release her distress.

Unfortunately, when we tried to neutralize the **anxiety** and **overwhelm** connected to her postpartum memories,

Thin Amelia had other things to say first: *"She is just scared—of feeling overwhelmed again. She is angry because I decided to have another baby. She does not mind another baby, but she does not want to go through postpartum depression again. She does not think it is possible not to happen."* She was the first new Part to utter what would be a refrain of doubt and anger.

A Trickster Appears

Another effort to blow away the **fear** of postpartum depression failed. I suspected a blocking Part because Thin Amelia had already agreed to do the intervention. I asked Amelia if she noticed any other Part in the neighborhood that might be interfering. She said, *"There is a child, a boy, about five, maybe, in jeans and a T-shirt. I cannot see his face. Now he is turning around. I can see him—Oh!—He is not a child! He is a* duende [a Latin American mythical being, a trickster, usually conceived of as a dwarf and roughly equivalent to the North American *boogieman*]! *They do things to you and then laugh at you. They are mischievous. He is very scary. He enjoys making her afraid."*

When asked his name, he said it was *Fear,* but Amelia preferred to call him *Duende.* He said that his job was to produce fear. Despite this, I coached Amelia to explain to Duende that the prime function of all her Parts was to help her. She relayed his answer: *"He does not care if he helps me or not."*

Negotiating with Duende

Initially, I thought that, like most managers, he just needed assurances that we were all on the same team. I thought that if we could show him the benefits of healing painful emotions, he would allow us to continue our work with Thin Amelia.

I decided to start over with Duende, to get acquainted with him as we tried to do with each new Freestanding Part. I hoped we could soften him a bit and then negotiate his cooperation with the intervention.

He responded to a series of our questions, insisting that he didn't have an earliest disturbing memory; he wasn't angry; and he just enjoyed making Thin Amelia suffer. Amelia added, *"He feeds off her anxiety and fear... Yes, he knows my mother. He is indifferent to her... Yes, he knows my father. He does not like him... Yes, he knows my husband and my children and he does not like them. He only likes making her scared. He doesn't like my husband and my father because they are never there when they are needed."*

Armed with hindsight, I can see now that Duende was another of The Witch's creatures. His views were her views. His job was one assigned to him by The Witch. The job was to cause Amelia to give up the idea of having another child. He would accomplish that by keeping Amelia afraid of again dealing alone with postpartum depression.

In trying to get past Duende so that we could continue with Thin Amelia, we tried to neutralize some of his issues. He agreed to a wind intervention to release his **irritation** with Amelia's father. This resulted in him becoming indifferent rather than irritated with the father. We were unsuccessful, however, in using a wind intervention to bring the same indifference toward Michael: *"He is very angry with Michael. He says he was never there for me and never will be."*

I decided to try to help Duende learn that things had changed, that both Amelia and Michael were different now. Further, Amelia was the owner of the body (not quite right but acceptable to many Parts) and she had decided to have another baby. Since she was the owner, he should help her do what she wanted. Duende wasn't going for it. And then, when Amelia tried to convince him that Michael had changed, he wouldn't accept it: *"He is angry with me. He says I am stupid to have another baby and stupid for believing Michael. He refuses to cooperate. He laughs. He is scornful He says he is going to make my life miserable."*

UNMASKING INTROJECTS AND MONSTERS

At this point, frustrated that Duende wouldn't bend at all, I decided to try an intervention that I usually reserved for *negative introjects* and *monsters*. These entities show themselves as hostile Parts and usually function to use anger and threats to prevent other Parts from cooperating with the therapy.

Most often, negative introjects present as images of parents or stepparents and encapsulate their worst, most frightening traits. Duende wasn't a parental introject, but he did share some traits with monsters. In parts of Latin America, he's a fearsome creature.

Monster Parts show themselves as ferocious, threatening creatures of various sorts, depending upon your life history. For one person a monster might present as a witch or a demon. Another person, a fan of horror movies, might find her monster in a Freddie from *Nightmare on Elm Street* or a Jason from *Friday the 13th* movies.

The technique for helping monsters and introjects to relax their intensity is what I call *unmasking*. It's based upon the simple idea that all internal self-states are Parts of the self. There can be no internal Parts that are not also parts of the self. Even if other Parts—and the conscious self of the patient—believe the entity to be a parent, a monster, a spirit, or a demon, it's necessarily still a Part of the patient. Everything that's in the mind is a part of the mind. If there appears to be a *not-self* Part, that appearance represents a costume and the costume can be removed. Underneath the costume is a version of the outside person. After utilizing the unmasking intervention for many years, I've routinized it to the following five steps:

THE UNMASKING PROTOCOL

1. Thank the entity for being a part of the patient's life and for helping the patient to make safe choices and avoid danger.

2. Congratulate the Part for doing such a good job of protecting the patient.

3. Praise the Part for being an outstanding actor in playing its role as mother stepfather, etc.

4. Assert that the Part is a part of the patient and not separate from the patient.

5. Direct the Part—usually a child Part—beneath the costume to un-zip or otherwise remove its costume or mask and just *be* the self inside the costume.

A New Adult Amelia

Sometimes the Part inside the costume doesn't show itself as a child, but the general approach remains the same. In this case, the unmasking protocol led to the appearance of a very-angry, adult Amelia. My experience has been that the age of the Part beneath a costume roughly corresponds to the age at which the Part was formed. In this case, that age appeared to Amelia to be sometime in the last three years, somewhere between thirty-two and thirty-five.

This *New Adult Amelia* was *"angry for all the rough times, being alone, getting no help, being away from home with no one to share with."* And also *"for feeling weak and out of control, not having anyone to help solve problems, frustration, feeling incapable, not good or strong enough to solve anything."* This Part was overflowing with negative emotions. The big question now was whether this transformation of the intransigent Duende into an angry New Adult Amelia would be more responsive to Amelia's desire to have another child.

I coached Amelia to explain to New Adult Amelia that she was now good enough and strong enough to have another baby. She was good enough to find the therapy to heal all those Parts who suffered. She could do additional therapy if needed. I also suggested that Amelia acknowledge New Adult Amelia's right to be upset, frustrated, and angry. But right now, Amelia needed support and help in order to do what she wanted to do.

I'm not sure how many of my suggestions Amelia used in communicating with New Adult Amelia. She was silent with her eyes closed. But she soon received permission to heal the new Part's **pain**. Within seconds of a wind intervention, she opened them again to say, *"Okay. She is very tired now. She is not angry."*

Thin Amelia Heals Too

We could now return to Thin Amelia whose fear Amelia had been trying to heal before the appearance of Duende. When Amelia checked, she found that Thin Amelia was no longer afraid. She required no further healing work. Thus, healing Duende, who originally said his name was Fear, also healed Thin Amelia of *her* fear.

We were at the end of our session and planning for the next when Amelia observed, *"It seems like these Parts were re-minding me what it was like after my son was born by mak-ing me miserable during my period and today. I am afraid of having the baby now. The pregnancy is not the problem. I love that feeling. And the delivery is painful but temporary. It is what happens after the birth... Yes, there is still a Part that is afraid. It says, 'What if it is like before?' It is true that when Michael told me it will be different this time, I did not believe him. He does not get it about how miserable I was... Yes, there is still a Part with fear that postpartum depression will hap-pen again."*

As Amelia prepared to leave for the day, she said, *"It is funny. The Part called me stupid and said 'You do not get it!'"* Amelia was passing along information here from a Part she had not yet visualized. I would try to bring us back to this Part in our next session. I believe it was The Witch.

SUMMARY OF PARTS

The three new subpersonalities we first met in the New Year, Thin Amelia, Duende, and New Adult Amelia, were easily healed of their issues. Their memory banks were shallow and easily neutralized. When I looked back on the therapy later in our work, it was clear that these Parts were driven by The Witch, perhaps even manufactured by The Witch as foils to thwart the therapy. The Witch believed that having another child was a very bad idea. Ultimately, the resistance had no effect on the treatment protocol. We continued to define a given problem, find the Part that carried the problem, collect the memories that underlay the problem, and neutralize the relevant memories. These three new Parts that had appeared had no further role in the therapy.

> **Thin Amelia**. She was a minor Part, with little substance. She was fearful of another postpartum depression that might follow the birth of another child.

> **Duende**. He was a kind of "mini-monster," representing Amelia's previously unconscious image of a Latin American boogieman. He insisted that his job was to frighten Thin Amelia so that she would influence Amelia not to have a third child.

> **New Adult Amelia**. She appeared as the transformation of Duende, carrying a lot of anger that masked her feelings of loneliness and helplessness.

Chapter 8

The Witch Appears

Amelia began our next session with her PMS-at-ovulation report: *"I am exhausted! And a little irritable. I have a full schedule of clients during the week and I am catching up on the weekends. There is not enough time! Right now, I just feel tired."*

Despite this glum news of ovulation fatigue and irritability, there was also good news. Amelia added, *"A few months ago I would have had to cancel my clients and go home to bed. Now I continue to work."* It looked like some of our gains had been retained after all! I was hopeful that the renewal of intense PMS symptoms was only temporary and that we could maintain our progress.

THE WITCH

We reconnected to the end of the previous session, and Amelia sought out the hidden Part that had called her "stupid," blaming Michael in advance for a new postpartum depression. Amelia had become adept at locating internal Parts. She quickly located this one and said, *"It is an angry old lady—witchlike and ugly."* Like Old Woman of our earlier work, *The Witch* showed herself in black and white. She wore a shapeless, floor-length dress, and her straight white hair was mixed with

141

streaks of black: *"She says* Loneliness *is a good name for her. She does not like to be called a witch. She thinks I am stupid, naïve, and will never learn."* In spite of the new Part's wishes, Amelia called her The Witch: *"She has a cold and almost cruel look as she enjoys making me feel down. Her face has hard features of coldness and accusation. Her eyes are big and black and very judgmental, like she knows all your secrets and enjoys your pain; very cruel. She has a half smile on her face of confidence and power. Her eyes and smile express her cold and cruel character. I think she looks about seventy years old but she is strong not weak."*

The Witch

It would become clear that this new Part was the most powerful of all of Amelia's internal managers. She controlled a host of other Parts and hundreds of long-dissociated painful memories. We would eventually learn that healing The Witch would require healing many other Parts of their painful memories as well.

Surprisingly for a Part so powerful, she was deceptively mild in her interactions with us. Her criticisms of Amelia had an angry and exasperated tone, but I had the sense that they were delivered with love, perhaps similar to the criticisms of a mother to a not-too-bright child. The disruptions she caused in Amelia's life were real, and emotionally painful, but when the three of us had conversations, she was always calm and seemingly cooperative. Unfortunately, her cooperation was sometimes passive aggressive—apparently agreeing to requests in session but ignoring her agreements between sessions.

The Witch's Memories

When asked about the earliest disturbing memory she had of Amelia's problems, The Witch brought up memories of Amelia's college years: *"I was dating a guy in my country."* The Witch rated the memories as disturbing at an 8 or 9 on the SUD scale. Amelia elaborated, *"I was very much in love and he was selfish. We broke up and got back together two or three times, but he was never in love with me. I got manipulated, played, cheated on. She says I was not strong enough to leave him. She is angry about how stupid I was."*

For The Witch, this earlier boyfriend had much in common with Michael. That meant that some of Amelia's negative reactions to Michael were partially reactions to triggered memories of the former boyfriend. This is the way our minds work. So whenever you find yourself overreacting to someone in your life, it's likely you're also reacting all over again to someone from your past.

The Witch seemed to be the kind of internal manager that didn't directly experience a person's life; instead, she collected a set of Amelia's memories, but didn't claim them as her own. She reacted to them in a negative way in a vain attempt to protect Amelia from reenacting her errors. For this reason, I believed it would be futile to try to heal The Witch directly of her pain—because she didn't experience the pain directly. It was Amelia who directly experienced the pain. Amelia felt the primary emotions of sadness, fear, and loss, while The Witch felt the secondary emotions of anger and disgust toward Amelia. She found fault with Amelia's current choices and berated her for her previous choices.

I chose to sidestep direct work with The Witch by locating the Stuck-in-Time Parts that had participated in Amelia's disturbing historical events. Our strategy was to soften The Witch's criticism of Amelia by healing the memories she used as ammunition for her attacks on Amelia.

Amelia, Dressed in Brown and Green

With this in mind I asked Amelia if she could visualize herself as she was when she made The Witch so angry with the way she allowed her boyfriend to treat her: *"Yes, I can see my college self. She is not in love with him anymore—Wait! Now I see two different Parts. They are both me when I was twenty."* Except for their clothing, they looked alike. To help us keep track of the two Parts, we called them by the colors of the clothes they wore: *Brown Amelia* and *Green Amelia*.

Brown Amelia was *"dressed in brown. She is wearing tight pants and a shirt. I won a singing contest with this Part of me. It was the happiest day of my life. The next day was a really bad day. Because multiple people criticized me for getting the prize. They said I should not have won. They were people who were friends of the other girl—who was the favorite of my director. She was unhappy. Those who criticized me confirmed what I believed about myself. I could not retain the positive statements of people who said I was great. Instead, I believed I did not deserve to win. I should not have won."*

Green Amelia *"is in a long green dress. She knew she was pretty but was always unsure if she was pretty enough, could sing well enough, was nice enough, good enough for anyone."* When Amelia spoke inwardly with this Part she found that the Part knew that Amelia was an older version of her, but *"she is the self who is still in love with the guy... Yes, she wants to give up the love—and the hurt."*

The two twenty-year-old Parts show us that Amelia's low self-esteem wasn't just a recent attribute. She had undervalued herself as a lightweight for many years. The Witch agreed with Amelia's doubts about herself and was also critical of how Amelia related to all males. Green Amelia's love for the old boyfriend was the first piece of evidence—there will be more—that The Witch used in building her case that Amelia couldn't be trusted with men in general and Michael in particular.

LETTING GO OF LOVE

Healing you of your lingering love for a past sweetheart is sometimes necessary when that love interferes with your attachment to a current love. Later in the chapter, we'll do some of this work for Amelia. However, neutralizing Green Amelia's love for the old boyfriend was intended to reduce The Witch's criticism of Amelia.

Letting go of love, or other *positive* emotions and sensations, is accomplished in the same way as letting go of *negative* emotions and sensations. But a different scale is needed to measure the intensity of emotion. For this reason, I created the SUE scale (for "Subjective Units of Energy," described in Chapter 2), which provides a scale of intensity for *non-negative* emotions or sensations just as the SUD scale (for "Subjective Units of Distress") does for *disturbing* emotions or sensations. Green Amelia still carried a love for the old boyfriend that measured 7 or 8 on the SUE scale.

Once Green Amelia had reactivated her level-7-or-8 **love** emotion, Amelia visualized a powerful wind blowing through her, breaking it up and blowing it away. It took less than ten seconds.

Giving up the pain of the boyfriend memories was more complicated. Amelia tried another wind intervention for the hurt, but three different efforts were unsuccessful. Finally, we recognized that some other Part was blocking our work.

Amelia at first believed The Witch might be doing the blocking. But then, when The Witch denied it, she soon observed, *"There is an image coming up—It is my musical director. She frequently embarrassed me. She heavily criticized Green Amelia—and she was the expert—so Green Amelia felt she would never be good enough. She got the same message from anyone who criticized her."*

THE MUSICAL DIRECTOR INTROJECT

The blocking Part showed herself to Amelia as her former musical director, an important person in Amelia's life for four years of college. During those years Amelia participated in the choir and other musical productions at the university. The woman represented by the introject held considerable power over Amelia. She directed the university choir and was instrumental in all of the university's musical activities and plays. We called this Part *The Director*.

She refused to recognize that she was a Part of Amelia. Instead, The Director insisted that she was separate from Amelia, and that she was indeed the actual university musical director. She further insisted that Amelia wasn't good enough to win anything. She admitted to blocking the healing of Amelia's hurt by her old boyfriend because she judged Amelia to be *"undeserving."*

More about Introjects

Parts of this sort are internal introjects, creations of your unconscious mind, drawing upon certain of the characteristics—usually negative ones—of a real-world person who had a significant impact on you. If you have a critical voice, a voice that regularly finds fault with what you do, say, or think, then you probably have an introject of your own. Most likely that critical voice is the voice of the demanding parent or stepparent of your childhood.

The Director claimed that she wasn't a Part of Amelia. Consequently, she felt none of Amelia's pain. Such introjects take your real, painful experiences of mistreatment and reframe them as appropriate and due to your own defects. For example, a beating by your father for something you didn't do, might be reframed by a father introject as appropriate punishment for your being a liar. The dynamic involved here is the belief that if your dad punished you, you must have deserved it. He's too powerful to be wrong. The general function of a negative introject appears to be to keep you timid and fearful—and consequently safe—by discouraging you from standing up to powerful others.

Introjects are interesting phenomena, and a different kind of therapy might explore them for the insights they bring you about how they formed out of your childhood. However, in Parts and Memory Therapy, they interfere with the efficiency of healing. My efforts in past years to directly neutralize introjects' negative emotions have been therapeutic dead ends. After all, these entities are themselves not in any sort of pain. Their function is to create or maintain pain. The best way to deal with them is, instead, to unmask them quickly and then to work with the Part underneath the costume until we can continue with the interrupted healing work.

Unmasking The Director

We followed the same procedure described earlier in the unmasking of Duende: praise the power of the introject and its skill in protecting the patient; thank the introject for enabling the patient to achieve the goal of adulthood; assert that the entity isn't who it represents, but a version of the patient; acknowledge that the Part underneath the costume is a great actor doing a very difficult job; and then direct this Part to remove the costume and just *be* the Amelia under the costume.

Following the ritual unmasking, the new Part that presented herself was Amelia at age twelve. *Amelia 12* had painful memories of her own, beginning with those of being *"criticized by a lot of people"* at her grandmother's house from an early age. Amelia clarified that those criticisms were mostly reprimands by her grandmother, but sometimes also by her mother and uncles. Examples of reasons for reprimands were interrupting the adults or getting grades less than an A in school. We quickly neutralized the hurt of the reprimands through a wind intervention.

The healing of Amelia 12 was important because the grandmother's criticism of Amelia at twelve unconsciously amplified the criticism of The Director (and The Witch) at twenty. The earlier hurts by a powerful person laid the foundation for the later hurts by a different powerful person.

Amelia 12 had other painful memories that she wanted to heal, but we had unfinished work that had been interrupted by The Director introject. We asked Amelia 12 to put on hold the remainder of her painful memories until we could heal Green Amelia.

Healing Green and Brown Amelia

As expected, unmasking The Director freed up the therapy to heal Green Amelia. Her **self-anger** was easily neutralized with a wind intervention. Simultaneously, without our working directly with Brown Amelia, that Part's distress also reduced to zero.

Because we had run out of time in the session, Amelia moved Amelia 12 and The Witch to a safe place until we could return to them in our next session. She visualized The Witch resting in a hammock on a Hawaiian beach with a Mai Tai in her hand, while keeping Amelia 12 close by. We would check in with them at our next session.

BAD NEWS FOLLOWING GOOD

It was a *"rough week"* for Amelia between sessions. Both of her children were sick and demanded extra care: *"I was overwhelmed and frustrated. I did something I have not done since I was a child. I hit myself in the head. I felt hopeless, that there is something wrong with me, and I should give up. I will never get better. I was irritable and crying all week. I am feeling that my daughter's problems are because of me. I am messed up and my daughter has inherited this from me."*

I was alarmed that Amelia suffered such emotional pain that she reverted to her behavior as an eight-year-old. We would heal that head-banging little girl in time, but my concern at present was what was happening with adult Amelia. Life's multiple sources of stress had brought her to a personal crisis. She had two sick children, work stress, and continuing PMS all coming at her at once—and Michael seems to have been of little help.

At our previous session, Amelia had been ovulating. She was now at Day 23 of her cycle. Unlike her usual pattern, she didn't get her normal break from intense emotions between ovulation and her second set of PMS symptoms near menses.

It's an understatement to say that Amelia had been in a dark place. The good news of the previous week, when she experienced less distress than usual during ovulation, was followed by abject misery during the time following ovulation when she normally had a few days of calm.

I, too, was distressed, concerned that I was missing something in the therapy that should have been clear. What I was missing was just how powerful and controlling The Witch was. We were now working through our twenty-first session. I had expected gradual improvement of the sort Amelia showed in our first eighteen sessions. Instead, Amelia had re-experienced painful mood states that had been absent since she was a child. Hitting yourself in the head isn't something normal adults do.

Certainly, having sick children, managing her household, and trying to maintain a psychotherapy practice is demanding, but it wasn't out of the ordinary for Amelia. She had been carrying an under-functioning husband for a long time. My best guess, not shared with Amelia at the time, was that The Witch and other Parts opposed to a third child were wreaking havoc in her emotional life in order to discourage her plan to have another child.

AMELIA 12

We returned to our unfinished work with Amelia 12, the former introject who had been costumed as the college music director. Her next memories involved a specific event—her father's no-show on an important day, and connected to a pervasive feeling of being unloved by him because he *"was never around."* The SUD score was 7.

After getting permission from The Witch (we wanted to remove a block before it appeared) to heal the girl's pain, Amelia visualized a wind intervention to neutralize the **anxiety** about her father's love. Shortly after beginning the intervention, however, Amelia opened her eyes to say, *"There is pressure in her head. I cannot get rid of it. She thinks too much— about her mother and father's problems, school, her grandmother's household, and stuff like that."*

I suggested that Amelia focus her wind intervention directly on the girl's head, in hopes that the either the anxiety would reduce or specific memories would arise that we could heal individually. In roughly ninety seconds, Amelia said, *"It is coming out. So many memories of what was going on back then!"* After another thirty seconds, Amelia laughed and said of the girl—who acted spontaneously without Amelia's direction— *"She is using a vacuum cleaner all around her head!"* That produced the desired effect of releasing the feelings of **being unloved**. *"She still feels a little sad that she was not a priority for anybody but she understands why."* Another pass of the wind intervention directed at that **sadness** reduced the girl's SUD score to zero.

THE WITCH'S INFLUENCE

We had succeeded in healing Green and Brown Amelia and Amelia 12, and I thought we could take some time off from deep work to get a bigger picture of what we were dealing with. I was curious as to how much The Witch might be influencing the therapy.

Once Amelia had located her again, I asked The Witch a leading question: why had she brought out the Green and Brown Amelia? My hunch was right. She admitted to pushing out Green and Brown Amelia *"because she thinks I will never learn... Yes, she made my life miserable this week. She does not mention me having a baby though. She just says it is because I am stupid."* When I pinned her down by asking whether Amelia having another baby was stupid, The Witch's simple response was, *"Yes!"*

I suggested to Amelia that she make a direct request for The Witch to refrain from making her life miserable, to allow her to make her own choices. The Witch was silent, which meant to me that she didn't agree. Stymied by her lack of response, I suggested The Witch take a week's vacation on her beach in Hawaii and continue to sip her Mai Tai. Amelia said, *"She is okay with that... Yes, I can visualize her there."*

The Witch's Power

The Witch seems not to have stayed in her Hawaiian hammock for very long. Amelia began our next session by saying, *"For two weeks I have been so critical of myself and irritable with everybody. Also, I had no interest in sex at all. Michael asked me what happened! I had to move The Witch back to Hawaii many times. It is like she is there and laughing and enjoying making my life miserable. She is in a hammock somewhere, but not in Hawaii. She is very present."*

Since The Witch was evidently close to Amelia's consciousness, I suggested that Amelia ask about the apparently failed Hawaiian vacation: *"She did not go to Hawaii. She did not want me to do something stupid—getting pregnant... Yes, she kept me from getting pregnant by keeping me from having sex. And she is critical about how I am raising my son—I think he is normal, but she finds things to criticize me about so she can say I am a bad mother. She is effective, because now I am doubting whether I can be a good mother to another child. And she says the postpartum depression will happen again. 'There is no doubt about it.'"*

It's difficult to believe that The Witch was so powerful that she could not only have a different agenda from Amelia, but that she could also carry out that agenda. She didn't want Amelia to have another child and so she prevented her from being sexual. It's so different from the way we normally think of how our minds and our actions work. Yet, that's what the evidence shows, and that's what Amelia and The Witch say.

Looking at ourselves

We generally believe that we're autonomous in our decision-making, that our minds are unitary and that we make decisions and carry them out as rational choices. The Witch's influence tells us otherwise. And if we take a closer look at our everyday behavior, we can see the Parts behind our own choices.

For example, sometimes we avoid sex without knowing why, and sometimes we avoid sex because we're angry or sad or focused on a problem at work. We might not connect our avoidance of sex with whatever it is that draws away our attention. But accepting the reality of non-conscious Parts allows us to see the sources of what draws us away.

Amelia's description of The Witch's actions suggests non-conscious sources for our own avoidances of sex. Not that we have internal witches, but that we have internal Parts with agendas different from our conscious selves. An angry Part wants to punish our partner by withholding sex; or a manager takes the position that no sex is better than tired sex. Amelia's experience with The Witch gives us insight into why we sometimes do or say things that are different from our conscious intent.

SCARLET, THE SEXUAL PART

All of us have at least one sexual Part, and some of us have more. For example, the sexual Part who likes wild and crazy sex is probably different from the Part who wants the sexual experience to be spiritual, and both are likely to be different from the Part who enjoys slow, sensual love making. We didn't explore Amelia's sexual Parts except to try to get a fix on who within Amelia might be avoiding sex because of The Witch's manipulation of her emotions. We did no direct interventions with the sexual Part.

To help Amelia locate a sexual Part, I asked her to think about a sexual memory or a sexual fantasy, any thought that would bring up a sexual response for her. She did so—but didn't tell me the source of the feeling—and I asked her to focus on her feeling and to speak to it and ask it to give her an image of herself.

When the picture appeared, Amelia laughed and said, *"She is me, younger, and she is dressed like a dominatrix. She is wearing leather underwear and bra, high boots, a sexy cop's hat, and she has a whip. She is twenty-five or twenty-six."* Amelia added that the picture surprised her because it didn't represent how she viewed herself. She had never acted as the dominant partner.

The dominatrix viewed Michael as her husband but *"my children are mine, not hers. She likes to dance, have fun, wear costumes, tease Michael. She likes it that she will be in a book. She has seen other Parts of me but does not like being around them. She calls herself Scarlet."*

WITCH WORK CONTINUES

Interestingly, even as The Witch continued to interfere with Amelia's functioning in everyday life, she also continued to respond to the treatment protocol. When asked, she shared with Amelia her next painful memory. It was disturbing to The Witch at a level 6: *"My best friend was arrogant and would say things to hurt me, like she was prettier or more popular than me. And she acted like she was better than me. The Witch was critical of me for taking it and for keeping her as my friend through high school."* (You can see the continued theme here of Amelia tolerating others' disrespect.)

Another set of memories, disturbing to The Witch at a level 4, related to Amelia's elementary school years: *"She remembers I was very shy. I did not join others or go to events. I was afraid of not knowing what to do."* Additionally, in her school-age years: *"I was pushed around by my boy cousins. She is angry with me because I did not stand up to them."* The Witch was upset about these memories at a modest level of 3 or 4.

Neutralizing The Witch's Anger

It's usually difficult to directly neutralize anger through work with the Part carrying the anger. Consequently, I generally work with the more vulnerable emotions of the Parts still stuck in the problem memories. However, because The Witch's anger seemed slow to reduce with this approach, I opted to try direct work with her anger in this session.

Somewhat surprisingly, she readily agreed to neutralize her **anger** with Amelia for not standing up to her cousins. After just a few seconds of a wind intervention, The Witch gave up her anger over Amelia's treatment by her cousins.

However, she continued to be critical: *"The Witch says, 'See! You have been stupid all along. People take advantage of you. You never stood up to them!' Even after the intervention, she continues to argue."* Amelia added here, *"I can hear an-*

other Part justifying my actions: I was young; I did not know what to do; I was afraid of getting into trouble; and stuff like that." We could not locate this protective Part then, but later it appeared to have been the revitalized Gypsy whom we had met earlier in the therapy.

Fortunately, we were able to easily neutralize The Witch's attitude toward the other two sets of memories. Only a few seconds of a wind intervention were necessary to neutralize her **anger** over Amelia's childhood shyness and her high-school tolerance of her best friend's arrogance.

High School Boyfriends and The Witch's Loneliness

We concluded the session by neutralizing The Witch's **upset** over how Amelia related to her first two high school boy-friends. *"My first boyfriend was flirtatious with other girls. I saw him as just being friendly. We had a two-year relation-ship. The Witch was upset because I did not stand up to him, for letting him flirt. My second boyfriend was my first love. He cheated on me more than once but I took him back. The Witch is critical of me for taking him back."* We combined the two sets of memories into a single wind intervention and quickly reduced The Witch's **distress** to zero.

As we wrapped up the session, Amelia answered a question I had asked of The Witch and added a few additional thoughts: *"No, The Witch does not like my husband. She likes the two guys I was involved with and thinks I would have been hap-pier with one of them. In every one of the memories we talked about today, I have been hurt and she feels lonely. Loneliness brings on her anger. My postpartum was lonely. She says Mi-chael will not be there for me if I have another child and I will be lonely again."*

When we first met The Witch almost two months ago, she said that *Loneliness* was a good name for her. Given her self-identification, it makes sense that her focus with the memories we had neutralized had to do with loneliness or the threat of loneliness. The fear of loneliness is a major driving force in how The Witch tries to manage Amelia's life. Another note of interest is that The Witch had finally owned her own vulnerable emotions. Until now, her anger was focused upon the pain that *Amelia* had experienced rather than what *she* had experienced.

PMS and a Huge Fight

Seven days later, Amelia began our session by talking about a *"huge fight"* she had with Michael the day after her expected ovulation: *"My son is three now and in preschool. His teachers regularly say he is disruptive. He came home that day and said that he is a bad boy. I got so angry at the teachers. Then Michael got angry with me for my anger at the teachers. Michael's reaction hurt me. I cried like a baby. I felt my protectiveness of my son increased. Even from Michael. I believe my ovulation triggered my emotions. I could not understand how I became so angry—it was overwhelming—over a small thing. Michael felt I was pushing the issue too much. He had been disconnected from us. When he is like that I reach out with my distress. That is when he exploded."*

Amelia had confirmed again that emotional distress in her relationship with Michael was linked to her PMS. I was concerned that such blowups were still happening, given all of the healing we had accomplished with Amelia's painful memories. This is not to say that Michael wasn't importantly contributing to their fighting. But to diminish couple-fighting significantly, often only one party of the couple needs to avoid provocation. Amelia could not control herself. And she was the one working on her issues. Evidently, The Witch required greater healing before the fights could diminish.

LONELINESS IN AMERICA

The next memory The Witch brought to mind was the loneliness Amelia felt after arriving in the United States from Costa Rica: *"It was very hard being alone in an apartment when I first came to America. The embassy held up my work permit for six months, so I had nothing to do, no one to talk to. Michael had his first teaching job in Utah. It was high stress work in a bad school and he worked really hard. But he had drinks with his friends every Friday and I had no one else to talk to. I did some babysitting but I saw no one else. Michael was angry with me because after we married I had to wait in Costa Rica four months before I could join him. During that time, I continued to talk to my ex-boyfriend. I told Michael after arriving in America. Part of my loneliness was because Michael was punishing me because he was hurt. If I had the money I would have gone back to Costa Rica during this time."*

With The Witch's permission, we began to neutralize the **loneliness** attached to the memories of Amelia's first six months in the United States. Shortly after beginning the intervention, Amelia said, *"It is hard. It is almost like she does not want to let go—Oh! Some of the pain is not hers. It is a Part we haven't met before. ... No, she does not know me."* The Part that blocked the intervention evidently did so unintentionally, just through the amplification of her own pain. Blocking Parts are more frequently powerful managers that intentionally prevent the healing ritual for reasons of their own.

A Homesick Part

The new Part was twenty-seven years old, the age of Amelia when she arrived in the United States. Amelia explained to *Amelia 27* that they were the same person but Amelia was older. The Part accepted this in a noncommittal way. This isn't unusual. Over time, once Parts come to understand their role in a person's life they come to accept the elemental truth that they exist within the person and do not lead an independent life—a common delusion when Parts first interact with the conscious self.

Amelia described Amelia 27 as *"thin, with long hair, and wearing workout clothes."* She was very lonely. Although she knew Michael was her husband, she knew nothing of Amelia's current life, including the fact that Amelia now had two children.

There was little time remaining in our session, but we tried to heal the Part's loneliness before we closed. We were anxious to finish our work with The Witch, and this was The Witch's memory too. Our first effort to neutralize the **loneliness** was a nonstarter. Within a few seconds Amelia said, *"She misses home a lot. She has a lot of emotion: loneliness, guilt, sadness, regret, confusion, disappointment."* A second effort reduced the Part's pain from a SUD score of 8 to 4, but we were out of time. In order to reduce possible negative effects of the unprocessed residual, Amelia visualized a container in which the Part could store her distress until our next visit.

Assessment of Progress

We had met now for twenty-two sessions, which was roughly the average number of sessions I expected to work with any given patient for moderate issues. Amelia's issues, as indicated by an official diagnosis of PMDD (and earlier postpartum depression) were severe. By now it was clear that we were not going to complete our work in the immediate future. But we continued to make overall progress, even as temporary setbacks discouraged both of us from time to time. The Witch remained our primary nemesis even as she highlighted significant issues that would allow us to improve Amelia's relationship with Michael. Among those issues were issues of love and loneliness held over from previous relationships.

PURGING PAST LOVES

We met again with Amelia 27 just three days after our previous session. The residual SUD of 4 had spontaneously reduced to a 2 sometime during the interim. Such a reduction isn't unusual. It may be due to the calm a person often feels after a session and the effect of this calm on the stored emotional memories before the memory circuit locks again five hours later (see Ecker et.al., 2012). But whatever the reason, Amelia now easily guided Amelia 27 in neutralizing this remainder with another wind intervention.

Amelia 27, when asked about other painful memories, shared memories of her ex-boyfriend: *"She misses him. She loves him."* Discovering that the Part carried memories of the loss of her boyfriend was important because it impacted Amelia's relationship with Michael. We had worked with another Part (Green Amelia) just a few weeks previously who continued to desire an earlier boyfriend. Amelia 27's mired-in-the-past lost-love gave us another opportunity to improve Amelia's marriage by removing blocks to fully engaging with Michael. We needed to explore and neutralize these unresolved feelings for the former boyfriend.

Having non-conscious Parts that continue to carry loving feelings for previous sweethearts is normal. Virtually every one of us with a history of romantic relationships—unless we married our first love—has Parts who continue to love one or more previous sweethearts. I'm sure Michael has such Parts, too. Having these usually-hidden Parts is also the source of the phenomenon of Facebook romances with someone from ten, twenty, or thirty years ago. The Facebook lovers have Parts who continue to love their earlier sweethearts.

I checked with Amelia to be sure that she wanted to neutralize the boyfriend memories. Her answer was an immediate *"Yes!"* She was powerfully committed to making things work with Michael and, especially as a therapist herself, she knew nothing could be gained by clinging to past loves. The positive emotions connected to memories of former lovers often lead to negative comparisons with current relationships.

Healing the Loss

This time, again using a wind intervention, Amelia shared the memories that emerged into her awareness as she guided

Amelia 27 through the neutralizing process. With her eyes closed, Amelia asked Amelia 27 to focus on her feelings of **missing** her ex-boyfriend as she visualized a wind blowing through the Part, breaking up the emotions into tiny particles of dust and blowing them away: *"They were in band together. They were involved in a lot of singing, performing—so she misses all those happy times."*

It might be possible to save the emotions of the *"happy times"* while somehow unlinking them from the boyfriend. But Amelia preferred to be sure to neutralize all the problematic associations with him. She continued to visualize Amelia 27 in the buffeting wind and asked her to focus on and release the **happy emotions** too. After a short time, she said of the Part, *"She is crying. A lot of regret about coming to America because she left so much behind."* Focusing now on the **regret**, Amelia then used the wind to reduce the overall SUD score to zero.

Amelia had healed Amelia 27 of missing her former boyfriend, and she had also neutralized the regret and loss of what she had left behind when coming to America. However, she had not yet healed the Part's romantic love for the boyfriend. That love had been largely sequestered out of Amelia's awareness for many years, but in difficult times with Michael, memories of that love would emerge again. It had to be neutralized.

LETTING LOVE GO, AGAIN

The idea that we can let go of our love for someone in the same manner as we can let go of our negative emotions may seem counterintuitive. How can something so basic to human functioning as love be *healed* in the same manner as sadness, fear, and anger? From a Parts and Memory Therapy perspective, love is just one more type of high energy experience. And old loves can be just as destructive to current relationships as old hurts, fears, and resentments. The romantic love we feel for someone from our past can interfere with our attachment to our current partner, leading us to fantasize about, or even reach out to, an old love rather than commit to fixing what needs to be fixed with our partner.

In Amelia's case, that old love surfaced when she felt lonely and distant from Michael. Amelia 27 was the Part who loved the former boyfriend. The love had been dissociated amid the memories of loneliness connected to moving to America. When things went well with Michael, Amelia 27 remained distant and out of mind. But when current circumstances triggered memories of loneliness or homesickness, Amelia 27 was there, reminding Amelia that there had been happier times with a different man.

Amelia explained to this Part of herself how her love for the ex-boyfriend made it more difficult to cope with her husband. She asked her to allow us to permanently neutralize that love so that Amelia could preserve her family of four (and potentially five). Upon agreement, Amelia chose wind, her favorite intervention, as a means of undoing the **love** Amelia 27 felt for the former boyfriend. Reducing her loving feelings to zero took just thirty seconds.

TRYING TO ATTACH TO MICHAEL

We didn't want to leave behind residual issues that might continue to impact Amelia and so we asked if Amelia 27 had other memories that needed healing: *"She wishes she could be more deeply attached to her husband. She felt it briefly on their honeymoon. But Michael left for the U.S. right after the honeymoon and she was alone for four months. She expected the love to be strong again when she got to America but the emotion was never the same."*

It's important to remember here that Amelia 27 had little actual conscious interaction with Michael over the course of the marriage. Other of Amelia's Parts carried the stronger love and attachment to Michael that sustained their relationship and drove Amelia to fix it. Amelia 27 was a relatively minor

Part in their everyday life, becoming important only when The Witch needed ammunition to discourage Amelia from having another child.

Neutralizing the **distress** connected to the wait for her visa was quickly achieved through another wind intervention, with only one hiccup in the form of guilt for not missing Michael more. A single pass of the visualization quickly reduced that **guilt** to zero. Similarly, Amelia needed only a single pass of the intervention to neutralize her **disappointment** for failing to reconnect with the same deep love of their honeymoon.

Still, she wanted a greater connection with Michael. Speaking of Amelia 27, Amelia said, *"She feels an emptiness within her. She does not know what that is about."* After a pause, she added, *"When she met Michael, she was coming out of the relationship with her boyfriend. She was guarded with her emotions. It was well known that Americans came to Costa Rica to have fun, not to find a wife. So she was careful with her emotions. So when he started getting serious, it was hard to drop her defenses. She wanted to but couldn't fully do so. She had the idea that love was painful. She had watched my mother love my father and experience a lot of pain when he divorced her. The closest she ever got to being in love was with her boyfriend. He was a calm person and so she felt safe to love him. She wanted to love my husband but was never quite able to do so. She thought things would get easier in a new country but they got worse."*

In an effort to heal Amelia 27's emptiness, Amelia brought a strong wind to heal her of the **sympathy pain** she felt for her mother's lost love of her husband. Her distress had rated a SUD score of 9, but she released it all within forty-five seconds. She felt less emptiness, but there was still a significant amount remaining. We hoped to further reduce that emptiness in our next session.

SUMMARY OF PARTS

The Witch. She finally allowed herself to be seen by Amelia after working behind the scenes to cause enough misery to prevent another child. The next two Parts were minor characters.

Brown Amelia. She and her twin in green were the fourth and fifth of The Witch's pawns to appear in the narrative. She believed that she was undeserving of anything good. Her healing occurred with the healing of her twin, Green Amelia.

Green Amelia. She continued to love an unfaithful boyfriend from Amelia's past and consequently wasn't very interested in making things work between Amelia and Michael. She carried a lot of self-anger. Both the green twin and the brown twin were of only temporary interest.

The Music Director/Amelia 12. The Music Director was Amelia's college music director, a negative introject who required unmasking because she insisted that she wasn't a Part of Amelia. Like Duende, the Latin American boogieman, she was a persecutory Part. When unmasked she transformed into Amelia 12, who required a significant amount of healing. Amelia 12 carried painful memories of criticism from her parents and grandmother and a sense that she wasn't very important to anyone.

Amelia 27. She carried all of the losses resulting from leaving Costa Rica and moving to the United States. She also carried the difficult experiences with past boyfriends.

Chapter 9
PMS/PMDD Overwhelm

Amelia's current issues forced us to put on hold our work with Amelia 27. We began our session by talking about the difficult times Amelia had experienced since we last met.

PMS, PMDD SYMPTOMS

"I think this is the real PMS now. My period is due in about five days. Two nights ago, I felt hit by tiredness and pressure in my chest. It was hard to breathe and I went to bed early. The next morning, I was tired and irritable and yelled at the kids for something small. My three-year-old said, 'Mommy, why are you so angry?' That night I was very impatient with getting the kids to bed—bathe them, dress for bed, get in bed. My current feeling is feeling upset about being tired, irritable, frustrated, and guilty about the kids. This is how I felt before starting therapy. Back then I had to cancel my sessions [with patients]. I was tempted to do that today.

"Last night I told Michael, 'Do not come home early! Stay out. Go for coffee. Read a newspaper or something.' I knew I would fight with him if he came home early. I had the kids all ready to say goodnight to him last night so he could put them to bed and I could have a few moments to myself. I felt like

crying some of the time but I did not. It is more anger than sadness."

Adjusting to the Setback

I experienced Amelia's news as an emotional blow. I felt badly for her and for her likely sense that six months of therapy had been wasted. And I felt a touch of panic about how well I was doing (or not doing) as a therapist. I had to remind myself that we *had* done significant healing and that we *were* on the right track in spite of the setback. The Witch had acknowledged that she was causing Amelia's pain in order to protect her from another round of postpartum depression and isolation—Amelia's fate if she had a third child. Strange as the idea might be that a largely unconscious subpersonality could have that much power, The Witch's claim of sabotaging Amelia's plan was believable.

I reminded myself to remain aware of the cyclical nature of Amelia's distress and to expect spontaneous improvement in a few days. At the same time, with Amelia caught in the throes of PMS, the therapist and researcher Part of me thought it was a wonderful opportunity to make progress. We might be able to explore and get to know whatever distressed Part presented herself in today's session. Hopefully, we could locate the Part that was responsible for the uncomfortable pressure that Amelia felt in her chest.

The PMS-Distressed Part

By first accessing The Witch and then asking her to bring the distressed Part forward, Amelia soon found herself with an internal image of herself at the age of eleven or twelve, wearing a floral dress and her long dark hair in a ponytail. We called her *Floral Dress*. She was clueless about who Amelia might be. As usual with this sort of disconnect, I coached Amelia to explain that she was the same as the Part, but grown up. Unfortunately, the child Part didn't accept the explanation: *"She does not believe it,"* Amelia said. *"She does not know who I am."*

When therapists help you to explore your internal world, they occasionally find Parts that aren't well oriented to your conscious self or your physical world. The first step is to find out how much such Parts *do* know. Sometimes, during the process of being asked and answering questions, the Part acquires a better understanding of your outside world as well as their place in your inside world. We asked a series of questions to assess the Part's awareness. Possibly, the interview would produce nothing of value, but we wanted to learn what we could about the Parts who were involved in Amelia's cyclical distress.

When Amelia flashed an image of her mother to the Floral-Dress Part, there was no recognition. A similar effort with an image of Amelia's father produced a recognition that he was someone Floral Dress knew, but a denial that he was her father. She recognized the grandmother, however, and claimed her as her own. This suggested that Floral Dress was a Part created after Amelia had been turned over to her grandmother for parenting during the week. Consequently, she had no memories of her mother or father performing in the week-day role of parent.

Amelia continued her exploration and noted, *"She says my sister is familiar but she does not know if she is also her sister."* Other questions similarly produced little information. She didn't know who *"the most important person in her life"* was. She didn't know if she had a boss or a protector. Yes, she had had her first period and yes, it was uncomfortable, but she didn't think it had anything to do with the pressure in her chest.

Finding the Source of the Pain

We tried to use a sensate bridge—"Focus on the pressure in your chest and let your mind float back to your earliest memory"—to locate significant early memories but nothing came up. When asked directly for her earliest painful memory, Floral Dress recalled her seventh birthday party, but it wasn't a painful memory: *"She liked it,"* Amelia explained.

With little gained so far in the interview, Amelia asked the young Part to say more about the party: *"She is wearing the dress—the floral one—that she got from her godparents as a birthday gift. She misses them. That was the last time she saw them because they got divorced and stopped coming around. There was lots of family at her birthday party. She liked being the center of attention. I think she misses all of the happy times with the family. She is not around them anymore."*

Tears appeared in Amelia's eyes as she said these last words. The seventh birthday party was a symbol of pain after all! The child was sad at the loss of her godparents and lonely in the absence of her extended family. (The Witch's loneliness theme thus appears once more.) At the birthday party, Floral Dress had been the center of attention. While she wasn't aware of Amelia's current life, or even that she was a Part of her, Amelia's PMS emotions triggered Floral Dress's implicit emotional memories of her losses—memories that she normally held out of Amelia's awareness. That's the first function of Parts: to wrap up painful experiences and dissociate them from the awareness of the conscious self.

Healing the Pain

Amelia tried to heal the **loneliness** of the Floral Dress Part through a wind intervention. After two minutes of silent work with her eyes closed, I interrupted Amelia's concentration to ask about her progress: *"It is coming out but very slowly,"* she said. Two minutes is a long time to work internally on releasing painful emotions, so I asked Amelia to look around for a blocking Part. It was The Witch. When asked for her permission to heal the child's loneliness, however, The Witch quickly gave it. It seemed that she just needed recognition as the one in charge. Again, Amelia visualized wind blowing the loneliness from the child Part, stopping momentarily to explain, *"The Witch is holding her hand now."* In another forty-five seconds, Amelia opened her eyes to say, *"It stopped."* The SUD score for the remaining distress was a 1 or 2. The little girl couldn't let all of her loneliness go *"because she will always miss her family."*

Healing requires accepting what is, and then moving on by releasing the pain of this reality. So Amelia acknowledged to Floral Dress that her extended family was in another country and that she probably wouldn't see most of them again. Still, she could remember them without hurting.

Then, she brought the more powerful imagery of a hurricane to blow away the remaining distress. In just a few seconds, Amelia said, *"It is now zero. She has no more chest pressure."* Our work had finally healed the pain of the Floral Dress Part but, unfortunately, didn't entirely heal Amelia of the pressure in her own chest. What this meant was that Floral Dress's chest pressure accounted for only *some* of Amelia's pressure. There was at least one other Part that amplified its distress onto Amelia as chest pressure.

As we concluded the session, Amelia's measure of the distressing pressure in her chest was a SUD score of 3 or 4, down from an 8. We would later need to find the Part that brought the remaining distress.

FATIGUE CONTINUES

A week later when we met again, there was more bad news. The primary pattern of PMS is that it ends on the first or second day of a woman's period. But Amelia felt no relief from her unpleasant mood and disturbing body sensations until the full five days of her period had passed. While technically not PMS, we had consistently treated Amelia's menstrual symptoms as just as much our therapy concerns as her PMS symptoms. She had remained tired throughout her period just as she had during her premenstrual days: *"One morning I was so tired that I cancelled my clients and went back home and slept for two hours. I am still tired today—for two weeks now. I am behind in my paperwork; I am not cleaning the house; I am angry with myself; I am feeling incapable of doing things."*

I was momentarily taken aback at the news. My own catastrophe Part was wringing his hands and thinking that the therapy wasn't helping. Yet, I again reminded myself, we *had* succeeded for a full cycle in significantly reducing the symptoms. And there *had* been several occasions where we reduced the intensity of either the ovulation or the menstrual symptoms during a given cycle. If we could do it sometimes, we should be able to do it all the time.

At times like this, I asked myself if it could really be true that The Witch Part was doing all of this, effectively sabotaging our work in order to protect Amelia from postpartum depression and an absentee husband. The idea certainly gives the concept of psychosomatic illness new meaning. We would see. Overall, I remained optimistic.

Finding Angry Amelia 9

Returning to the pressure in Amelia's chest, she said that it had come and gone in the days following the last session, but she could *"still feel a little bit now."* I coached her to try to talk with the source of the sensation by focusing on the pressure and speak to it as a Part and ask it to increase in intensity. When Amelia then felt an increase in pressure, I coached her to request that the pressure decrease. That, too, was successful. She was now communicating with the source of the pressure. It was doing as she requested. Her next step was to ask the Part to provide an image of itself. Initially, Amelia couldn't see anything, but when I suggested that she ask the Part's age, she responded, *"Nine. It is a girl. She says she is scared to come out. She showed me a photo. She is in her school uniform, brown and white. She has two pigtails."* We called her *Amelia 9* during our work, but changed that to *Angry Amelia 9* for this book because a different nine-year-old appeared later in the therapy. We called the later one *Lonely Amelia 9*.

The girl's earliest painful memory was of *"not being good enough in school. She was always in the top four of her class but she never got recognized as 'student of the month.' That really hurt her because she tried really hard to get the award. The same is true for musical performance. She was always just a little bit short."* The memories remained disturbing to her at a level 9 or 10: *"One time she earned the award by her grades but her teacher said, 'You do not deserve it,' and she gave it to another student without an explanation."*

Small and Large Traumas

It would be easy to discount Amelia's grade-school disappointments as forgettable experiences that hardly deserve mention when compared to the trauma and pain of major abuse experienced by children in other families. But every child has her own pain, regardless of wealth, social status, or family structure. Each of us is marked in some way and our adult personalities are affected by those marks. No one escapes childhood entirely unscathed:

"It was never a big deal to her family when she got good grades, but when she failed to do that, everybody in her family got on her. She was punished. For Halloween, she was not allowed to go out trick-or-treating. She cried all night. This is the Part who banged her head as a child. When she was frustrated, she would pull out her hair or hit herself in the head to make her brain better. She felt that there was something wrong with her."

We used wind again to heal the student-of-the-month and Halloween memories in turn, making just one stop in each case to ask and receive The Witch's permission to continue on with the neutralizing interventions.

Amelia tried to help Angry Amelia 9 let go of her false belief in her deficient brain by describing Amelia's adult accomplishments: a bachelor's degree in psychology, a master's degree in school psychology, and another master's degree in marriage and family therapy. And she worked as a therapist in America. She argued that she couldn't have accomplished these things if there were something wrong with her head. The little girl seemed to accept the argument, but as we ended the session, Amelia still sensed that something was wrong with her.

MOTHERHOOD

Amelia began our next session saying, *"I feel guilty for thinking or saying I cannot have another child. I feel selfish. I want another child but I do not think I can. Also, I worry that my first two might be neglected if I have a third—I might be disconnected from them as I was with my daughter. I go back and forth on having another baby. I feel something crying inside when I say no more children. The Witch doesn't want me to have another. She has almost got me convinced."*

This session took place in the week after Amelia's period: *"So I feel fine,"* she said. She was no longer irritable or tired, and looked forward to meeting her own patients later in the day. She easily located the image of The Witch so that we could do further work with her.

Changes in The Witch

"She seems relaxed," Amelia began. *"She is younger now— about fifty."* I took this to signify that we were making progress in our work. As noted earlier, it's common for internal images to show positive changes in appearance as the therapy progresses. It renewed my hope that we would soon heal The Witch and the small army of Parts she seemed to have marshalled to prevent another pregnancy.

Amelia went on: *"She is in a hammock, and drinking a cocktail since we sent her on a vacation. But it is like she enjoys seeing me in pain. Yes, she enjoys that. It proves her point that I do not make good decisions—like having another child."* We asked The Witch to locate her earliest, still-painful memory.

The Witch's Memories

"It was after my first pregnancy, after the birth of my daughter. I was feeling lonely and sad. Giving birth was very painful. I could not hold her for a few days. I had pain for a few days and the baby cried constantly. Even after she stopped crying, I still felt lonely. I wanted my mother there. I had mild depression. I was depressed because we didn't know how to parent."

Amelia was able to visualize and communicate with the young mother in her memories. When asked, the mother indicated that she knew Amelia: *"I am her, older. She is feeling a lot of responsibility, and alone. She knows she needs to be a housewife and cook and clean but she does not know what direction she is going. She is sad. Because she is lonely. She does not quite feel connected to the baby. She loves her and takes care of her, but it is not companionship. She quit working to stay home, and then her coworkers* [from the mental health agency] *were no longer around her. She expected her coworkers to stop by and be friendly but they did not.*

"She was very alone. She felt loss. I remember wishing I was home because I had lots of friends there, and family who would want to see the baby. Being a mother separated me from everyone. The people she knew were single and also had no children. I tried to join a group of new mothers but felt no connection with them." (Amelia's switching her self reference between a first person and third person is striking here, but I've regularly chosen not to correct her grammar in order to illustrate this common way of talking about Parts.)

Amelia 30's Memories

When asked, the young-mother Part indicated that she was thirty years old. This corresponded with Amelia's calendar knowledge of her actual age at the time. We decided to call this her *Amelia 30*. She's a kind of Stuck-in-Time Part because she has no awareness of Amelia's current life. And because she's contained within the memories that The Witch considers her own, she's also a subpart of The Witch. Her memories are thus also The Witch's memories.

Her earliest painful memories related to the time when, after coming to the United States, she found that *"she did not fit in well. She was lonely. We were not connected to anybody in Utah. No friends or family. My husband's family was in Pennsylvania. In her first job I was disrespected by my boss. He would yell and do other things to humiliate her. She would go home and cry every day."*

Rather than start the intervention and then have to stop and ask permission from The Witch to continue, we chose to request that permission first. She gave it. The two interventions went smoothly. Amelia 30 quickly gave up her **loneliness** to the wind—in just twenty seconds. In another minute she gave up her **hurt** and **humiliation**.

Struggling in the Desert Heat

Amelia 30's next disturbing memory related to her supervisor at the job she had while pregnant. He was highly critical and inflexible. In late pregnancy he would make no accommodations for her condition. In her seventh month, summer was approaching and it became difficult to drive to the homes of her in-home patients where therapy took place.

Many of these homes had no air conditioning and the stifling heat often made Amelia miserable as she tried to bring emotional relief to her patients. She asked her supervisor for fewer home visits and more paperwork. He refused her because he believed her English grammar wasn't yet good enough for report writing.

Additionally, she was on-call—available at a moment's notice—every other week because she was one of only two Spanish speakers in her agency. Monolingual American English speakers were on-call only one week per month. The stress of feeling constantly on-call for work was difficult for her. She gave up the **stress** connected to these memories with a wind intervention in just thirty seconds.

As we concluded the session, Amelia observed that she now realized that she had experienced postpartum depression after her first child as well as her second: *"It was just milder."*

The session had gone so well that I was feeling optimistic again. My unstated strategy all along had been to make The Witch flexible by quietly healing the earlier painful experiences that had made her so stridently opposed to Amelia's wishes. I expected that The Witch would eventually soften and become more of a kindly supporter than a critical opponent. She had already shown positive changes in her physical image.

I didn't have a position on whether Amelia should or should not have another child. I simply wanted her to have a choice. Currently, with all the obstacles of increased physical and emotional pain that The Witch had thrown up, Amelia didn't have a real choice.

MONSTER-HEAD

Amelia began our next session by saying, *"I was horribly angry last night. We had a big fight. I was angry before Michael came home. I just lashed out at him. I do not like it when I am so angry, out of control."* Her ovulation emotionality began on the weekend and her big fight with Michael occurred on Monday night, the night before our Tuesday session.

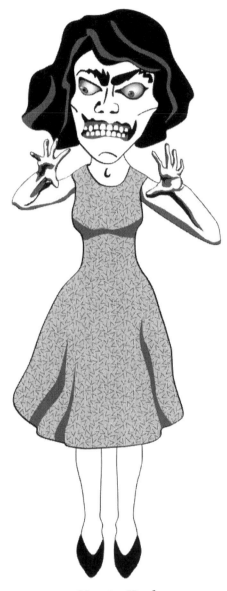

Monster Head

Because our session coincided with her ovulation sensitivity, it was an opportunity to more easily identify the Parts who were, knowingly or unknowingly, creating havoc in Amelia's marriage. When she looked within to locate the angry Part, she found an image of herself, but *"with a monster head—a big jaw and teeth, her eyes popping out. She has normal hair and the body is me."* Amelia gained only a little information with her initial questions of the Part. *Monster-Head* had no name. She was thirty years old: *"There is just growling when I ask if she wants a name. She knows who I am."*

When asked about her earliest painful memory, Monster-Head produced the memory of Amelia as *"a little girl, eight or nine years old, hitting herself in the head when she was angry. She would hide so that others would not see her doing that."* A second memory dated to Amelia at age eleven, angry because her mother and father were fighting.

Angry Amelia 9

The little girl who hit herself in the head appeared to be the same little girl—Angry Amelia 9—with whom we had previously interacted but hadn't healed. Amelia asked permission of Monster-Head to talk with the little girl. With permission granted, Amelia asked the get-acquainted questions. The little girl knew that Amelia was an older version of herself: *"She is angry with herself for getting in trouble. And at others for yelling. She thinks something is wrong with her. She does not say or do things right."* (Previously, she had told us that she hit herself in the head because something was wrong with her brain.)

As we began to heal the little girl's pain, I coached Amelia to focus on her **hurt** rather than her anger because, as noted elsewhere, anger seems always to be secondary to more vulnerable emotions. It's secondary to sadness, fear, embarrassment, etc. When we heal the more vulnerable emotions, anger disappears.

Shortly after beginning a wind intervention, Amelia added, *"She feels like nobody loves her."* I suggested that Amelia guide the Part in focusing on **being unloved**, and to expand her awareness to locate the memories that underlay the unloved feeling: *"She feels that people get bothered by her—she was the only child in the house... Yes, that is why she believes something is wrong with her."* This **false belief** that bothering adults meant something was wrong with her was the next focus for the wind. The wind blew it away: *"She sees everybody busy with other things and so she hangs by herself, trying to find someone to do something with. She is just lonely."* The next pass of the wind intervention focused on the child's **loneliness** (The Witch's bane). Healing that left just a feeling of **being lost**. Finally, after one more pass, the child felt no other negative emotions: *"She went off to play with the dog."* In general, the best way to know when a child Part has been fully healed is when she wants to go play.

Amelia 11

We turned our attention then to the eleven-year-old Stuck-in-Time Part in Monster-Head's second memory. *Amelia 11* was angry that her parents were fighting. She knew that Amelia was an older version of herself and she was ready for relief. She actually had several memories. In one, Christmas was ruined because of her parents' fighting. In another her father was drunk at Christmas. And there were other events, such as her First Communion, when her father wasn't there but should have been:

"Sometimes he showed up drunk or late or forgot to bring presents. My mother would get angry with him and they would fight. There were several years when special events were ruined by their fighting. Any special day was an opportunity for them to fight. I hated them both. I had to hide my anger because my grandmother said I had to show them respect no matter what. At special events I was always waiting for something to happen and for them to fight."

Amelia's wind helped *Amelia 11* release the **disappointment** linked to her special occasions. Soon Amelia said: *"She is cleaning it with wind—the First Communion, that is the pic-*

ture I have of her, in her white dress. My dad came but he left early and did not leave any money. So there was no customary party afterward for family and friends. So there was just the ceremony. My mom got in a big fight with him because he did not give any money. He did not love my mother and he did not love me. He wanted his own life—soccer or another woman or friends. And after he left, my mom would be sad, so she was not there for me either."*

Amelia refocused the intervention onto Amelia 11's **sadness** about the First Communion memory. Then she interrupted herself to say, *"I know now why I was so angry last night with Michael. Because it feels like it did with my dad, who did not care about my stuff. Last night I had papers I needed to fill out for my family in Costa Rica, and I had been asking Michael to help me for a few weeks. It feels the same as it did with my dad, that he does not care. His own world is more important than us. I feel very powerless because I cannot get him to do things. Later, Michael did what I asked but I had to be a crazy woman to get him to help me."*

We had reached the end of the session without healing Amelia 11's memories, and because we had activated them and talked about them, I was concerned that these old wounds might cause further problems in Amelia's relationship with Michael. Consequently, I guided her in visualizing the placement of Amelia 11's unresolved distress into a container until our next session. Monster-Head agreed to take a nap until then.

Amelia had a few more remarks before she left: *"That was interesting! I knew I had very angry feelings that would come out in our session. I did not know it was a Part. It was rage. I do not like it because it comes out with my kids, too, and I feel guilty. I got triggered last week—I do not know why—Last night it went kaboom!"*

SUMMARY OF PARTS

Floral Dress. She was eleven or twelve, a child Part who carried the childhood loss of a sense of family togetherness. She had no continuing role in Amelia's story.

Angry Amelia 9. She was angry because something must be wrong with her head; otherwise, adults wouldn't find so many things wrong with her. She was angry also because she felt unloved. She was lonely, the only child in a house full of adults.

Amelia 30. She was the adult Stuck-in-Time Part who carried the memories of dealing with the isolation that followed Amelia's first child.

Amelia 11. She carried memories of disappointment with her father for his absence at special occasions. She appears again for additional work near the end of the therapy.

Monster-Head. Age thirty. She was angry for feeling unloved by family members, especially her father. She carried a range of memories of Angry Amelia 9, and Amelia 11.

Chapter 10
The Problem with Fathers

Amelia had been trapped in the throes of PMS much longer than usual. The day of our previous session had coincided with Day 19 of her cycle. Our new session was on Day 26. Through it all, she had continued to experience the PMS that began with ovulation at around Day 14. Normally she would have had a week of relief between ovulation PMS (roughly Days 13-16) and menses PMS (roughly Days 23-28). But anger, oversensitivity, and low energy continued unabated. Amelia pessimistically expected it to continue even through her period, which should appear in three days.

DISCORD AT HOME

"This is a bad time, I have been consistently down for two weeks—since my ovulation. It was a horrible Sunday [two days ago]. I was angry and depressed all week. I was causing so much harm that I decided to stand back from everyone. Michael held back, I think, because he knew I had a cold. But on Sunday he exploded. He was very, very angry. It was so bad I thought of leaving him—which I had not done in a long time. I told him that what bothers me most was that he does not care if he says painful things and yells in front of the children.

"I took the kids to church, feeling empty and alone. I texted to him that I thought it was better for us to separate. At the time I said this, I meant it, but when I calmed down, I did not. Michael does not know how to handle it when she is [I am] sick or depressed. He may be helpful for a time, but eventually he explodes. He just cannot handle it when he has to take care of me and other household chores too.

"This is what happened when I was in postpartum depression. He would get so angry with me. He would help do what I could not do but then explode. It is bad for the kids. My daughter said on the way to church, 'Mommy, why is Daddy so angry?' I told him I would not have another child. I would fix myself. He said, 'No, do not do that. That is a big decision.' I said I am not going to bring another child into this situation. Since Sunday night, he has been so sweet. But I am so tired of this happening. The children love him and he is a fantastic father most of the time. But at some point, I am going to get too tired to do it anymore."

Based upon the Sunday events, and the anger and depression Amelia had been experiencing, The Witch's strategy appeared to be working. Amelia told Michael she wouldn't have another child with him. But things said in anger shouldn't be taken as the final truth (or perhaps not truth at all). Amelia didn't say during our session that she had made a final decision.

The College Part

Amelia continued her story of the Sunday experience: *"On Sunday night I tried to visualize Amelia 11 in her communion dress. But a different Part came out, a college Part. In college, it was financially difficult for me, although things were better with my father and we were closer. But sometimes he would forget to leave me money—he normally left me an allowance—and when I went to his office he would be gone and left me nothing with his secretary. Other times I would ask for something extra and he would say no—because he was 'short of money'—but he and his new wife and kid were doing well—two cars, plenty of food in the refrigerator—while at home my mother and I would eat rice and beans for weeks because we could not afford meat."* Amelia didn't visualize or describe further interactions with this college-age Part of her, but I expected we would meet her again later.

Amelia 11

Late in the session, we returned to the deep work we had begun with Amelia 11, the young Amelia wearing her communion dress. She still held onto the container of negative emotion from the previous session. Amelia asked her to open it up so that we could continue our healing work:

"She still wonders why my dad did not show caring for me. Why did he not love me?" In preparing Parts for healing when they feel unloved by a parent, or who yearn for a closeness they never had, I emphasize how important it for the adult conscious self to let the child Part know that *she* will never leave the child and will always love her. In this way the conscious self takes over the role of the parent who failed the child. Amelia did this for Amelia 11. She also explained that we had listened to her with love and that it was now time to accept that her dad is who he is and it's time to let go of the container of pain.

This time, instead of her usual wind intervention, Amelia chose a bonfire. She visualized Amelia 11 standing in front of the fire and urged her to burn up her container of **pain**: *"She threw it into the fire. Now she feels sad, a little bit."* Amelia then guided Amelia 11 in giving up her **sadness** to the fire: *"Now she is indifferent to her dad. She wants to be with someone who loves her. But she still does not seem happy. She feels fear—of being alone."* Amelia explained to the 11-year-old that she would never be alone. She had Amelia, who would be with her always. But even an additional pass of the fire intervention failed to reduce the child's distress to zero.

A Mother Introject

This resistance to healing led us to look for a blocking Part. This time it was a mother introject, a Part that looked and acted in some of the ways as her mother had acted. Amelia found her easily by looking around the scene of the intervention: *"My mother is there... Yes, she is preventing Amelia 11 from healing. She is very angry."*

I previously described the procedure for unmasking an introject, and we followed that protocol here. Amelia praised the mother image for helping her to grow up, and then congratulated her for doing a good job. She also praised and congratulated her for being such a good actor. Finally, she emphasized that she wasn't her mother but a younger Amelia wearing a mother costume. She directed her to take off the costume and *just be* the younger Amelia underneath.

The Five-Year-Old in the Costume

The introject quickly removed her costume: *"There is a five- or six-year-old there now. She feels lost and confused. She says she is five."* The child Part revealed that she didn't know Amelia—who then explained that she was the same as the child but grown up. She emphasized that she would take care of her now and would always love her. Continuing with a fire intervention, Amelia urged her to throw into the fire her **fear** and **confusion** and burn it up: *"She's trying to throw things into the fire but she is still confused about what to throw."*

We were nearing the end of the session and I suspected another blocking Part. But I wanted to check whether Amelia 11—who had been blocked by the mother introject/five-year-old—could now neutralize her negative emotions. Amelia again tried to heal her with the fire intervention. She directed her to burn up her **fear** of being alone, but then said to me, *"She wants to be with the five-year-old. She feels she has to be with the five-*

year-old. That way she will not be alone. Now she is standing next to the five-year-old, who is asleep."

The work of Parts and Memory Therapy can't be accomplished through force. We can't simply demand that a Part give up its distress and expect it to happen. Persuasion will work, and cooperation between Parts will work. Our continued failure to heal the two child Parts clearly indicated the presence of still another powerful manager. But we were out of time. Before leaving, Amelia said, *"Monster-Head was observing everything but she seemed very tired."* Thus we caught a glimpse of the likely blocking Part.

Our session had been about the effect of Amelia's father on her growing up. Amelia described a bit of history before leaving: *"My father was just nineteen when I was born. He probably would not have been with my mother if she had not become pregnant. In his twenties he became an accountant. I was twelve or thirteen when he graduated college. That is when he met his second wife, who he loved like he never loved my mother. He had a five-year relationship with her before divorcing my mother."*

RESOLUTION FOR CHILD PARTS

We didn't meet again for two weeks, but Amelia shared that she had been in a good mood, just a few days of mild irritation. It was the week after her period and she didn't expect any problems. The uncomfortable body and emotional concerns had evidently ended after three consecutive weeks, from ovulation through her period. She thought the mild irritations she currently experienced weren't due to any hormonal source but rather because she couldn't involve Michael in her decision-making about having another child:

"We had a couple of arguments. I wanted to discuss the question of having another child. He was not ready to discuss it. But I am the one who has to make sacrifices and go through it all. For him it is about money, whether we can af-

ford to do it. For me it is also that he has to make a commitment to help me and not leave me alone like before. We argued because he does not want to make a decision. Finally, I told him I would not use birth control for another two months. If I get pregnant, okay. If not, then I will get fixed. He said okay, but then had second thoughts again later."

Amelia had actually stopped her birth control five months previously. So, despite The Witch's efforts to prevent another pregnancy, Amelia was nevertheless able to stand up to her inner nemesis and leave open some possibility of pregnancy.

Amelia 11

We returned to the deep work of two weeks earlier. We had been unsuccessful in helping Amelia 11 (the first-communion Part) to let go of all of her fear of being alone. As we ended the session, Monster-Head, the Part with the body of Amelia and the head of a monster, had seemed to be the likely blocker of that work. However, Amelia now said of Amelia 11: *"She says she is not afraid of being alone because she has to take care of Amelia 5."* I wasn't sure what to make of this. I had expected we would begin by negotiating with Monster-Head for permission to do the healing. I wondered whether Amelia 11 would still need healing if we succeeded in our treatment of Amelia 5. We would have to wait and see.

Amelia 5

"The five-year-old is lost and confused," Amelia began. *"Around this time my mother went back to work and I went to live with my grandmother. She does not clearly remember. But she does remember being in both houses and having a lot of relatives around her. She was the only kid, no cousins. She played by herself. She went places—like errands—to stores. She enjoyed that. She was not allowed to play with neighbor kids often. She had to be well-behaved because she was al-*

ways around adults. She had to be well-contained. She was not allowed to be loose. She has no memories of having freedom. She felt restricted."

Relief from Grandma's Control

I suggested to Amelia that we neutralize her painful memories of **being restricted** by using a fire intervention, in which she would burn up the negative emotions. Amelia said that the little girl didn't know how to do that. Instead, Amelia suggested a water intervention, and visualized Amelia 5 in a swimming pool: *"She started swimming around this time and it was where she felt the least restricted."* Amelia visualized the feelings of **restriction** as ropes around the little girl, and imagined the ropes being dissolved by the water in the pool. Soon she said, *"She feels now like a bird and she can fly. She feels now like a loose animal. She has wings and she can fly and she can dive into the water and be a dolphin."*

With Amelia 5's memories of restriction neutralized, we checked Amelia 11's mood state. As I had feared, with the younger Part no longer needing her protection, Amelia 11 was again distressed: *"She feels alone again. She wants to dive in the water too. She **feels restraints** also."* Amelia visualized the same restraining-ropes intervention she had used with the younger Part: *"She is free now. They went to a water park and are just having fun. Amelia 11 is no longer feeling alone. She is fine now."*

Timing Interventions

I was surprised by how easily we were able to accomplish the interventions, given how much interference we had faced in the previous session. Monster-Head hadn't made an appearance. When we located her, Amelia said, *"She is lying in bed and watching the girls. She is happy for them now."* For me this raised another question. When we previously worked with

Monster-Head, Amelia was in the throes of PMS. Now she was in the usually-best-time in her cycle, the week after her period. I had already been thinking that the best time to locate PMS Parts was during PMS episodes. And now I began to think that once located, healing PMS Parts might best be done when the symptoms had diminished. That seems to be what happened. Monster-Head blocked our work two weeks previously but stood aside during the positive part of Amelia's cycle.

MONSTER-HEAD

Since Amelia was thinking about Monster-Head, it was a good time to collect autobiographical memories from her. Monster-Head recalled her teenage years *"when I was rebellious. I turned to anger and defiance of my mother. My parents divorced when I was thirteen and I blamed my mother. And I was disappointed by my father for not showing up for his visits.*

"There are many memories but I do not have a clear image of myself... Yes, they are Monster-Head's memories. Oh! There is a memory of my mom having a miscarriage when I was thirteen. Before that, my dad was drunk and wanted to hit her because he did not want another child. She kicked him out at three months and miscarried at five months. She was very depressed. Divorced during pregnancy and then a miscarriage! She was depressed for six months, would cry almost every weekend, playing songs and being with friends. She would cry and cry and blame my dad.

"So I was missing my dad and sad about not getting a little brother—my mom already had a name for him. She was thirty-five and I am thirty-five now. Maybe that is where my desire to have another child comes from."

Progress in Therapy

Amelia began our next meeting by reporting that she was four or five days into her ovulation phase: *"but the week was pretty good. It is usually worse. I felt some mild irritation about small things and I was moderately tired but that is all. And my relationship with Michael is not too bad. Two weeks and only a couple of fights."* Good news! We were making progress again!

Michael had begun doing his own therapy. *"Monster-Head is really pleased that my husband is doing therapy. It is the first time in his life that he is opening up to someone. I think he is more self-aware now. Before, he would just act or react and be surprised if I got upset with him."* (Michael was doing therapy with me, with a focus upon his pornography addiction. His therapy, like Amelia's therapy, involved healing difficult life-history experiences that underlay adult issues.)

"We are still having conversations about having another child. We are probably going to do it. We just have to agree on the details and the changes we will have to make; for example, taking the first two kids out of private school so we can afford a third child. I was surprised that his only concern was financial. Mine was that, but also—and especially— postpartum depression and possible isolation from my husband."

More Monster-Head Memories

We returned to Monster-Head. Amelia said that the therapy hadn't yet improved her appearance. She had Amelia's body but *"her face—a big face—was of an angry monster with bared teeth. Right now she is calmer, lying on a bed, more tired than angry and no bared teeth."*

Continuing with Monster-Head's memories, Amelia returned to her parents' divorce when she was thirteen: *"Yes, I can see myself after my parents' separation, with my mother depressed. After they split up I had to do a lot of caring for my younger sister, a kind of parenting of her. I would try to distract her when my mom was depressed."*

Amelia 13

We called this thirteen-year-old Stuck-in-Time Part *Amelia 13*. She seemed to be a subpart of Monster-Head, like Angry Amelia 9 and Amelia 11. And like them as well, she had no awareness of Amelia's current life:

"*My dad was very present right after the separation. He would pick us up on weekends and do things with us. I enjoyed his attention for two or three months, then less and less. I remember sometimes waiting for him and him not showing up. Eventually, I stopped waiting for him. I joined the choir and went out with my friends. Then my dad would get angry when he would show up and I was not there. So he would take out just my sister. But gradually he stopped coming more. I got angry with him and then angry at my mom. The anger with my mom lasted throughout high school.*"

We turned our attention to healing Amelia 13 and asked her to focus on her painful feelings for the separation of her parents and her mother's depression. Amelia took over from there: "*I used water and fire. I threw her* **emotions** *on the fire from the big fight of my mother and father and for the separation. Then I washed away her* **sadness** *and* **disappointment** *for when my dad no-showed for visits and the other stuff.*" Amelia 13 quickly gave up her painful emotions. Monster-Head similarly had a SUD score of zero for the memories.

Amelia 16

Monster-Head, however, was still angry with Amelia's mother—she didn't know why. Amelia asked her to focus on her anger with her mother and connect to the memories that were the source of her anger. The result was an image of Amelia at age 16, wearing a purple dress and high boots. Amelia described the memories of this Stuck-in-Time Part and named her *Amelia 16*:

"She was very hurt when her father went to live with his girlfriend and got her pregnant right away. He bought an apartment in a better part of town and tried to get her mother to reconcile with him there. After her mother refused, he moved his girlfriend in. I was very angry with that lady and for my mother's refusal to move to the new apartment. We struggled with food and clothing because my dad gave little support. I was angry with him and that lady and their son in that nicer apartment and better finances. My mother would sometimes have to beg for support. Later they had a daughter. My sister and I would visit them and they had food and things we could not imagine."

Another of Amelia 16's painful memories had to do with her personal interview for college, an ordeal that was necessary for admission: *"I had to borrow shoes and a jacket to be appropriately dressed for the meeting with all the professors. My shoes were so tight I got a blister. I was embarrassed to be so poor."*

Although it was late in the session, we tried to neutralize the first of Amelia 16's memories before closing. Utilizing a rainfall intervention, Amelia asked her to focus on the **sadness** and **disappointment** over being treated as less important than her father's other children. Unfortunately, the rain had no effect. But when Amelia switched to a different intervention and helped Amelia 16 to vomit up her distress, she reduced the SUD level from 8 to 4. Then we were out of time. In closing our meeting, Amelia visualized Amelia 16 temporarily storing her remaining **distress** in a suitcase.

FATHER'S FAILURES

Returning to Amelia 16 in our next session, the SUD level for the **distress** in the suitcase was now down to 2, a further reduction that sometimes happens between sessions. Amelia quickly guided the Part in producing complete neutrality for the emotional memory. She described her intervention: *"She* *opens her mouth and the wind blows it out of her mouth like vomit."*

We then asked Amelia 16 to scan for other painful memories. She soon identified the anger she felt toward her father for his frequent failure to help with her college expenses. She was also angry because she had to *"smother"* her resentments for fear that he would do even less. She was also angry with her mother for not reconciling with her father.

Anger with Mom

Amelia continued to describe the teen's thoughts and feelings: *"My mom could have reconciled with my dad. But she was afraid of change. She did not want to move to my dad's new apartment because it was too far away from my grandmother. And she did not know anybody over there, and she was a very social person. But I wanted us to go to the new apartment."*

Amelia chose a wind intervention to neutralize Amelia 16's **disappointment** with her mother for refusing to move. The healing was quick. As expected, neutralizing the vulnerable emotion also neutralized the protective emotion of anger: *"Now she thinks they would have divorced anyway and it was probably better that her mother stayed with her friends to help her deal with it."*

Amelia 16's changed outlook provides a good example of how healing brings insight and understanding. Often therapists work too hard at trying to bring insight to their patients as a means of healing rather than recognizing that insight is better achieved following the healing—at least when neutralizing emotional memories.

Disappointment with Dad

We continued our work with Amelia 16: *"She is disappointed with her dad's inadequacy, and his selfishness, and his ab-*

sence from seeing her, and his lack of loving affection unless he was drunk. I wanted a different father, someone like my grandfather who was loving and caring." Amelia tried to use a wind intervention to relieve the teenager of her **disappointment** with her father but the wind she visualized simply blew around the Part rather than through her: *"She cannot let go of the* **disappointment**. *She is trying but she cannot. And I have a pain in my stomach."* The resistance to the intervention was strong.

Monster-Head Blocks

We looked immediately for the blocking Part, who, not surprisingly, turned out to be Monster-Head: *"Yes, she is blocking the healing but she does not respond when I ask why."* Amelia then complimented her strength and asked permission to heal the emotional memories: *"She does not want to. It is almost like these emotions for my father are part of the core of her, like we are touching a nerve, and she does not want to let go. It is like she feels she might disappear if she lets go of these feelings."*

This sort of fear is common, especially so with blockers and other managers. Their identity is so bound up with the emotions they carry that the idea of healing them, even when the emotions are painful, threatens their existence. It's clear that Parts have a desire to continue to exist, just as the external person does.

The Two-Step

I've found it useful in these cases to suggest a two-step intervention. In the first step, the negative emotions are initially moved out of the Part and into a container, but still under the control of the Part. The Part can monitor the process and stop it if it begins to disappear. Then, in the second step, once the Part understands that it won't disappear, the negative emotions can be permanently released. In only rare cases have I seen a Part insist upon taking back the negative emotions from the container.

Occasionally, a blocker finds that, although it has shown no signs of becoming weaker or less substantial, it still wants to hold onto the container for a while before finally letting it go. In such cases, I return to the Part in the following week so that it can finally dispense with the container's negative emotions.

Monster-Head agreed to the two-step intervention and Amelia began the transfer of Amelia 16's **negative emotions** into a large trunk: *"She is throwing up into it, like she is throwing up oil, very dark, sticky things. She is using water, too, to wash it out of her through her mouth. And it is not coming from her stomach but from her spine. It is coming out like a pressured water hose. She is done. She is very happy."*

When Amelia checked with Monster-Head, she found: *"Now she is scared. She does not have a monster head anymore. She is just a woman. She is thinking of all the things my father did and all the hurt he did, all the things he caused, his lack of responsibility for his actions. She hated him but also wanted his approval. She would do anything to make him proud and she would be hurt when he did not notice her. So she hated him and she hated herself for being unable to make my dad proud and for being unable to help my mom. He did acknowledge her in time as he got older—more than before. She hated him and she loved him."* (Remember that Monster-Head is Amelia too.)

Without a specific memory to focus upon, we nevertheless went ahead with trying to neutralize Monster-Head of *"hundreds of* **hurts***"* by Amelia's father. We expected that the memories would flood Monster-Head and Amelia as the intervention proceeded. Shortly after beginning, Amelia said, *"She is using water and it is black and sticky like with the sixteen-year-old. It takes a lot of water and chemicals to wash her clean."* After a full two minutes, Amelia sighed and said,

"Okay. Sshe is probably at a zero." Although I was concerned about the lack of a definite SUD score of zero, I decided not to push the question—we were near the end of the session. Instead, I coached Amelia to express her thanks to Monster-Head and to let her know that we would talk to her in the following week.

Monster-Head's Transformation

But Monster-Head had suddenly changed. Amelia exclaimed, *"Now she is empty! Just a silhouette! She seems to be disappearing."* Perhaps Monster-Head was at least partially correct in her fears of disappearing. Although our healing of Amelia 16 didn't affect her, somehow, when we healed her directly, the result was this transparency, an unusual effect. I quickly urged Amelia to tell Monster-Head that she still needed her, that she would always need someone to help assess the men in her life. Amelia did so and then responded, *"Now I see her face and her upper body. Half of the body is coming back. She looks sad. I still feel some pressure in my chest."*

We had forestalled the unusual effect of a Part seemingly on her way to disappearing. Very occasionally, a Part *does* disappear, but not when there's more work to do. My personal preference is to assign another task to a Part when its original function seems outdated. I had the sense, though, that we had more work to do with Monster-Head. Unfortunately, we had no time left to explore her sadness and half-body. Nor was there time to examine Amelia's chest pressure. Another patient was in my waiting room. I noted before closing the file that we also needed to check Amelia 16's container for the emotional content she had placed there.

SUMMARY OF PARTS

Amelia 11. She first appears in the previous chapter and carries memories of disappointment with her dad for his absence on special occasions.

Monster-Head. She was angry for feeling unloved by family members, especially her father. She carried a range of memories located in her subparts Angry Amelia 9, Amelia 11, Amelia 13, and Amelia 16. Her head was evidently a monster because Amelia's child Parts thought something was wrong and abnormal about their head.

Mother Introject. An internal manager costumed as Amelia's mother, she prevented Amelia 11 from releasing all of her burden. When unmasked she had transformed into a five-year-old girl that we called Amelia 5.

Amelia 5. She was the child Part who wore the mother costume and who carried the fear of being alone. This was the age at which Amelia's grandmother became her primary caretaker. Amelia 5 struggled with the constraints on her behavior she endured in her new home.

Amelia 13. She was a subpart of Monster-Head, like Angry Amelia 9 and Amelia 11. She carried the pain for the events surrounding the breakup of Amelia's parents.

Amelia 16. She was hurt and angry over her father's choice to be with a new woman and for the lesser support he gave to his first family in comparison to his new family.

Chapter 11

The Problem with Men

We seemed to be making slow but definite progress. Sometimes it seemed we had made clear breakthroughs, but then Amelia would have another difficult PMS episode. However, she regularly commented that life was much better than before she began therapy. There was still significant work to do and other Amelia Parts to meet. And The Witch continued her efforts to protect Amelia by interfering with the process of what we knew to be deep healing.

THE WITCH BLOCKS WORK

We met again eleven days later. Amelia began by saying that, after leaving our last session: *"I felt a heaviness in my gut. At first it was mild, but in the next hour, I became very nauseous. I thought I was pregnant. The worst was on Saturday* [four days later]. *I cancelled my clients that day. On Sunday I got my period. Then on Thursday* [yesterday], *the nausea came back. It is very strong, like I could throw up."* She had just described the classic PMS/PMDD pattern except that after the initial relief at the beginning of her period she became nauseous again in her period's late phase.

As I frequently did for Amelia's other body sensations, I coached her to focus on the sensation and to request that it provide an image of itself: *"It is the monster lady that became more a shape than a person and was almost disappearing. She is still half present but her bottom part is empty, just an outline with no content. She is still sad."* When Amelia asked the Part if she was the cause of the nausea, *Half-Lady* (formerly Monster-Head) wasn't sure. In my experience, being unsure like this generally means that the Part isn't involved.

We decided to check with Amelia 16 and the negative emotions and sensations she had placed in a container. The contents were all of Amelia's disappointments with her father and, by implication, all of her similar disappointments with her husband: *"It is still there,"* Amelia said. *"but Amelia 16 is not there anymore. I do not know where she went.... Yes, maybe it is the container causing the nausea. Because she filled it by throwing up."*

Since Amelia 16 was absent, we asked Half-Lady to neutralize the contents of the container by burning it up in fire. Amelia 16 seems to have been a subpart of Monster-Head, who was now Half-Lady; thus the contents of the container would belong to her as well: *"She is burning it up."* But two minutes later, Amelia added, *"It is still burning; it seems like a lot of it is still there. She does not feel connected to it."*

Confusion of Emotion with Knowledge

Since the healing process had stopped, we looked for a blocking Part: *"It is The Witch. She says she has been watching all along. She does not want to let it burn. She says if I give up the memories I will get hurt all over again."* We explained again—as we had so many times before—that we weren't getting rid of factual memories but of emotions. Amelia would retain all of her explicit memories as well as the wisdom that came with them: *"She is not sure,"* Amelia said. *"She says Half-Lady is too fragile and might not remember and I am too stupid to remember."*

Finding a Hidden Part

It seemed clear that The Witch was unable to perceive Amelia as I saw her, sitting in my office and working hard at healing her full set of Parts. If she did, it would be obvious that Amelia wasn't stupid, fragile, or weak. There had to be another Part of Amelia that The Witch perceived. With a technique I often used in similar situations, I suggested that Amelia speak to The Witch and request that The Witch speak to the Part of Amelia she perceived as stupid and weak, and ask *that* Amelia to step away from both Amelia and The Witch. In this way, both Amelia and The Witch would see the Part that The Witch had been calling stupid.

When the Part stepped away, Amelia said, *"I see myself in my twenties, with long hair, jeans, and a green sweater. Kind of how I looked when I got married."* The Part claimed an age of 27, so we called her *Amelia 27*. With this Part now stepped aside, Amelia explained to The Witch that she wasn't stupid, but a high-functioning adult. The Witch responded, *"She does not think I am stupid but I do not have it together yet."* The Witch admitted that she was causing the nausea: *"She enjoys me being in pain. She thinks that if I have some pain, I will remember my postpartum, my problems. She is not happy we neutralized the monster. Now I am weaker and unable to defend myself. Monster-Head was the angry one that would come out to protect me. The first time we found her I just had a fight with my husband. She thinks that the monster cannot protect me now—as a woman with a half-body."*

Understanding Anger

The Witch had again claimed to be the cause of Amelia's suffering. Our continuing work should tell us whether her claim was accurate. Previously, she seems to have sometimes overstated her power. But it's important to see here that The Witch and Amelia have different views about what is helpful. The

Witch wants Amelia to express anger to protect herself. Amelia wants to be less angry in order to improve her marriage. This is a familiar scenario in work with couples. Angry Parts are not generally concerned with the wellbeing of a spouse. Instead, they want to create distance with the spouse to keep the conscious self safe.

Another claim here, that Monster-Head was the Part that was angry with Michael, was probably only partially accurate. My sense was that there were several Parts that functioned to bring on protective anger. Later sessions would also tell us whether neutralizing Monster-Head's anger would also reduce the frequency of Amelia's angry moments with Michael.

AMELIA 27

We had so far been unable to elicit painful memories directly from The Witch, memories that she claimed as her own autobiographical experiences. We tried again, asking her to share her earliest painful memory: *"She does not remember anything. She is focusing now on Amelia 27, attacking her verbally. She is saying she was stupid to get married because she knew what kind of man she was marrying. She should have stayed in Costa Rica. It was a foolish mistake. She should have listened to her and made a different decision.*

"There was a situation with Michael when he broke up with me. I knew he had issues and I knew he had problems. I could see it in the way he related to others, his lack of self-confidence. So when he broke up with me, I was going to leave the company where I worked to get away from him, but I could not get a transfer. I felt very sad. I went to a park for two hours, thinking about it, if he was worth it. I probably did not feel love so much as the basis for my decision. It was more my dreams of what we might do, travel and other things. I loved him but I had lots of doubts. But I thought I could have a good life. He repented almost immediately and I could have left him, but I chose on the basis of hope. The Witch says to

Amelia 27 that at that moment it was not a good choice and it caused so much pain and bad consequences.

"But I think I wanted to be more in love with him. I thought that it would grow eventually, that it would grow stronger as we lived together. I could see he was a good man in spite of his problems. At that moment, I was not sure. And The Witch says she should have chosen with her heart and not for the reasons she did. I think she was still in love with the old boyfriend. She was still thinking about him and she knew the relationship did not have a future. It would probably have been a miserable life with him. She wanted to be in love with Michael but she knew he was a difficult man, that he was troubled. Before I met Michael, I did not think I would ever get married—because of my parents' relationship."

INVESTIGATING THE NAUSEA

We were out of time again, but I wanted to know whether Amelia was still nauseous. She was. I coached her to bargain with The Witch, to remind her that she had listened to her the entire session. The reward should be that The Witch would take away the nausea: *"She is not responding but she does not want to take it away."* I suggested here that Amelia promise The Witch that she would listen again during all of our next session if she would take away the nausea: *"I think she likes me to be in pain. She reduced it but did not take it all away."* I suggested further that Amelia promise redoubled attention to The Witch if she would take away the nausea: *"She says she cannot. She does not have the power over it anymore."* The Witch seemed to have overstated her strength.

Since we had reached a stalemate in negotiating with The Witch, we decided to treat the nausea as the production of a new Part. Amelia asked the sensation to step back. The nausea diminished but didn't disappear. Amelia then asked the hypothesized nauseous Part to provide a picture of itself in Amelia's mind: *"It is me, pregnant with my daughter, my first child."*

We were rushing now to stabilize things before ending the session. Amelia thanked the pregnant Part for showing herself and told her we would talk to her more at our next meeting. Amelia visualized moving this Part to a safe place in hopes that the nausea would dissipate. Instead, *"she moved to a safe place but did not take the nausea with her."* Amelia asked the Part to reach back and take her nausea too: *"She is taking it, yes."* After about one minute, Amelia added, *"As she is taking it, her stomach is expanding."* Not knowing the symbolic meaning of the expanding stomach, I asked Amelia to stop the process and check her own subjective level of distress. She said her SUD for the nausea had reduced from an 8 to a 4 and that she could live with that for now. We planned to return to the pregnant Amelia and The Witch in our next session.

Depression and Self Criticism

Our previous session was on a Friday and we met again the following Tuesday. Amelia's period had ended on Monday. On Sunday and Monday, she had experienced mild depression, *"feeling like a horrible mother, a horrible wife. I should quit everything since I cannot do anything right. I should stay at home with the kids. I work on Saturdays and so the kids miss me. I come home and they are already eating or are in bed already. My son is sometimes clingy, experiencing separation anxiety—I feel the guilty Part of me. And I see The Witch's face: 'You see how bad you are and your children are suffering!'"*

These emotions are typical PMS symptoms experienced by millions of women, especially those who try to pursue a career as well as a family. For Amelia, though, these emotions were often experienced during her period as well as premenstrually. Although the experts would say this is *dysmenorrhea* (i.e., painful menses rather than painful pre-menses) rather than

PMS, for Amelia there was little or no difference. Consequently, we hoped to reduce the symptoms of both PMS and dysmenorrhea.

We returned to our work from the previous session as Amelia said, *"After last session, the nausea was not strong at all. I do not remember being nauseous on Saturday or Sunday."*

AMELIA 29

This was more good news; our work was indeed able to reduce physical symptoms with purely psychological techniques. We returned to the internal source of the nausea—hijacked by The Witch—the nauseous Part, locked in the experience of being pregnant for the first time.

In their conversation, Amelia learned from the pregnant Part that she viewed herself as twenty-nine years old and that we could call her simply *Amelia 29*. Her earliest difficult memories were those of being pregnant while stressed with the requirements for the first of her two master's degrees. She was taking her final course, a practicum (directly-monitored counseling) in school psychology.

She was also a healthcare worker at that time but not yet in training in psychotherapy. She worked in the homes of troubled families doing "psychosocial rehabilitation," meaning that she tried to teach everyday life skills, such as scheduling, cooperation with other family members, budgeting, etc. She was seven months pregnant and her bosses wouldn't permit her to reduce her workload as the summer birth of her child approached. She recalled being uncomfortably hot and sweaty in some of the homes that lacked air conditioning.

Pregnant and Overworked

"I was overworked, pregnant, and doing my practicum. I was disconnected from my husband. He stopped having sex with me after I got pregnant and I was highly aroused throughout.

He would say things like, 'I do not want to hurt the baby,' and that is ridiculous. He was caring but he was always distant and distracted. Later I found that he was deeply involved in watching porn."

I asked Amelia to get a SUD rating from Amelia 29 for her last two months of pregnancy. She said, *"It is making me nauseous! It is like a 10. I was very stressed, and afraid my stress would harm my baby. And I needed my mother with me but her visa was denied. It was very difficult and sad that she could not come. I would call her all the time for advice."*

Healing a Difficult Childbirth

Amelia chose a wind intervention to strip the **negative emotions** and **body pain** from the memories of the last two months of her pregnancy and birthing. The **sadness** and **fear** of harmful stress for the baby healed right away. Neutralizing the physical pain took longer. Amelia said of Amelia 29, *"She remembers the pain she felt after the birth."* Amelia directed the wind toward the **pain** and observed, *"It looks like she is bleeding."* After forty seconds, she added, *"The wind cleaned out the pain and it came out of her mouth and stomach. Then she started bleeding and the wind healed that. The doctors didn't cut me and so I ripped both sides and I bled a lot. In my culture, mothers help you heal the wounds but she was not there so Michael had to do it. It took two months of aftercare after the birth. He was very hands on and that was helpful."*

The healing had been successful: *"Amelia 29 is fine now."* I asked whether the Part had any other painful or troubling memories. She did: *"Years later Michael told me of his porn addiction and he said that sometimes he just let my daughter cry while I was in evening classes. She feels guilt for not knowing her baby was not being cared for."* Unfortunately, when we tried to use wind again to neutralize that **guilt**, we could not: *"The Witch is not letting her release the guilt. She is telling her that is why she should never have married Michael."*

We were again at the end of the session and would have to postpone this healing. We planned to return to Amelia 29 and The Witch in our next session. Before leaving, Amelia added that Amelia 27 had also been present during the healing of Amelia 29, and we still had not healed the younger Part of her regrets for having married Michael.

PMS Success at Ovulation

We began our next session with good news about Amelia's ovulation. She had been ovulating over the weekend—beginning Thursday and Friday: *"I felt very anxious for one day, but I had five clients in crisis, so that makes sense. I felt some mild depression. But it was a calm weekend. By Saturday I was much better. Just two days of emotions. Before, it was four or five."*

Sharing Therapy with Michael

Before returning to our work from our previous session, Amelia revealed that she had talked to Michael about having a Part who had never loved him, i.e., The Witch: *"He was hurt but he said that he had always thought there was some Part of me who did not love him."* By now Michael had begun to work with me on his porn addiction and therefore with his own Parts. Consequently, he had some idea of what Amelia meant when she referred to a *Part* of her. But I still cringed at such honesty in their relationship. I was pleased that they could be so open, but if Amelia had asked me about it beforehand, I would have urged caution in sharing so much. Evidently, I can sometimes be too cautious.

RETURN TO AMELIA 29

Before returning to take up the unfinished work with Amelia 29, I coached Amelia to request permission from The Witch to heal the previously pregnant Part's guilt for going to class and leaving her daughter with Michael. I suggested also that she make the point that the five years since the birth of her daughter was enough punishment for Amelia 29.

The Witch gave her permission, and Amelia was then able to neutralize the **guilt** in seconds with a wind intervention. Because managers like The Witch need their power acknowledged, I asked Amelia to thank her for her help. One can never be too polite when working with powerful managers.

Amelia checked with Amelia 29 regarding other painful memories. She found that the Part could still feel some of the mild depression she felt following the birth of her daughter: *"She was **lonely** because my mother couldn't come, and my co-workers did not visit. She was isolated and alone. She was **sad** that nobody cared. And she did not have anyone to share her joy with."* Amelia 29 released these negative emotions fairly quickly to the wind, requiring just one detour from the visualization to again ask The Witch's permission to complete the task.

Another of Amelia 29's memories was her **longing** to be with her family in Costa Rica. A wind intervention took about fifty seconds before she released her **homesickness**, this time without any interference from The Witch.

Healing Amelia 29 at 30

One year after the birth of her daughter, Amelia was diagnosed with precancerous lesions in her uterus. These memories were also contained within Amelia 29's memory bank. Notice that the presenting age of a Part doesn't mean that she can't have memories later than that age—in this case the twenty-nine-year-old Part had memories from age thirty. The presenting age of a Part is best viewed as a handy hook for recall and not as a reliable predictor of memories held: *"She was very scared that she would not be able to have another child. It was her first time ever for surgery with complete anesthesia."* Amelia guided Amelia 29's healing of her **scared** feelings in just thirty seconds.

As always when working with distressed Parts, we want to be sure we've healed all of the painful memories. Otherwise, these memories may be triggered later in the therapy, or later in the patient's life. When Amelia inquired about additional disturbing memories, we appeared to be finished: *"She is okay. I think that is it."*

Triggering Unconscious Parts

Amelia 29 had no memories of Amelia's second child, Nathan. So, while Amelia 29 wasn't stuck in just the final months of Amelia's first pregnancy, her active memories ended after a roughly two-year period. Until now, Amelia's emotions from that period could have been triggered by events in her present-time life. Thus there is a connection between conscious life and non-conscious stored emotional memories. The triggering events might have been guilt or fear similar to what she had experienced at twenty-nine or thirty. But with the emotional memories now neutralized, they could no longer be triggered.

Drama at Session End

As we began to plan for later work, we checked with The Witch in order to get a sense of whether the healing work might have softened her views. Evidently not: *"She is okay. She is kind of irritated with all of these memories. She does not want to talk about them anymore... No, she does not want to heal her irritation."* I would continue to look for changes in her outward appearance and her attitude for signs that we were making progress in the therapy.

With only a few minutes left in our session, Amelia exclaimed, *"Amelia 29 has just showed me another memory! When my daughter was four months old, Michael had heart surgery and then he could hardly move. My daughter got very sick, vomiting everywhere. She was vomiting in the car when I went to the hospital to pick him up. I had to stop the car to be sure she did not choke on her vomit. And she vomit-*

ed throughout the house when we got home. I had to deal with her by myself. I remember crying because I did not know what to do. I was just scared." When I asked about healing those memories, Amelia said, *"She is already letting it go. Yes, she is using wind. It is gone now... Yes, the SUD score is zero."*

A dramatic end to the session! Fortunately, the healing intervention went quickly. The Witch seems to interfere only when the painful memory has something to do with Michael's actions toward Amelia. I was also quite pleased that Amelia had done the healing without guidance from me. She gave us a positive glimpse of what she would do on her own later in the therapy.

AMELIA 27

We met again on Day 10 of Amelia's cycle, a calm time for her. It had been three weeks since we last met. In the interim, each of the four members of Amelia's family was stricken with strep throat as they infected each other. Amelia took two weeks off from her work. Michael was off for the summer and so his work schedule wasn't affected. I had seen him once for his own therapy during the three weeks. Amelia remarked, *"He is less angry as the result of the therapy. He is cute when he talks about his new insights from therapy."*

We finally returned to work with Amelia 27. Amelia described her as *"a Part who married Michael and upset The Witch for making a rational choice rather than a love choice. She seems sad."*

Breaking Up with the Old Boyfriend

Her earliest painful memory was that of breaking up with the boyfriend she had before she met Michael. The **loss** was disturbing to the Part at a level 8 on the SUD scale. Amelia chose wind again for this healing, and after one minute, she opened her eyes to say, *"Okay."* The SUD score had reduced to 2.

The healing had stuck at a level 2 because *"she always wondered how life would have been if we had stayed together. The breakup was mutual. We lived in different cities. I was working already and thinking of the future. He was still in college and in a different place, not thinking of his future yet. We loved each other but he was immature. He had a wealthy family who provided everything for him. He knew nothing about independence and working for a living. I did not think I could trust him to be a good husband."*

Following this narrative, Amelia easily reduced Amelia 27's remaining pain of **loss** to zero with just fifteen seconds of wind visualization. This is a good example of how talking about the issue—even briefly—can break through a stalled intervention.

Holding Back from Michael

Her next disturbing memory involved the way she related to her future husband: *"After meeting Michael and beginning our relationship, there was a missed communication—she was very guarded—maybe it was the language barrier, maybe it was her fear that he would leave her and go back to America, but she could not fully commit to him."* Amelia asked Amelia 27 to focus on that **guardedness** that still affected the way she related to Michael, and then to visualize the wind breaking it up and blowing it away. After twenty seconds Amelia said, *"It's very hard, like a shield."* She continued for almost two minutes before adding, *"I had to break it up with a hammer. It was very thick. Now the pieces are coming down."* But thirty seconds later, Amelia added more: *"Now she feels exposed, like you can see her bones; you can see her insides, like she does not have skin."*

When neutralizing emotions, and there's this much struggle in doing the interventions, it usually means there's interference from other Parts. However, we were making progress, and for this reason I stayed with the process rather than look for blocking Parts. If we could accomplish the healing without confronting the outside interference, we could keep the work from getting too complicated.

Amelia asked Amelia 27 to focus on the feeling of being **exposed** and to permit the wind to carry it away. As an aid to the Part's healing, Amelia explained to her that she and Michael had been together now for nine years; they had two children and were thinking about a third. They were well into a long life together. With her eyes still closed, Amelia said, *"Now she's growing skin. It is just growing on its own. I am not using wind or anything."* In another two minutes, she said, *"She is better... No, she does not feel **exposed** anymore."*

Clearly, Amelia 27 was a Stuck-in-Time Part, holding onto the doubts and fears she had when Amelia first married Michael. But now, after Amelia shared the positive history of life with Michael, the younger Part was able to accept the healing.

Letting Go of Home

Having healed Amelia 27 of the loss of her previous boyfriend and of her guardedness toward Michael, Amelia turned to the Part's next disturbing memory. It was the **sadness** of saying goodbye to her family when she came to the United States. She rated this loss as significant, but only a 5 on the SUD scale. Amelia guided Amelia 27 in releasing the **sadness** of the loss to a gentle wind and blowing it away. That took just 10 seconds, but Amelia added, *"She was **nervous** too."* That feeling also gave way quickly to the wind: *"She is thinking now of the honeymoon on San Andreas island. She wishes she could stay there forever."* I suggested that she could actually do so, since the inner world doesn't have to correspond precisely with the outer world: *"It makes her happy to think of that. It was her last happy three days before coming to the United States."*

We ended the conversation and the session with Amelia recalling, *"After we returned to Costa Rica, Michael left for America. Then it was three months before I came. It was a big disconnection between us and I do not think we ever fully re-covered from it."*

THE WITCH GROWS YOUNG

Our next meeting was on Day 17 of Amelia's cycle, a some-times-peaceful time for Amelia and sometimes not. We were meeting on a Wednesday: *"I have been ovulating since Sunday night* [Day 14]. *I have been irritable for no reason and having light headaches and tiredness. But this is better. I used to be sick and depressed. I would lose one or two days of work. Now I can push it through. All of these changes have come since we started therapy."*

With this very good news about the effectiveness of the therapy, we returned to our work with The Witch: *"Did I tell you that she is not like a witch anymore? She is like a forties person. Her hair is brown and curly. I cannot see how she is dressed because she is lying in a hammock with a drink in her hand. She is very relaxed. But she still enjoys my pain. Re-member, she thinks I am stupid... No, she is not concerned with my ovulation distress. She could care less."*

Amelia's new description of The Witch as a brown-haired woman in her forties was further confirmation that we had made significant progress in the therapy. Such positive sym-bolic changes—old to young, scruffy to well-dressed, sores to clear skin—are common as we make progress in healing the pain of earlier life experiences. Soon, I hoped, The Witch would be fully on our team.

Another positive development in the therapy was that for the first time, The Witch was willing to rate certain memories on the SUD scale, although she still wouldn't claim them as her own autobiographical experiences. She rated as an 8 on the SUD scale the next memories that she brought to Amelia's awareness.

DOMINANT MALES

"Before I met Michael there were three men in one year I was getting to know. They were all physically aggressive and pushy, ordering me around. One was a friend who tried to have sex with me when we were drunk. I was disappointed with myself for putting myself in that position, and disappointed in him too. I was alone in the city and I did not know many people and I wanted to get to know people. After these men, I became guarded. The Witch was angry about the situation because I was stupid and naïve—to let these men be so rude to me just so I would have friends."

These men and others who Amelia experienced as dominant, pushy, rude, etc., had a profound effect on her relationship with Michael. With Michael, she eventually came to take the lead, to be the one in the relationship who pushed for change, and who took charge of running everyday life. She gave up the passivity her grandmother required of her, and rebelled also against dominant men in her life. She eventually became the household leader in the family she established with Michael. But it took some time.

Amelia 24

We asked The Witch to bring to Amelia's awareness an image of the Part who had felt humiliated by the dominant males. This Part, *Amelia 24,* had *"short hair and jeans with a blue T-shirt."* She wasn't initially aware of who Amelia was. When Amelia explained that she was an older, wiser version of her, and that she was married with children, Amelia 24 was surprised but pleased. She rated the memories at an 8 or 9 on the SUD scale, similar to the rating The Witch gave. She felt **disgusted**, **used**, and **alone** when she connected with those memories. She very much wanted to release the pain of them.

Amelia began a wind intervention to neutralize these emotions, but after thirty seconds she said, *"It is hard!"* Once more we suspected that The Witch might be blocking the work. When asked for permission to do the intervention, The Witch at first refused: *"She does not want to… Yes, she is blocking—because she* [Amelia 24] *needs to remember. She wants her to feel pain."* I asked Amelia to remind The Witch that healing the emotions doesn't remove the memory and that the pain wasn't necessary to keep the Part alert to possible new threats. Amelia did so and then responded, *"Okay, she says okay."*

Being Passive and Naive

Amelia visualized the wind blowing through Amelia 24 to break up and blow away the **negative emotions** she carried. After a minute, she said, *"They are talking to each other. The Witch is saying she has allowed people to take advantage of her. Amelia 24 is saying, 'I am sorry; I did not know.' She is showing her many situations in which she put herself in vulnerable positions, like with men who only wanted sex. So, even though she did not have sex with them, she was still naïve and stupid. Amelia 24 is feeling very ashamed for doing that. The Witch is acting like an angry mother. She does not let me do the work because she is angry."*

Stymied again by The Witch, I tried to coax her to locate earlier of her memories that produced this sort of anger. I was thinking that if we could neutralize the foundation memories of the anger, The Witch would be more flexible with the current issue. Amelia asked her for these earlier memories and soon described them: *"She was always taught to be passive, to avoid arguing, to accept everybody's position. She was the youngest, a child—required to submit to her dad, her mom, her grandmother, her uncles and aunts. So she never learned how to defend herself, especially with men. She would be compliant to avoid further problems. It makes her be in pain. She is afraid to give up her pain because then somebody will take advantage of her again."* Amelia cried as she told The Witch's story. Amelia's tears were The Witch's tears. I was pleased to see that she had finally trusted us enough to share her vulnerable emotions rather than her anger.

The Witch's Suitcase

Getting The Witch to acknowledge her own experienced pain was a major therapeutic advance. It meant we had a chance to heal her directly. We struck a bargain with her and used the two-step intervention. We asked her to put her **pain** into a suitcase, but keep the suitcase with her. Then she could examine herself to see if she were just as vigilant without the pain as with the pain. She could check whether she needed the pain to protect herself. If she found herself less vigilant, she could open up the suitcase and take the pain back inside of her. But if removing the pain had no negative effect on her vigilance, she could release it permanently. Amelia closed her eyes and concentrated deeply as she tried to visualize The Witch moving her **pain** into a suitcase. After a full minute, Amelia reported that The Witch had placed some of her pain into the suitcase, but was reluctant to do more.

Knowing that time was short and that we needed something more to complete the intervention, I thought out loud, "Maybe we should find the little girl who became compliant and avoided argument." I didn't intend to actually work with another Part that day, but Amelia quickly said, *"She is about nine."* Amelia was already aware of her. We now had a nine-year-old Part with whom we had to coordinate our work with Amelia 24 and The Witch. I suggested that Amelia move the two younger Parts to a safe place and return The Witch to her hammock. Amelia responded that The Witch would keep the other two Parts with her, as well as the suitcase of pain.

We wanted to continue our work with all three Parts in our next session. Before parting, Amelia mused, *"Now I know why I have a hard time saying no."* She also added, *"The Witch finally broke. We touched a nerve with her. Before it was always about everybody else."* I agreed. For the first time, The

Witch accepted some autobiographical memories as her own, and acknowledged that her pain was about *her* experiences and not just about the experiences of other Amelia Parts.

PMS Intrudes

When we met a week later, it was two days before Amelia's period and she was in full-blown PMS: *"Yesterday I felt very emotional; actually, it was all weekend. I cried at night. The Witch was there telling me what a bad mother and bad wife I was. I had a difficult time yesterday with my clients—one is cutting again, so I felt like a bad therapist. I'm feeling frustrated—frustrated, irritable, everything bothered me yesterday. Today I still feel I wish I did not have to work. I would rather stay home in bed. I have no interest in sex or intimacy with my husband. The Witch says all men are incapable—you ask him to do this and he cannot, and you cannot rely on him."*

The only positive takeaway from Amelia's distress was that she continued to go to work, unlike her actions before beginning therapy. With this as a measure, she had made progress.

LONELY AMELIA 9

We returned to our planned work with The Witch, Amelia 24, and the nine-year-old Part. We called the child *Lonely Amelia 9* to distinguish her from the Angry Amelia 9 we had met in earlier therapy, and who seemed to be a subpart of Monster-Head. Lonely Amelia 9 seemed to be a subpart of The Witch and carried an entirely different set of memories from those of Angry Amelia 9.

Our new work seemed especially important because the memories we had accessed in the previous session were actually claimed by The Witch as her own. Lonely Amelia 9 was a Stuck-in-Time Part who continued to experience those memories as they happened in childhood. Until now, Amelia had been unaware of their influence in her life.

Amelia found all three Parts together. The Witch remained in her hammock but gave us permission to work directly with the little-girl Part. This was important to our strategy: we wanted to do enough healing of The Witch's early memories to make her flexible enough that she would allow us to work with Amelia 24 and other Parts without interference.

When asked, Lonely Amelia 9 didn't know Amelia (unlike Angry Amelia 9 who was fully aware of Amelia). She accepted with skepticism that she was a Part of her: *"She is still trying to believe it,"* Amelia said.

When this happens, we continue the therapy anyway, expecting that, having explained the relationship between person and Part, the Part will eventually recognize this truth.

Playing Alone

Her earliest painful memory was that of playing alone: *"She had no brothers or sisters or cousins. She had to play alone. Her grandmother was strict and wouldn't allow her to visit the neighboring children. She had a much younger sister but only saw her on weekends. If a visitor came to play with her, her grandmother only allowed about one hour."*

We began with Lonely Amelia 9's experience of playing alone, with a SUD rating of 8 or 9. Amelia visualized a wind intervention for thirty seconds before opening her eyes to say that the **loneliness** had reduced to a 2 or 3. She explained that it was momentarily stuck there:

"Because of the isolation, she did not know how to interact when around other kids. She was very shy. She would get red cheeks with embarrassment and she would get teased for her red cheeks. People called me tomato face—El Tomate. She was very disappointed to be red—because she knew people would tease her. That lasted into high school and college even, when I got into the choir. Sometimes I avoided activities so I would not get red and made fun of."

Amelia thanked the child Part for the explanation and told her that she would help her to remember her experiences from now on. We wanted to reassure the child Part and the watchful Witch that the factual memories wouldn't disappear during the healing. She then directed the wind at the nine-year-old's remaining **distress**. But Amelia was immediately deluged with other, related memories.

Learning to be Passive

"Other memories are coming up, of situations in which she was not allowed to talk, to explain or defend herself. It was not accepted to talk back to Grandma or any adults. The only one was my mother, who allowed me to explain myself, but I was not living with her. But with my grandma I was never allowed to explain myself if I got in trouble. I would be punished if I tried to say why I said or did something. So I had to be perfect in every way. I learned to do that and was praised for being a good child—all the way until I was twelve when I rebelled."

Amelia began a new wind intervention to strip these memories of **distress** but immediately ran into new resistance. After thirty seconds, she said, *"It is hard to let go of everything— anger, frustration, loneliness, shyness."* She tried to focus just upon the **loneliness** and **shyness** but again was unsuccessful. When asked for permission to continue, The Witch denied that she was blocking the work. We had run out of time and we needed to stabilize Amelia's emotional state before she left my office.

Checking SUD scores for the different emotions, we found that the nine-year-old now rated her loneliness at a 4, her red embarrassment at an 8, and her inability to defend herself at a 10. We tried to move all of the unresolved emotions into The Witch's suitcase but Amelia found they wouldn't fit. She felt an uncomfortable pressure in her chest that linked to an image of her grandmother.

A Grandmother Introject

I thought this probably meant Amelia had developed a *Grandmother Introject,* a Part that wore the costume of the grandmother and reminded her of how she had to behave in order to please her grandmother. I suspected this introject of preventing our healing the memories of the grandmother years. In a large number of cases where a dominant parent demands strict rule-following, a child develops a parental introject. In this case the grandmother was the strict parent.

Amelia could easily visualize a grandmother image. In hopes of reducing Amelia's chest pressure before she left, I directed her to speak to the Grandmother Introject and ask it to step back. Immediately Amelia said, *"She went away."*

Unfortunately, Amelia continued to feel the pressure in her chest. Further attempts to communicate with the grandmother Part were unsuccessful. After several more attempts to reduce the pressure, a second image appeared, this time of Amelia's mother. While this seemed to confirm that the problem originated in one or more introjects, we were not ultimately able to reduce the pressure.

We ended the session with Amelia going off to work still feeling the unrelenting discomfort in her chest. This may have contributed to the difficulties Amelia experienced during the following week.

We could not immediately follow up with the mother and grandmother introjects. However, both Parts required attention some months later during the final phase of therapy.

Complexity in Amelia's Therapy

The therapy had become quite complex. We had healed Amelia 27 of her losses—including the loss of her previous boyfriend—caused by marrying Michael and coming to the United States. We had returned to The Witch for her next set of disturbing memories. Amelia 24, another subpart of The Witch, carried these memories, all or most of which seemed to be linked with Amelia's passivity and naiveté with respect to aggressive men.

To summarize, we tried to bypass The Witch's blocking of our healing work. We located Lonely Amelia 9, the Part that resentfully adopted the passivity she needed in order to meet the demands of her caretakers—especially her grandmother. We were blocked again when we tried to heal the child Part's earliest memory (playing alone), this time by mother and grandmother introjects. Getting past these introjects would allow us to heal both the initial memory and the additional ones that that had popped up for the little girl. Then, with the child Part healed, we could return to work with the 24-year-old. Once she was neutralized we could finally return to The Witch for the next set of painful memories.

Meanwhile, outside events in Amelia's life intruded into our work. It was summer vacation from school, and Michael would take the children to visit his family in Pennsylvania, leaving Amelia alone to maintain her small psychotherapy practice.

SUMMARY OF PARTS

Monster-Head/Half-Lady. Age thirty. She was angry for feeling unloved by family members, especially her father. She carried a range of memories of Angry Amelia 9, Amelia 11, Amelia 15, and Amelia 16. As she healed she morphed into Half-Lady.

Amelia 16. She was hurt and angry over her father's replacement of her mother with a new woman and for the lesser support he gave to his first family in comparison to his new family.

The Witch. This is the persecutor Part who dominates Part 2 of the narrative. She appears again in this chapter as Monster-Head heals. Her goal was to prevent Amelia from experiencing another postpartum depression of the sort that followed the second child. She hated Amelia's husband Michael.

Amelia 27. The Witch blamed this Part for choosing Michael as a husband. She carried the losses of breaking up with her previous boyfriend and of leaving her family behind to come to the U.S.

Amelia 29. She's the Part who experienced the final stages of Amelia's first pregnancy and the work and school stress of that time in Amelia's life.

Amelia 24. She carried the burden of victimization by aggressive males as well as the passivity necessary to please her grandmother.

Lonely Amelia 9. This nine-year-old was a subpart of The Witch, unlike Angry Amelia 9, who was a subpart of Monster-Head. She carried the loneliness of being the only child in a sea of adults. She also carried the passivity of childhood and significantly influenced how Amelia related to aggressive males in adulthood.

Chapter 12
Michael Vacations, Amelia Rages

As he had done the previous summer, Michael took his vacation from school as an opportunity to visit his family in Pennsylvania. He took the children with him, leaving Amelia to handle things in Utah. Money was short for the family, and Amelia couldn't take a month off without endangering her private practice.

AMELIA, ALONE

We met again on a Tuesday, after Michael and the kids had gone. Amelia was very angry. Michael was supposed to leave in the week after our session. But he had misinformed Amelia. When he checked the airline tickets over the weekend he found the departure date was actually yesterday. Both he and Amelia believed that they had another week of preparation for the trip. Now they had to cram a week of planning, packing, and last-minute details into two days.

Meanwhile, Amelia's twenty-year-old half-brother had arrived from Costa Rica for an extended stay to master his English. Amelia was left with the job of tending to a brother she hardly knew—she had agreed to their father's request to look after him—while dealing with the sudden absence of her husband and children. Further, her brother, while using her car, had been pulled over and ticketed for lack of a driver's license.

Michael was supposed to have helped his young brother-in-law get his license before he left.

Fear and Loathing in Utah

On Monday, after her family had flown to Pennsylvania, Amelia had to cancel sessions with some patients in order to pick up her brother from his language school. She was overwhelmed. She told Michael—angrily and accusingly—before he left that it had been *"the same thing for ten years, mistake after mistake after mistake! The Witch came out and blasted him. I have to do everything! All he has to do is take care of the car!*

"I got angry on Friday when my period started. I was shaking with anger and crying. It is never going to change! He is never going to come to planet Earth and take responsibility! Every time I need him he is not there. All he can do is take care of himself. He left scared that I will divorce him."

For Amelia, the days of her period were usually days when she experienced the same sorts of emotional symptoms that she felt at ovulation and again just before her period. Michael's sudden departure with the kids happened at a bad time. She was sensitive, irritable, physically uncomfortable, and easily hurt and angered:

"Right now I am reconsidering my private practice. Maybe I should get a full-time job. He goes on a thirty-day vacation and I work to pay the bills. Everything I make goes for home expenses and I barely pay my rent. How is that fair! I am absolutely tired of my life! He can never perform. He can never do what I need him to do. I cannot hold this together anymore. He promises he will change but I have heard that before! I have had it! He might think it is just a small mistake but it is huge! I have to find two or three thousand dollars in the next thirty days and he goes on vacation!"

When asked about which Part was blending with her as we talked, Amelia said, *"It is The Witch. She says 'All men are un-*

reliable!' I am very angry. More than that, I am hurt, disappointed." Amelia cried softly, releasing her anger: *"I feel like a fool—for trying, for getting my hopes up, for thinking things are going to change. All men in my life have been unreliable. Why should he be different? I always end up cleaning up the mess. The Witch is agreeing. 'Yeah, I told you so!'*

"I think next summer I am going to leave. Go to my country or go to another city. At least in Costa Rica I have family. I can be broke in Costa Rica. He can follow or not. I tell him to go into administration but he does not want to. He loves to teach. But we need more income. I have no energy, no patience for him anymore. It has been ten years. He spends so much time thinking about everything in his head. He is so distracted. I think it is actually better that he left. It might have become physical."

WHAT SHOULD I DO?

"So what should I do?" Amelia asked me. If a patient has to ask me a question that stymies me, it's this one: "What should I do?" Answering that question with direct suggestions is usually counter-therapeutic. I want my patients to take full responsibility for their actions. I rarely feel that I know what is best when it comes to this question.

There are exceptions: when a patient is in danger from others or herself, I must be directive. But when the problem is an unsatisfying relationship, especially when the question is asked during a time of high expressed emotion, there's no safe suggestion I can make. Divorce him? Work harder at fixing things? That isn't my decision to make. I directed our attention inward, to Amelia's internal dynamics.

I suggested that Amelia speak to The Witch—because she was the dominant subpersonality currently affecting her mood—and ask her to permit us to heal the hurt that produced the anger. That would cause the anger to dissipate, allowing Amelia to do her job of meeting with her own patients. At first

Amelia said that The Witch was unsure if she was hurt. But then she quickly added that she wasn't hurt, just angry. And when asked to help us find the hurt Part, The Witch indicated that it was Amelia herself.

Amelia 36

Amelia focused upon the **hurt** she could feel at that moment, and asked that Part to provide an image of herself in Amelia's mind: *"I see myself crying, me in bed, crying, devastated. She's thirty-five... Yes, she knows Michael and the kids have gone to Pennsylvania. No, she won't give up her hurt... Okay, she agrees to put her hurt into a temporary container. She put some of it in. Now she just wants to sleep in bed. She thinks nothing will change Michael."* Amelia first called this Part of herself *Amelia 35*, but then remembered she just had her thirty-sixth birthday. She changed it to *Amelia 36*.

Clearly the issue wasn't resolved, but we hoped to gain a bit of temporary stability in Amelia's emotional life. We asked The Witch to permit us to further neutralize Amelia 36's **pain**, rationalizing for her that there was plenty of other hurt that she would still retain. We just wanted her to be able to function well in her job while remaining civil with Michael: *"The Witch is not sure; she is so angry. And I am not sure if Amelia 36 gave it all up. I still feel pressure in my chest... Yes, she feels it too."* Amelia brought a wind intervention to neutralize the **pressure** in Amelia 36's chest. And because neutralizing a body sensation that isn't connected to a specific memory almost always brings memories to mind, we instructed Amelia 36 to strip those memories of their associated **pain** as they popped up.

Continuing her wind intervention, Amelia observed, *"She is remembering all the other disappointments."* I suggested that Amelia ask the Part to put away those other memories for now and just focus on the **disappointments** of the last four days: *"She put them in a container. She is going to be sleeping so* *she does not have to think. I feel better. I am still hurt but no, I am not angry."* With that we ended the session and Amelia went off to see her own patients.

In fairness to the assessment of how well the therapy was working for PMS/PMDD, Amelia's great anger here doesn't coincide with the PMS phases of her monthly cycle. She was between her period and her ovulation. I have the sense that most women would feel similarly to Amelia in her circumstance. She had a lot to be legitimately upset about.

Negotiating with Michael

We met again a week later. It was Day 11 of Amelia's cycle, three days before her expected ovulation. She felt no additional stress or emotional upset. But she continued to be disappointed at Michael's failure to keep track of the earlier-than-expected departure date for Pennsylvania. We talked about her continuing issues with Michael and about how much she missed her children. She had a lot to say and seemed to just want to be heard. For this reason, I didn't urge her to return to the deep work with her subpersonalities:

"I have been working on the hurt that Michael suddenly left and I had to do everything. A few days after he left our car broke down and I was stranded in the middle of the street. He always gets the easy path. We are married and I do not feel I have equal rights. I broke down yesterday and attacked him on the telephone. He understood me after I listed all the things I had to do and he got to go on vacation two years in a row while I worked. He says it won't happen again. He will not travel again without me, and he acknowledges he has to be more aware and pay attention to detail—like knowing what day his flight is on. He says when he comes back everything will be different. I felt very supported by him."

I wondered to what extent our intervention with Amelia 36 might have led to Amelia's greater calm, or whether the calm appeared because Amelia was between the PMS days of her cycle.

Amelia continued, *"I do not feel as hurt and disappointed now. I am still upset but it is more: 'Okay, I gotta fix it. I gotta move on.' I know something else will happen but I will be ready."*

Before closing, Amelia shared her observations about our work: *"Even with PMS I can still go to work. The physical* [discomfort] *isn't even close to what it was. When I came to see you, I never expected to be working on anything that had to do with my period or ovulation. I expected to work on some of the things I knew from my postpartum depression. I thought that my problems with my body were something I had to accept as part of the rest of my life—or until my body changed with menopause."*

MICHAEL WILL COME HOME

Amelia called six days later on a Monday to cancel our Tuesday appointment. We met on Friday, when she quickly brought me up to speed. A lot was going on: *"My family is coming home in two days. Because I flipped out!*

"I ovulated last Friday. I was sensitive, sad, and weepy, some nausea, mild body pain. I went out on Saturday to get the car washed and had a flat. I waited for two hours but AAA still didn't come. So I drove on the flat to get the flat fixed. It took four or five hours total to get the tire fixed. I was so angry with Michael. He had been saying forever that he was going to get an emergency kit in case of a flat tire. He is always like that, does not do what he says.

"Sunday was my birthday. I was deeply depressed. The second year in a row I was alone on my birthday. Michael called to say happy birthday. Later in the evening we talked again and he asked what the problem was. I went off! I told him I did not get married to be alone! I said I will leave with the kids in a year after I finish my contract. I did not care if

he followed or not. I was very sad and crying. Since then he talks about how much he loves me and he is bringing the kids back three weeks early. Michael asks me if I love him and I tell him, 'Do not ask me that!'

"The Witch is full-out against my husband. I do not trust him. He is always going to let me down. I do not even want to see him. He has been emotionally unavailable in six of the nine years we have been together. He disagrees, says he has been there, supportive. Why did he go on vacation when we are struggling financially! Why did he not find another job for the summer?

And I got angry with myself for being the one to provide for him to go on vacation. I have done this for two years straight and no vacation. I am the one who sees the kids less because I am always working. He says he is the primary provider and I am just working to maintain my small practice— but every bit of cash I get goes for groceries or for the house. He says he is coming home with a plan to make a budget and develop a financial plan. I just became aware that I have been an enabler for him to do as he pleases.

"On Wednesday I felt low blood sugar or something and cancelled two clients and went home. I ate something and watched a movie and went to bed early. It has been like that since Sunday. It has been very hard to keep it together." Wednesday was Day 19 of Amelia's cycle and she would normally be emotionally centered at this time. It appeared that her situation with Michael—rather than cyclic hormone shifts— was responsible for her cancelling work.

AMELIA 11 AND AMELIA 36

Amelia had a lot to share in this session, but it was also important to continue the deep work we had begun. I asked her to describe what she was feeling in her body. She found *"a deep hurt"* in her chest. When asked to focus on that sensation and to ask it to provide an image of itself, there was, surprisingly, no response—surprising because Amelia usually had no difficulty linking an inner Part to the body sensation she felt: *"I cannot see anything."* She could, however, locate The Witch: *"She is angry. She says the hurt Part is the child—the one who felt alone and abandoned by my dad. I cannot see her but she is telling me that… Yes, she is triggered by my husband being gone. Because my dad had a bad habit of not showing up for my special events. He did not care that I was alone."*

Amelia 11

At my request, The Witch brought out the child to work with Amelia: *"It is Amelia 11 in her First Communion dress. Her head hurts. It is that day of the First Communion when my dad did not show up. It is the emotion of not being loved, that she is alone. It is not the event that bothers her. It is feeling alone, that my dad does not care for her, that he does not love her."*

Amelia asked The Witch if she had revived the little girl's pain to teach Amelia a lesson: *"She says she did not do it, that Michael did it. By leaving me alone on my birthday."* That is, the pain was triggered spontaneously by the experience of Michael leaving her alone. (Her visiting half-brother didn't count in determining what "alone" meant.) The Witch had nothing to do with the trigger, and she agreed to permit us to do healing work with Amelia 11.

The young Part rated her distress at a 9 or 10 on the SUD scale, but it wasn't just about her father's no-show at her communion. It was about all the times he let her down with his absence or thoughtlessness. Our intervention would then target her entire father-generated **abandonment pain**. We expected several steps before we were done. Amelia asked Amelia 11 to focus on the **pain** in her heart. Let the wind break up that **pain** into tiny particles of dust and blow it away forever, and to expect that memories of her dad would flash through her mind. She could share these memories if she wished, but she should continue to strip the memories of their attached **pain** as they popped up.

After seventy seconds Amelia said, *"It is down to a* level *3 now. She is still a little bit* **sad**. *As she washed her heart—I chose wind but she changed it to water—the blood came out and stained her dress. She feels like it is her fault somehow. She remembered all those times when he was not there or he forgot to bring a Christmas present and other times. Why does he not love her?"*

Amelia 36

This time we asked her to focus on her feeling that it was **her fault** and to wash that feeling away. After another seventy seconds, Amelia reported, *"It is hard. It is like all of her body is stained with black oil."* With no further progress in the intervention, we looked for a blocking Part: *"I feel a pressure in my chest that has increased... No, The Witch is not blocking. She does not know who is. I can feel it but cannot see it. It seems to have to do with Michael and the pain I have felt with him. Yeah, it is me, in black sweats, my age now, thirty-six."* She seemed to be the same devastated Part we had met earlier who we called Amelia 36. We could now work with her more deeply.

Amelia asked this image about her earliest painful memory: *"When we were dating and he would come to the States for his vacation time every six months. It became harder and harder each time he left. He made me feel like I was supposed to wait for him. And he would take short trips in my country with his friends, and I was not invited, so I just had to wait for him to come back, and I could not allow myself even to feel bad about him being gone."*

We were near the end of the session, again with unresolved issues. Amelia guided Amelia 36 in packing away her **pain** in her grandmother's storage chest until our next visit: *"Yes, it is similar to my dad's situation. It is being stuck away while someone else is leaving. As a child I had no choice. As an adult*

I had a choice, but I just accepted it because I guess I was supposed to accept it. I did not realize until right now that I have just been accepting it and I could not ask for anything different. I never asked him to get a job and stay here. I did not even think of that. He worked so hard for years; it was okay to let him go. I did not know how hard it would be for me. I did not know I would feel so unfairly treated."

SUMMARY OF PARTS

The Witch. She appeared again a few times in this chapter and was always in the background.

Amelia 36. This is the Part who was overwhelmed and hurt by Michael and the kids' vacation in Pennsylvania. Her pain briefly kept Amelia from going to work. She was a Freestanding Part, co-conscious with Amelia and fully aware of present and past. She carried the pain of abandonment, both in childhood by her father and in adulthood by Michael. She carried all the disappointments with Michael, accumulated over the years of their marriage.

Amelia 11. This is the Part who wears her white First Communion dress. Amelia's disappointment in Michael triggered Amelia 11's memories of disappointment in her father.

Chapter 13
Family Reset

Amelia cancelled our next appointment as she settled in again with her family. We met a week later in the first week of August, the middle of summer, almost two months before school began again. They had reunited two days after our last session. Amelia was overjoyed to have her children with her again, but she took a few days before she could be comfortable with Michael.

MOVING FORWARD

The missed session had been scheduled on a Thursday and her period began on the following day, Friday, and lasted four days. On Thursday (premenstrually) she was *"bloated, anxious, irritable, with a lot of anger."* These symptoms were problematic. However, she wasn't sad or self-deprecating. These were positives. During the first two days of her period the symptoms continued while adding *"body aches, cramps, craving sweets, breast tenderness; no fatigue. I was in overdrive with anxiety."* Clearly, we had more work to do, but under the circumstances, Amelia was doing pretty well.

It was now Thursday again, Day 7 of her cycle, and Amelia felt back in control of her life: *"During my period, Michael was more patient—only one day with a little fight. He's taking his ADD meds so he's calmer and so am I because there are two of us to handle things. Now I gave him the financial work and he can finally see my income is necessary for us."* Meaning that Michael could no longer dismiss her earnings as negligible in comparison to his salary.

Amelia now planned to end any further efforts to have a third child. This ought to please The Witch since the idea of having another child seemed to be what triggered her into such an active role some months ago. Despite The Witch's objections, Amelia and Michael had intentionally gone several months without contraception: *"I told him I didn't want kids after thirty-six and I turned thirty-six three weeks ago."* However, she had not yet done the surgery. She continued without birth control. She thought she was probably no longer fertile.

Reconnecting to the Deep Therapy

We had taken up almost the entire session just catching up with events in Amelia's life over the last two weeks. Amelia had one more observation before we returned to the interrupted work from our last session: *"I think The Witch really came out with a vengeance during my period. She was so mad at him for being gone and leaving me doing all the work here."*

Returning to Amelia 36, her greatest issue was that of having had to suppress her feelings about Michael's trips away from her when they both worked in Costa Rica, especially trips when he went off with friends to tour her country. The SUD score for those experiences was a 7. Using a wind intervention for the Part's **negative emotions**, Amelia quickly reduced the level to a 2, but the Part was *"still upset that she's always the one waiting—seeing other people go, and staying behind."* We were able to reduce the SUD to a zero by twice repeating the intervention while Amelia 36 blamed herself for passively accepting Michael's separations. The Witch agreed with that assessment. It was her fault because she was so *"weak!"*

Unfortunately, Amelia 36 could not yet release her hurt for Michael's last two summer trips to Pennsylvania. She agreed to leave that distress in a container until our next session.

Checking PMS Progress

We met again on Amelia's Day 14, during ovulation. This gave us another chance to assess our progress. Amelia listed her symptoms: *"I am depressed, irritable, acne, something like cramping, tired. Since yesterday. I wanted to cancel my afternoon appointments today but I did not. I have not felt this bad in a long time. We are very strict right now about money. I am busy but not making the living I need to make. Maybe I should take a full-time job with a salary so I do not have to pay rent for my private practice."*

I couldn't give us a superior rating for progress, but overall we seemed to be moving forward. After all, Amelia didn't cancel her appointments with her patients. We had been doing well enough that I thought we might finish our work within a dozen more sessions, but the summer break and Michael's vacation had thrown my mental scheduling into disarray. My hope was that this month's ovulation report represented only a temporary setback.

Amelia's Depression

We turned our attention to Amelia's depression. I wondered if The Witch was still influencing her PMS during ovulation: *"The Witch is there, but I do not know if she is depressed... No, she is not depressed... Yes, she is causing my depression. She is doing it so I will learn that I am stupid. For working so much for so little money, for having bad dreams, for going so long without a vacation... Yes, she still thinks a baby is a bad idea, but she does not say she is concerned with that. She says I will never get better so why bother trying to end my depres-*

sion... No, she is not causing the depression but she is either allowing it to happen or making it stronger."

The Witch seemed to have softened her view of having another child, now simply asserting that it was a bad idea. This, too, showed progress with her. Regarding depression, the contradiction by The Witch in first saying that she was causing it and then saying she wasn't causing it, isn't unusual when interacting with Parts. While Parts are capable of intentionally misleading the conscious self (e.g., Amelia), more frequently they simply make errors in judging the degree of their influence. Later, they sometimes correct themselves with more accurate assessments.

Seeking the Depressed Part

In looking for childhood sources of the depression, we asked The Witch about early childhood memories. Amelia recalled occasions in her fourth and fifth grades, and again in high school, when she had to do homework or projects on her own without help. (Note the theme of having to go it alone, just as she had to do when Michael was gone.) When asked who the depressed Part was, The Witch indicated that it was Amelia herself. We tried unsuccessfully to coax the depressed Part to step away from Amelia—because all strong emotions come from Parts and can't directly emanate from the conscious self.

We tried another technique to help the depressed Part show itself. Amelia said that she felt the distress most strongly in her chest. When she focused on that chest sensation and asked that it become stronger it did so. Then, having coaxed the hidden Part to interact with her, Amelia again asked it for an image of itself. This time Amelia found herself viewing an image of herself as a teenager.

Amelia 16

This Part initially denied knowing who Amelia might be, but when asked to guess, she accurately communicated to Amelia:

"You are me." She was sixteen years old. She then acknowledged that she and Amelia had previously interacted (in Chapters 10 and 11). We had called her Amelia 16 and worked on her hurt that her father took a second wife and treated his second set of kids better than his first.

As Amelia recalled this, she smiled grimly. She explained that her half-brother from Costa Rica, now twenty, was temporarily living with her while taking a class to improve his English: *"I see how my dad is protective and concerned with him. He calls frequently to see how he is doing. My brother is very pampered. He does not know how to do things on his own. He misses his family and wants to go back earlier than planned. I am irritated because he does not help or does not do what we ask. I think I have talked to my dad more often in the last month than I usually do in a year. It used to be not even once a month."* Evidently, her father's attention to his son triggered old wounds in Amelia for his lack of attention to her as a child.

"With me now as an adult, I am happy I had to work hard to take care of myself. It makes me self-reliant now. But my teenager Part [Amelia 16] is maybe wishing she had more from my dad and maybe it is because we are struggling right now financially that it reminds me of life back then."

Problems with Healing

I thought it likely that Amelia would feel better if we could heal some of the teen's hurt. Amelia chose her favorite intervention—wind—to blow away the teen's **disappointment** in her father—triggered by the concern he presently showed in calling Amelia to check on his son. After twenty seconds of visualizing, Amelia said, *"It is hard!"* As we suspected, The Witch was again blocking our work. She relented, however, when Amelia explained that she was only trying to neutralize the teen's momentary mood state, not the entire history of disappointments by her father. Returning to the wind intervention, Amelia now said, *"She is letting some of it go. She is feeling tired now."* But when Amelia changed her focus from disappointment to the **tired feeling,** the intervention produced no further relief: *"The Witch says she is not blocking. And I do not see another blocker."*

I suggested that Amelia 16 connect to that tired feeling and bridge to the earliest memory that came up. This brought Amelia's recollection that:*"It did not matter how much we did, how much we tried. Nothing changed. What is the point of trying—there was still not enough money. She had to wear a lot of her mom's clothes in college because she had a uniform in high school. And in college she had to choose sometimes between food and photocopying and so sometimes she was hungry."*

Amelia had graduated high school and begun college at sixteen. Amelia 16, although triggered by Amelia's current financial stress and by her father's phone calls to check on his son, seemed to have no autobiographical knowledge beyond her difficult first year of college. Despite this disconnect in historical information, Amelia's hopelessness in relation to Michael triggered Amelia 16's hopelessness in relation to her father. And this triggering made Amelia's depression in the present, worse. That's why we were trying to heal Amelia 16.

Hopelessness

The teenager's tiredness was linked to a sense of **hopelessness** about things ever changing, and that became the focus of our efforts. I suggested that Amelia share with the teen the memories she had earlier shared with me—about later getting a job in college, buying her own clothes and even having enough money to help out her mother. But this had no effect on the Part: *"It is hard. She is absolutely convinced it will never get better."*

Stymied in our efforts to heal the teen, we had also run out of time in the session. Amelia helped the Part to store her hopelessness in Grandma's antique chest. We planned to return to healing work with her in our next session.

I was puzzled about our lack of progress with Amelia 16. The Witch had given permission to do the healing and Amelia could not locate any other blocking manager. I thought again about the two sources of blocking: either a manager saying no, or an earlier memory amplifying distress onto the Part we worked with. Then I recalled that just prior to locating Amelia 16, Amelia had spoken of memories from the fourth or fifth grade. Maybe there was a still-hidden eight- or nine-year-old yet to be located.

HEALING AMELIA 16

We met again on Day 21, a week before Amelia's period. With many women, this is the beginning of PMS/PMDD symptoms, but for Amelia those symptoms didn't usually appear until Day 25 or 26. She was in relatively good spirits. She was anxious, but attributed this to having two of her own patients in crisis. Additionally, her children were returning to school or preschool and needed her attention for their clothing and supplies.

Updating me on life at home, Amelia said that her brother was trying to return to Costa Rica earlier than the planned completion of his English training in January. It was now late August: *"I hope he goes home early. He is a lot of extra work. He does not talk to Michael or interact with the kids. He seems to be bothered by them. All he does is watch TV or play with his tablet. My dad kind of apologized for his kid. He wants him to finish the English training. He asked me to challenge him to interact with us."*

A Good Time for Healing

We returned to Amelia 16 and her grandmother's chest of **hopelessness**. This time the Part easily let it go. Amelia had first tried to use a wind intervention, but Amelia 16 wanted to use fire—another demonstration that Parts can make their own choices (i.e., they have "volition"). Visualizing **hopelessness** burning up in a fire quickly produced a SUD rating of zero for the hopelessness.

My speculation regarding interference from a younger Part seemed to be in error. One possibility for this day's ease of neutralizing in comparison to last week's blocking is the state of Amelia's cycle. In our previous session Amelia was ovulating, a usually difficult time for her. This week she was safely between her ovulation and her period, a usually smooth time for her. Perhaps the best time to carry out healing rituals with internal Parts is when the patient is in a positive mood state— although the best time to locate problem Parts would still seem to be during a difficult time in the cycle.

Father's Penny-Pinching

Amelia asked Amelia 16 about her next disturbing memory and was soon remembering experiences that the Part rated at a 9 on the SUD scale: *"She used to have to go to her dad's office for money. Sometimes he forgot to leave me money. I would come for lunch money and for other things every morning. His secretary would loan me money or I would have to walk back to college to borrow. Two or three times he left me coins. I felt like a beggar! I wrote him a letter about how humiliating it was to feel like a beggar and not his daughter. But it changed halfway through college for the better."*

Amelia did the healing work with a fire intervention, visualizing a large bonfire with Amelia 16 in front of it: *"She is throwing the coins into the fire. My dad would complain that I was just a daughter for money. She is throwing both paper money and coins into the fire now. Okay. It is down to a 1 or 2. It still hurts because he never tried to give me anything extra. I would have to lie to him to get money for a dress or shoes. I had to say the money was for a book or a college pro-*

ject. If I said my jeans were worn out, he would say he had no money.

"I had student loans for tuition that paid some of the tuition and he gave me money for the rest. Later I got scholarships and did not tell him so I could still get money from him. For Christmas he would give me money that would pay for just one set of clothes. My mother paid for our living expenses with lots of different sales jobs. We had to be careful with what we bought to eat. We had a piggy bank that we always had to empty to pay for transportation and things like that."

Releasing Resentment

We turned our attention to the resentment Amelia 16 felt for her father's miserly doling out of financial support. Amelia again used a fire intervention to neutralize the teen's **resentment**. After thirty seconds, she said, *"That one is hard. The black stuff comes out of her chest and into the fire but very slowly... Yes, The Witch is there. She is fighting to prevent the healing because that was the first man who could not be trusted."*

Amelia assured The Witch that her father's lack of trustworthiness wouldn't be forgotten, and that it was Amelia 16's job to remember those things. With The Witch momentarily pacified, Amelia redirected Amelia 16 to releasing her resentment: *"She let a lot more resentment go, not just about college money but about **not being cared for** by her dad. Now she feels tired and sad for all of the difficulty with her dad at that time."*

Resentment, like more expressive anger, is a response to hurt. With the resentment carried by Amelia 16 neutralized, the underlying hurt became evident. That was our next target for healing. Amelia returned to the fire intervention, and asked Amelia 16 to burn up her **tiredness** and **sadness** in the bonfire: *"She is peeling off her skin because that's where all over she feels the tiredness and she burns it up. She became young-*

er, like ten or eleven. She took off the costume of the 16-year-old to become a ten- or eleven-year-old. But she is not well. She has problems, too."

We were out of time again and consequently Amelia placed the child Part in a "Sleeping Beauty Bed," a safe place we had developed to hold a hurt Part until our next session. By imagining the canopied, four-poster bed, and tucking the child Part under the pure-white sheets with her head resting on the pillow, Amelia hoped to avoid emotional upset from her during the week between sessions. Hopefully, she would "sleep" until then.

Before we closed, Amelia observed, *"That was weird when the ten- or eleven-year-old showed up. I felt a pressure in my chest and I remembered that there was a ten-year-old with The Witch* [after a previous session] *and we did not finish with her. And Amelia 16 seems to be gone now."*

I, too, was surprised at Amelia 16's transformation into a younger Part through skin-peeling. I had worked with Parts previously that peeled their skin during an intervention, but I hadn't seen the appearance of a younger Part underneath except in cases of monsters and family introjects of the sort we had previously unmasked. I wasn't sure that the teenager was gone permanently. More likely, the ten- or eleven-year-old was a subpart of Amelia 16 who was activated by the intervention with the teen.

FINDING PROGRESS IN NEW PROBLEMS

At our next meeting on a Thursday, Amelia was in Day 3 of her period, three days earlier than expected: *"I was very angry for two days before my period. Then on Tuesday it started. I was physically ill—weak, tired, could not concentrate, nauseous. I cancelled clients. I was not irritable, just so tired. It is like the day before you get the flu—something is wrong but you do not know what. I was tired on the second day, too, but I worked. I think I was early because of stress—finances, paying for school and school uniforms, getting the kids ready for their first day. It was odd cancelling clients. A year ago, I was cancelling every month. Now it is maybe one time in three months. And it is not as intense."*

I was relieved to hear that Amelia saw progress in our work. I had begun to be pessimistic again about success in the near future. A little shot of encouragement is good for the therapist too! I also saw as somewhat positive that she cancelled her clients during her period but not during her PMS.

She added, *"Today I am fine. And I am excited that my employers have chosen me to do parent training seminars for the PSR workers... Those are the workers who visit the homes of poorly functioning families to coach basic parenting skills."* This was a job Amelia knew well because she did this work part-time before she became licensed to do therapy.

Amelia 10

We returned to the child Part in the Sleeping Beauty Bed: *"She is ten... No, we have not talked before... Yes, she says she was inside the teenager. She is another Part, somehow."* Her earliest disturbing memory dated to the time when she became aware of her parents' constant fighting. The extent of their unhappiness became clear when they brought her home from her grandmother's to live with them full time. She rated these memories at a 7 on the SUD scale. She readily agreed to neutralize them, and The Witch gave her permission to do so as well.

Amelia returned to a wind intervention to neutralize the child Part's pain. She soon said, *"She let go of some of the **fear** and **sadness** but more memories came up. She remembers my mom crying after my dad left. Mom cried a lot. My dad never showed any sadness when they divorced or when my mom miscarried. Mom was sad for more than a year. She had hatred for my dad for not caring about my mom and for not showing any remorse, especially after the miscarriage. He*

did not seem to have any caring about my mom's suffering.
She is very angry with him."

Note here that the divorce came when Amelia was thirteen. The fact that the child Part shows herself as a ten-year-old illustrates again that the apparent age of a given Part doesn't preclude her from having awareness of events after that age. The Part's age is more representative of a kind of mood state or attitude that can last well beyond the apparent age of the Part.

Amelia 16 Reappears

Clearly the anger needed to be neutralized, but a frontal assault on this emotion is difficult to carry out. And in the occasional case where anger can directly be healed, there's still the omnipresent hurt underlying the anger that must be healed. For this reason, I suggested that Amelia work with Amelia 10 by asking her to focus on her **sadness** and **disappointment** with her father rather than her anger. Amelia followed my suggestion and in less than a minute said, *"It is in her chest and still coming out. Oh! I still feel it! I feel the pressure... No, The Witch says she is not blocking. The pressure is great... No, I do not see another blocker. Amelia 16 is there but she is not blocking."* As I suspected, Amelia 16 hadn't permanently disappeared.

Amelia 16 might not have been intentionally blocking, but she was the only other Part that had showed herself. Maybe we could work with Amelia 10 and Amelia 16 together. Amelia brought together both Parts for her wind intervention, visualizing the wind blowing through both of them at the same time. Shortly, Amelia said, *"Oh, you are right! It is working!"* Then, chuckling, she added, *"Okay! They did it! They high-fived each other!"*

Before closing for the day, I wanted to be sure that the resentment and hurt Amelia 10 felt for the relationship between her mother and father had been neutralized. When she found that the child Part still carried some **distress**, Amelia again brought the wind to bear on her. "It is clearing. Okay. She has a little pain in her chest but it is not clear what it is. Something is missing that is causing the pressure."

She moved the child and the teenager to Sleeping Beauty Beds so that we could end our session, but that didn't provide Amelia relief: *"It is weird. I have this pressure in my chest but when I came in I felt neutral."* She asked the two Parts in their Sleeping Beauty Beds to take the distress with them: *"They put it into a container. I feel better but I still have some pressure."* Amelia appealed to The Witch for help, emphasizing that she had to drive directly to work from my office: *"I can see myself pulling it out of my chest and into a container, but it is not yet neutral. The Witch is trying to help. She says it is me. I can feel the Part. It is my age but I cannot see her. I asked her to step back because I have to go to work and that helped. There is just a little left."* With that we ended the session, with plans to return to the ten-year-old, the sixteen-year-old, and possibly a new thirty-six-year-old in our next session.

SUMMARY OF PARTS

Amelia 36. She released her pain for Michael's early absences in their relationship, and then, more slowly, for his trips to Pennsylvania.

Amelia 16. She was hurt and angry over her father's choice to be with a new woman and for the lesser support he gave to his first family in comparison to his new family. This left Amelia frequently struggling to find enough money to pay for college and necessities.

Amelia 10. She's the Part who carried the distress over her parents' divorce and her father's lack of remorse for abandoning her mother. She was a subpart of Amelia 16.

Chapter 14

Performance Anxiety and a False Alarm

We met again on Day 10 of Amelia's cycle: *"I feel pretty good; a little cranky but I think that is because of our finances and rushing to get the kids into school."* Good, normal emotions.

OPTIMISTIC OUTLOOK

With more good news about her marriage, Amelia talked about Michael: *"He has started taking his AD/HD medicine. He is so nice, helpful! He is doing the financial stuff. This helps me so much because now he understands how much trouble it was for me to keep us surviving. Now we do it together and it is companionship for us. He is so focused! Why on earth did he stop taking his medications? But I also think the big fight we had made a difference in his focus too."*

After our previous session, Amelia went on to successfully present her work seminar. She impressed her employers enough for them to ask her to expand her presentation and talk directly to groups of parents.

She felt no interference from the adult Part that had caused her chest pressure at the end of our last session. We could return to our unfinished work with Amelia 10.

Healing Amelia 10

When asked about Amelia 10's painful memories, Amelia responded, *"It is more than memories. It is wishing her dad was around more and not playing soccer or drinking with his friends. She wished her dad had more time for her as a dad when he came home and not just in conflict with my mom. It is like loneliness."*

We moved forward with a wind intervention to neutralize **loneliness** *and* **longing**. Within a few seconds Amelia 10 felt complete relief. Amelia added, *"One positive memory that came up was that there were other people around, like my uncle and my grandmother and mother who loved her and cared for her."* This was the perfect result. Not only were the problem memories healed, but doing so removed the block that prevented recollections of positive memories.

Neither Amelia 10 nor Amelia 16 could locate any other painful memories: *"They want to hang out together in someplace like a park or something."*

VIOLET APPEARS

We returned to The Witch since she was the internal manager that claimed to cause Amelia her greatest emotional pain: *"She is okay. She is not as angry."* But then Amelia noticed that she was feeling the same chest pressure she had felt at the end of the previous session. The Witch denied that she was the source. Following the Parts and Memory Therapy protocol, Amelia addressed the chest pressure and asked the Part responsible for it to show herself: *"I see myself, kind of raggedy. Her clothes are old, kind of broken* [i.e., worn], *and she is kind of neurotic. Her hair is messed up; her eyes are not focused— like a crazy homeless person. It is me but it does not look like me at all."*

Violet

The new Part's age was thirty-six, Amelia's current age, following her recent birthday. She knew Amelia by name, but denied that it was also her own name. She had no name of her own, but accepted Amelia's middle name *Violet* when Amelia pressed her. She was aware of Amelia's current life with Michael but denied that he was her husband too. She felt similarly with respect to the children; they were not hers. She remembered being present in the previous session when we worked with Amelia 10 and Amelia 16. She was drawn to that scene because those were stressful and anxious times.

Her earliest painful memories had to do with being nervous or ashamed at school: *"She remembers things would make me nervous when I was young. Like trying out for sports, because she felt she was not going to be good enough or might do poorly, or if she had to talk in front of people or write on the board, she would be afraid or nervous. Even in elementary school there were a couple of times—dances for school or plays, or playing music with a flute—she would do it but it would be very uncomfortable. She graded herself at a level 8 for her anxiety for childhood performances, partly because she actually liked dancing and performing but her anxiety kept her from doing more."*

Violet quickly released her **performance anxiety** to a blowing wind, giving us with a positive closure to our session. Before parting, Amelia added that The Witch explained that this was the Part who always felt *"not good enough, like a little scared-girl Part. This is a physically strong Part. I feel her strongly in my chest when she comes."* Although we were unaware of it at the time, Violet would play an important role in Amelia's PMS/PMDD experiences during the final phase of therapy.

MOTHER ARRIVES

We met again three weeks later because Amelia had been too busy with the new school year—getting her kids enrolled in their private school, getting uniforms, supplies, and doing other things. Additionally, she had been doing intensive training in a new therapy for working with couples.

More than that, Amelia's mother, having finally acquired a permanent resident visa to live in the United States, had arrived. She would add an entirely new dynamic to Amelia's life, a quite positive dynamic. She would live with Amelia's family. Amelia now had a family of six, with husband, two children, mother, and half-brother—although the half-brother was scheduled to return soon to his family in Costa Rica. Surprisingly, Amelia's mother and half-brother got on well. Her brother was the first child Amelia's father had with "the other woman" after leaving Amelia's mother: *"Actually,"* Amelia said, *"my brother has been more comfortable because my mother brings more of the family atmosphere he is used to. He has come more out of his shell and is talking more with Michael. And he is acting as a translator between Michael and my mom, who only speaks Spanish.*

We didn't return immediately to work with Violet. Instead, Amelia caught me up on the changes in her life in the last three weeks: *"Michael is having more issues from work pressure. He sold his prep* [i.e., preparation hour] *and now works without a break to make more money. He is reactive again and blowing up with our daughter, like with doing homework."*

Today was Day 7 in Amelia's cycle, an emotionally positive time for her, but she had kept records of her emotional and physiological responses during the critical times since we last met. Her period lasted just three days. Before that she had experienced five days of significant PMS/PMDD symptoms, with acne and breast tenderness, irritability, and anxiety through Day 28: *"Day 28 and Day 1 knocked me out. Day 2 was also bad. Cramps, dizziness, and physically sick—nauseous. On Day 1, I had to leave my training and go home."*

Not much good news here. Premenstrual symptoms abated a bit, but the issues with her period (dysmenorrhea) were temporarily devastating. It was impossible to tell whether the symptoms were due to current stress or something else, perhaps related to an absence of therapy for three weeks. The only positives here seemed to be that most of her symptoms were physiological ones rather than the emotional ones that had been the focus of our attention.

POSSIBLE PREGNANCY

Amelia cancelled her next appointment because she was sick, and when we met again two weeks later, she continued to feel unwell. At first she thought her distress was due to her ovulation but when the nausea continued, she suspected a stomach virus. On the day of our missed appointment a week previously, she had felt *"depressed, dizzy, no appetite, lethargic, and nauseous."* Since then she had felt non-stop nausea. A week ago, she had felt so poorly that she found herself unable to drive safely. She cancelled her clients for a day.

The nausea raised the question of whether Amelia might be pregnant. Interviews with The Witch and Violet indicated that these two Parts didn't believe she was pregnant. But both Amelia and Michael had wondered about the possibility. We were unable to produce any reduction in the nausea through our usual techniques. This led me to think that there was more likely a physiological cause than a psychological cause for the symptoms. We hoped to have a definite answer by our next session because Amelia had scheduled an appointment with her physician.

Pregnancy would leave our work on healing PMS/PMDD unfinished. I thought Amelia had shown significant improvement some of the time, but I wasn't yet convinced that we could claim that psychotherapy had permanently reduced her symptoms. Although I thought we were close to doing so.

False Alarm

Amelia cancelled our next appointment because she was still in her physician's office at the time we were scheduled to meet. Meeting again after another two weeks, Amelia said that she was *"feeling better physically, but not so good emotionally."* She wasn't pregnant. A week ago, she had started a course of antibiotics for a powerful, long-lasting ear infection. According to her physician, the drainage into her stomach from that infection had caused an ulcer and that was the source of her nausea. She had also been suffering from allergies that led to inflamed sinuses. Because of the physical issues, she couldn't distinguish between PMS symptoms and the symptoms of her illness. She didn't go to work on Thursday (the day of our cancelled appointment) or Friday, but returned to work the following Monday. She was still recovering from the infection.

Amelia remained under pressure from work and home life, both sources making demands upon her limited time: *"I have a deluge of clients who want to see me and I am moving again to a new office. And I need to be at home more with my daughter between four and seven in the afternoon, but that is also the time I need to see my cash clients* [i.e., private rather than agency clients]. *My daughter is regressing with her anxiety. She says, 'Mommy, you are never around. I never see you.' Her OCD about her clothes has come back* [i.e., her clothes had to fit and feel just right, with seams aligned and socks that were neither too loose nor too tight]. *I am taking Mondays off now to be at home and help her with her homework."*

The Possibility of Pregnancy

Regarding our discussion two weeks previously about her possible pregnancy, she said, *"I realized that I saw being pregnant and having a child as a way to get away from the pressure and put it all on Michael. And also to push him in his career so he will go into administration—he loves teaching too much to do that. I am so resentful that I have to carry so much weight and I wanted to let go of that. And then I could really enjoy my kids at this special time.*

"The nurturing Part of me is sad I am not getting pregnant and we are getting ready to sell all our baby stuff." With tears in her eyes, Amelia added, *"When I got ready to put them on Craigslist, I could not. It is too hard to give up the idea of having another child. We are still not using birth control but I am not getting pregnant."*

I hadn't known that Amelia was still hoping to get pregnant. I had believed her a couple of months earlier when she said she'd closed the door on that option. Evidently, pregnancy was still an option, but Amelia was moving forward with the idea that it wasn't going to happen.

AMELIA'S DAUGHTER

We were near the end of the session when we checked in with The Witch: *"She is feeling stressed about my daughter. She wants me to be there more with her. She says, 'Think about when you were little and your mother wasn't around.' I feel intense guilt for what my daughter is going through."*

Her daughter was seeing a therapist for a traumatic experience she had suffered a year previously at a church summer camp: *"One time we were going to church and she did not want to go. She was scared. We can go to church with Michael but if we go without him, she is anxious and looking for him. She sees him as her protector. I feel horrible every day. Huge guilt."*

PMS CHECKUP

Our next session coincided with Day 15 of Amelia's cycle and she wasn't feeling depressed or irritated. Her sinus inflammation and ear infection had made her miserable; she couldn't tell how much of her misery might have been due to infection and how much might have been due to her hormonal shifts. But we took the time to look over the last year of sessions and get Amelia's impression about her progress. She said, *"Absolutely. My symptoms are less now."*

She also observed that before therapy she was miserable every two weeks for three to five days at ovulation and again before her period. Her symptoms just prior to her period had become inconsistent. While she regularly felt greater anxiety, depression, and physical symptoms, they appeared sometimes before her period and sometimes during her period.

When she checked in with The Witch, Amelia found that the Part continued to be subdued in her attitude toward Michael, leading me to think that the therapy was showing success in reducing Amelia's rages—because The Witch seemed to be the primary source of PMS rage. She was frustrated now with Michael but not significantly angry. She was relaxed about the possibility of pregnancy, and didn't believe that it would happen.

SADNESS ABOUT BABIES

Amelia was considering birth control again to be sure that they were not surprised by an unplanned pregnancy. At her daughter's school, Amelia sold some baby things at their flea market but could not bear giving up the bassinette she had used for both of her children. *"I just did not feel ready for it."*

Near the end of the session, because Amelia was sad when she spoke about the bassinette, I asked her to recall telling me about her plan to have her tubes tied. I did this to help her find the sad Part of her. Her response was a feeling of even greater sadness and a sense of defeat. When asked, The Witch could not identify the affected Part. I asked Amelia to notice where in her body she felt the sadness (her chest), and then to ask that sensation to provide her with an image of itself.

The Twins

What came to her mind were the twins with whom we had previously worked, Big and Little Twin. Amelia said, *"I see them now as the same size. The sad one wants another daughter because she craves the connection she has with my son. The connection with my daughter got better but it is worse again. She is acting now as she did after my son was born—she is clingy again, and compulsive about how her clothes fit."* We would return to the twins in our next session. Hopefully, we could also return to the continued assessment and treatment of Amelia's PMS/PMDD.

When we met again, we barely touched on deeper work, focusing instead on family issues. Primarily, we talked about Michael's neediness and daughter Noelle's sensitivity to touch.

Noelle was going through a difficult time, feeling painful sensitivity to hair brushing and irritation when her clothes were too tight or too loose. She had her own child therapist. Big Twin, who had not originally bonded with Noelle, now felt rejected by her because of the irritability she showed when Big Twin blended with Amelia in brushing Noelle's hair. Thus Big Twin was thwarted in giving Noelle the love she had previously withheld from her. Amelia described dealing with her daughter as *"like handling a porcupine."*

MICHAEL'S NEEDINESS

Michael was feeling ignored somewhat because much of Amelia's available time at night was taken up by her mother, who had now become a fixture in family life. Amelia felt a comfortable amount of connection with Michael simply by being near him. Michael, however, was *"a high-demand person who needs a lot of attention from me."* They had had two or three blowups in the last couple of months but that was an improvement over their history prior to therapy.

SUMMARY OF PARTS

The Witch. She continued to be nearby, but was calmer now, more helpful.

Amelia 10. She completed her healing in this chapter, releasing the loneliness and longing for a closer relationship with her father.

Big and Little Twin. These Parts appeared again, linked to issues of daughter-love. Little Twin is sad that she won't have a daughter to love as she loves her son. Big Twin feels pushed away and unloved by Noelle's discomfort with touch.

Chapter 15
The Witch, Transformed

We met again at the beginning of November, fifteen months after we began therapy. Initially, I had no idea how complex and deep our work would be. I naively believed that a dozen sessions might be enough. Ultimately, I realized that the issue wasn't just rage, postpartum depression, and marital distress. Nor were PMS and the more severe PMDD the primary issues. These were just the spaces in Amelia life where themes of abandonment and attachment loss from early childhood, continuing into early adulthood, were played out. Addressing the content of those themes had so far taken fifty-two sessions over fifteen months, exactly one year of sessions if we had met once a week.

PMS AND PMDD CONTINUE

Bad news was at the top of our agenda when we met for our fifty-third session. Amelia had gone through a difficult three days of PMS/PMDD, including one day in which she couldn't finish her workday. She cancelled her final two appointments and went home to bed. We didn't meet in the previous week because I had been out of town, but her period started during that week. Day 1 was a Wednesday, the day before we would have met if I been in town. Her PMS symptoms began on the

255

Sunday before that, Day 26 of her cycle. She was symptomatic on Sunday, Monday, and Tuesday. From her notes, she reported that she had *"felt dizzy, headache, anxiety, frustration, anger, impatience, stressed, and mean and irritable."* On Tuesday, her anxiety had been so great that her hands shook uncontrollably. Not recognizing her shaking as a symptom of PMS, she was fearful that she had contracted a new physical illness. She went home from work. The shakiness was a new symptom for Amelia, and scary because it *was* new.

The next day, when her period began, she felt immediate relief. This is the normal pattern for PMS, but infrequent for Amelia. It appeared that her symptoms had begun to conform more closely to the typical pattern of PMS.

The Witch's Transformation

There was also momentous good news! I became aware of its significance only slowly, as Amelia matter-of-factly described the week's events. On Sunday, the first day of her PMS, she had argued with Michael. While he was upstairs with the kids, Amelia stood at the sink, doing dishes. She was teary-eyed as she reviewed her faults: *"I am a bad person, and a failure in so many ways. I am not a good mother or a good wife. I am incompetent as a therapist. All my problems with Michael are my fault! I will never get better! I am broken, and nothing will heal me no matter what I try."*

Then, her self-deprecations were interrupted by new thoughts: *"No! I am a good mother! I am good in my profession and as a wife!"* She decided to look inside to see where the self-deprecating thoughts came from. The Witch was there in the forefront of her mind, and it was she who was feeding Amelia the painful self-criticism.

Amelia Heals Herself

"I was experiencing those thoughts in the first person until I

thought, 'This is not true!' And then I felt it was coming from The Witch. I closed my eyes and she was right there. I went there with anger. I told her to 'shut up! I am tired of you! I am a good mother and wife. I do not want to hear from you anymore.' I told her, 'You should burn in hell!' and I threw her into a fire. She fought to get out but I kept her there, burning. She burned almost to ashes, down to the size of a baby. I did all of this while I stood at the sink. And the fire inside my head made me sweat I was so hot. It was intense! Then I had to go upstairs for something with Michael, so I put her into a box and locked her up in a safe. I did not think any more about her until just now."

Visualizing her at the sink, doing her own intervention with The Witch, I could almost feel my own sweat. It was a dramatic story! And I was pleased that Amelia had carried out her own neutralizing ritual without my help. While the imagery was violent, and different from what I would have coached, it was effective. She felt some relief on Sunday, and from then until our session eleven days later, she felt no more of her earlier depressive, down-putting thoughts. It was a major healing. The likelihood of it being permanent shows in the remainder of our discussion.

Parts Don't Die

Twenty years of experience in work with Parts has taught me that they don't die, and rarely disappear. They might appear to die in one session but then reappear in another. A Part maintains its function as a repository of memories, regardless of changes in appearance. And as we've seen in this book, the image of a Part often changes as the result of therapy. In one form or another, I expected that we could talk with The Witch right away.

Amelia showed some reluctance when I asked her to locate The Witch: *"Oh, I do not like her! I do not want to talk to her!"* Because all strong feelings represent blending with the conscious self by other Parts, I asked Amelia to speak to the Part who didn't like The Witch and ask it to step back. With that Part stepped back, she was willing to look inside. At first she said, *"I cannot see her"*—unusual because The Witch had been so close to Amelia's consciousness for so long. I asked her to find the safe where she had placed The Witch's burnt remains and open it. Reluctantly, she did so. Later, she said that she was afraid that The Witch would bring back the bad thoughts about her.

An Angel Appears

But Amelia opened the safe: *"There is something coming out of the safe but it is not clear... It is a woman. She does not look like The Witch. She is younger. A woman. She does not look like me. A younger woman with curly hair in a dress, a white, flowing kind of dress, long... Yes, she is The Witch, but she is different. Younger and happier. She says she is the same person but does not feel like that anymore. She is cheery, happy. It is like she burned off the anger. Like the fire burned the costume she was wearing. Whoever did this really helped."*

The Part Who Burned The Witch

It made sense that the Part who carried out the intervention with The Witch might be the Part who Amelia had earlier asked to step back. When Amelia looked inside she said, *"It seems to be Gypsy."* This is the Part who appeared in Chapter 5, who had transformed over the course of therapy from Old Woman to Gypsy. She had slowly acquired color as opposed to black-and-white, and youth as opposed to age as the healing of Old Woman took place. Amelia continued, *"Yes, she is the Gypsy. Yep, she is the one who burned up The Witch. She says it was like performing an exorcism on her. The Witch seems thankful to her. It was helpful to get rid of that demon. The Witch doesn't want to be called that any more. She likes the name* Angel.*"*

Amelia recounted the process once more: *"The Witch was telling me how worthless and hopeless I was. Then I said, 'Shut up! I work hard! I do not deserve to be treated this way!' Then Gypsy came over and started a fire and threw The Witch in it. She did not want that and she fought it, but I made her stay and burned her. She burned down to ashes and I had to go upstairs for something, so I just tossed her into the safe. I was anxious and sweating. I think I had another argument with Michael, but within an hour I felt calmer.*

"It did not take away the irritation and anxiety. I remember saying, 'Burn in hell!' to her. And today I was afraid to find her and afraid to open the safe. Somewhere in the burning I had the sense of an angel helping me, so I guess that is why she changed her name to Angel. I think it was Gypsy who intervened because she had experienced a lot of that kind of attack on her when she was growing up."

Sudden Changes

Sudden, violent changes like The Witch's transformation into Angel are unusual. More often a Part's image and role changes incrementally as we do the healing of painful autobiographical memories. Early in the book, Old Woman also showed herself in black and white. As we neutralized the memories that created and sustained her, her appearance slowly changed. Her skin acquired color; her hair first took on streaks of brown and then became fully brown and curly; and her clothing changed from drab to bright and multi-colored. She had become Gypsy.

In contrast, the final act for The Witch to become Angel was dramatic. But it followed many months of therapy, with slower changes as well. By the time Amelia brought about the final transformation, she had already acquired color and appeared to Amelia to be in her forties rather than her seventies. She had also begun to view Michael less harshly.

But while we had done the healing with all or nearly all of her painful memories, she still hadn't completely changed her image nor given up all of her harsh criticism. That change was overdue. When it happened, it did so suddenly through the intervention of Gypsy. It was a metaphorical changing of the guard, with a new leader in charge. I preferred slower, incremental changes, but I was pleased with the result. I was optimistic again about healing Amelia.

VIOLET'S ANXIETY

As we ended the session, I suggested that we return at our next meeting to Violet, the Part we had located some weeks previously, who had claimed responsibility for the anxiety Amelia experienced as a strong pressure in her chest. She could feel the pressure again as we approached the end of the session. She said of Violet, *"She is very present right now. I forgot we got connected before and I wonder if that is why the anxiety was so bad in my PMS."*

At our next session, in the first week of December, Amelia was in Day 23 of her menstrual cycle, six days before her projected period. As yet there were no PMS symptoms. She didn't, however, escape the PMS of her earlier ovulation. On Day 15 of the previous week, when we didn't meet because of the Thanksgiving holiday, she had felt *"frustrated and impotent."* Day 16 was even worse. She noted that she *"felt frustrated, mean, irritable, angry, stressed. I was snapping at everybody. My poor husband took most of it. On Day 17 I felt irritable, stressed, impotent, and anxiety.*

"Those three days were horrible. The anxiety was probably from Violet and really bad every day, snapping at everybody. I was even aware of it. By the third day I was feeling guilt for my behavior. It was really self-anger. 'Why am I doing this? I am a bad mother, a bad wife! I will never get better!' I am losing patience with my daughter. I am just so short with her. I am angry, yelling at her. So she does not want to be around Mommy. When my son comes to me, I hold him close and it just feels so good, but not with her."

BIG TWIN

The PMS during Amelia's ovulation was bad enough to warrant immediate attention. We had planned to finally work with Violet in order to reduce Amelia's anxiety. But because Amelia had now identified significant new issues with Noelle, I thought we should first work with Big Twin, the Part who lacked the appropriate mother-daughter bond with her.

Amelia quickly located Big Twin: *"She is very angry and anxious. She is angry with my daughter. She is the one yelling at her. She says things to me like, 'Why did you get that daughter? Why did you not get a normal girl? Why does she have to be like that, having tantrums, crying, irritability? It is hard to love her.' She feels that everything my daughter does is directed at her."*

I suggested that we do a short-term intervention in order to give Big Twin and Amelia temporary respite from feeling negatively about Noelle. The intervention would target only the current-time anxiety related to Amelia's anticipated next interaction with her. I thought that if we could succeed in reducing the Part's current reactivity, we could do the deeper work of healing the memories later. Big Twin hesitantly agreed.

Amelia visualized a bonfire and asked Big Twin to lift the **anxiety** about next interacting with Noelle out of herself and throw it into the fire. Soon after beginning the intervention, Amelia said, *"She has so much anger, too!"* I coached her to guide Big Twin in ignoring the anger while focusing just on the anxiety. After twenty seconds more, Amelia added, *"She is trying, but she cannot let it go."* In this case, we were trying to neutralize anxiety about the future, not entrenched memories from the past. But Big Twin couldn't even do that. We looked for a blocking Part.

Healing Little Twin

Because Little Twin was also present at the scene of the intervention, we thought she might be the blocker. She was curled into a ball again, just as when we first met her: *"She is scared of the big one. She does not know if she is blocking her."* Amelia invited Little Twin to neutralize her **anxiety** about interacting with the daughter. Within thirty seconds, Little Twin had released her anxiety. She had also grown to the same size as Big Twin. (We would continue to use their original names to identify them as having differing personalities.)

A Pile of Bones

Amelia then repeated the fire intervention with Big Twin: *"She is feeling more anger than anxiety, so the anxiety was from the little one."* I knew the anger would dissipate if we could find the vulnerable emotion that anger shielded. Consequently, I suggested that Amelia try healing Big Twin's hurt over feeling rejected by Noelle. Amelia confirmed that the Big Twin felt *"pushed away, rejected."* Then she guided her in the bonfire intervention, directing her to burn up her **hurt**. After one full minute of the visualization, Amelia said, *"She is throwing in a lot of it. She is feeling a lot of guilt. Like why cannot she love her? Why is it so frustrating to be connected to her child? What is she doing wrong? Why cannot it be different? Why is it so difficult to understand her, be connected to her?"*

Amelia refocused her work and asked Big Twin to find her **guilt** and burn it up. After a few moments of silence, Amelia said in surprise, *"She threw herself into the fire and she is burning up—skin, bones, organs, and now she's just a pile of body parts."*

Parts Make Choices

This is another good example of how Parts have volition (decision-making ability) of their own. They can and do sometimes act independently from the conscious self. Spontaneously, Big Twin had burned herself up in the fire. I had previously used fire interventions in which I suggested that Parts jump into a fire to burn up the sensations and emotions they carried, but I had always made sure to add that the fire wouldn't harm them. Instead, it would burn right through them and neutralize the targeted feelings. It was a first for me to have a Part immolate herself intentionally.

It was a good reminder for us to keep in mind that all images of Parts have a strong symbolic component. The image isn't the Part. It just represents the Part, and it can change its shape as needed—although most images have considerable continuity across time. What to do about a pile of body parts? Speak to the pile as if nothing had fundamentally changed. *"She says this is exactly how she feels about her daughter—broken down into pieces and she cannot put herself back together."*

Pre- and Postpartum Distress

We bridged to the earliest of Big Twin's memories that connected to her present feelings. What came up were her memories of *"being stressed while pregnant, and struggling after her daughter's birth. Changing her formulas, the baby being constipated and in pain, and giving her baby enemas and prune juice. Breast feeding and being afraid my milk was harming her. And when she was sleeping, wanting to hold her because she was calm, but then she was too exhausted to just hold her. So whenever I held her it was at fussy times, painful times."*

Amelia continued to release a flood of painful thoughts and memories, almost without pausing to breathe: *"She was born with a fever and I hardly saw her for three days, and I was very weak and had lost so much blood, and I was anemic. And Michael was the one who did the caring for those three days and the next three months of summer before going back to work at school. I remember I did not feel connected to my daughter and I did not know why and I thought it would come later. I felt most connected when breast feeding. It was not until after the birth of my son that I learned what connection re-*

ally was. When she cried, I went to her but out of duty and not love—Oh my! I did have postpartum depression with her!"

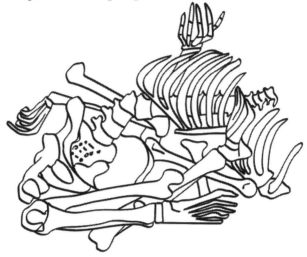

Pile of Bones

As we helped Big Twin burn up her memories of painful postpartum **emotions** and **body sensations**, Amelia interrupted to say, *"I do not know when it happened but the fire stopped burning."* She switched to a wind intervention to blow away all of the **frustration, depression, exhaustion** of the first postpartum year. After a minute of silent concentration, Amelia said, *"Yes, it is blowing away. She is now a Pile of Bones with all the organs burnt up. She feels hurt now and that she did something wrong."* Amelia tried to neutralize the **hurt** and **guilt** but soon said, *"She has stopped. Nothing else is coming from that Pile of Bones."*

We were at the end of the session and would have to return later to continue the healing—and locate the cause of the latest block in the therapy. Amelia moved Big Twin (the Pile of Bones) to a safe place where Little Twin could watch over her. They chose to stay in the house where they lived when Noelle was born.

VIOLET AGAIN

These end-of-session adjustments failed to quell Amelia's continuing anxiety. Looking inside, Amelia found the anxiety's source in Violet, who was impatient with us for taking so long to get back to her. It appeared that Violet and Big Twin had been competing for our attention, and Violet's needs had inadvertently blocked our work with Big Twin. Amelia assured Violet that we would soon return to her.

Travel Versus Pregnancy

We met on Day 30 of what was usually Amelia's 28-day menstrual cycle. She should have been on Day 2 of a new cycle. Ordinarily this wouldn't have been a cause for concern, but now she and Michael had given up trying to get pregnant and had begun to look forward to traveling without a baby. She expressed some concern about possibly being pregnant. She added, *"That would be funny! All these months of trying and now that we are not trying to get pregnant, we could be."*

They both liked the idea of visiting new places and learning about new cultures. For Amelia, the revival of her Gypsy Part gave her a renewed desire for travel and adventure. They had begun to look for places in other parts of the world where they could work, perhaps where there were American military bases: *"If I am pregnant, that would change our plans because we could not travel for at least a year."*

Their marital relationship was much improved: *"Things are so much better. And his therapy with you has helped so much."* I agreed that Michael was making good progress, although I maintained confidentiality with both of them regarding the content of the other's sessions.

Violet's Anxiety

Returning to deep therapy, we looked for Violet, the anxious Part who had seemed to be trying to get Amelia's attention for weeks with a ball of anxiety in Amelia's chest. I now believed that working with Violet might hasten progress in our work with Big Twin and Little Twin. Perhaps it was Violet's anxiety that was slowing our work with Big Twin.

When Amelia acquired an internal picture of Violet she said, *"She looks like a crazy version maybe of me—no, it is hard to say if she looks like me. Her hair is messy, and maybe she has not showered in months. Her clothes are ragged and dirty, worn out, looking grey with dirt. Her eyes are unfocused. She looks like a crazy person."*

Violet was confused. She seemed not to recall our previous work with her a few weeks earlier: *"She says she does not know who I am, and she does not believe me when I tell her that I am her or that she is a Part of me. She does not know Michael, but she knows my mother. She says my mother is not her mother. She is not sure if she knows my children but she does not have any."* Violet's responses are uncommon. Most Parts are better oriented to the conscious self and have a clearer recognition of the important persons in her life.

However, as is usually the case, talking about the Part's memories helped her to better understand her relation to Amelia. Violet's earliest disturbing memory was of Amelia's birthday party at age six or seven: *"My family was having a party for me. I was upset about something. I did something inappropriate, like yelling. I ran away and hid because I was afraid of being punished. She is embarrassed and ashamed of what she did."*

Healing Violet

The **embarrassment** Violet felt at a level 4 on the SUD scale quickly vanished as Amelia neutralized the memory with a rainfall intervention, visualizing rain soaking Violet and dissolving and washing the emotion away.

Violet's next memories had to do with getting reprimands for bad grades, especially in high school: *"She was always a good student so when I got bad grades it was a big deal. I did poorly at about the time my parents got a divorce. I got reprimanded by both of them."* Amelia again used a rain intervention, this time to neutralize the **hurt feelings** she experienced when scolded for bad grades. After closing her eyes to visualize the falling rain, Amelia opened them again to say, *"She thought that my parents always expected too much. She had to perform for them to make them happy. So when she made a mistake, they came down on her. When she did well they did not notice."*

The first pass of the intervention reduced the SUD level from 7 to 2, with a stall on the way to zero because: *"It was the injustice of it. She did not have a right to make a mistake."* A second pass of the intervention produced no improvement. *"It is hard!"* Checking for blocking Parts, Amelia found Little Twin and the bones of Big Twin in the scene too.

REMEMBERING THE LESSONS LEARNED

"Oh! Maybe it is the little one. She is telling Violet I better remember how they treated me because that is what I am doing now to Noelle. And so I am causing pain for someone I want to protect. She does not want to neutralize the memory because she is saying Violet is hurting Noelle with her reactivity. She does not even know Noelle but she reacts when Noelle does something wrong." [Amelia is describing the unconscious process by which internal Parts often respond to external stimuli even when they aren't conscious of actual external events.]

Little Twin displayed a common belief that healing the memories of painful emotions would lead to forgetting the memories, and that would mean that the patient would forget the lessons learned from experiencing the pain. The belief is untrue. Factual memories aren't forgotten, nor do Parts forget that the events were once emotionally painful. Healing means only that the emotions attached to the factual memories are neutralized. When doing Parts work we have to repeat this correction frequently in order to break through different blocking Parts' resistance.

Amelia explained to Little Twin that our work would help Violet to not be reactive to Noelle's irritating behaviors. Instead, she would learn to be calm in interacting with her.

With that explanation, Little Twin responded, *"That is okay then. We can do it because it will help her not to be like that."* Amelia then easily guided Violet in releasing her **distress** for being reprimanded. Then Amelia said, *"She does feel guilt for reacting to Noelle, so she does know her after all.* [Not uncommonly, Parts may be at first unaware of current-life events, but then they acquire that awareness during the interview.] *She does not want to do that. Overall, she feels like a victim herself, so it is hard to hurt someone else."*

We still had work to do with Violet, but we were again at the end of the session. Amelia tucked Violet away in a Sleeping Beauty Bed until we worked with her again. We would wait and see whether our work permitted us to help the Pile of Bones that now represented Big Twin.

Before she left the office, I asked Amelia to text me when her period began. The next day she texted me that while her period hadn't begun, she had taken a pregnancy test and the results were negative. We both expressed relief. Amelia because she and Michael were hoping to travel, and me because we could continue our therapy and further reduce PMS/PMDD symptoms.

CHRISTMAS BREAK

Our next session was our last for three weeks. Amelia, Michael, their two children, and Amelia's mother would visit Michael's parents in Pennsylvania over the holidays. Amelia's half-brother had returned to his family in Costa Rica, three months ahead of the original plan. That was a relief for both Amelia and Michael. It was a good time for a break. We seemed to have done a lot of healing of both Amelia's PMS and her marital relationship. We would tie up several loose ends in this session.

Amelia shared that her period had started on the previous Saturday, two days after our session—Day 32 counting from the first day of her previous period: *"I think it is my thyroid because I am gaining weight too. It lasted four days. I had no PMS for the three days before my period and I hardly had any symptoms during my period either. I was a little cranky on the first day and that is all."* We were doing well.

Regarding possible pregnancy, Amelia said, *"I was happy when my period came. But there is still a little Part of me that wishes I was pregnant."*

VIOLET'S GUILT

We returned to the deep work of our previous session and planned to retrieve Violet from her Sleeping Beauty Bed. Before we could engage her, however, Amelia complained of a disruptive headache. It began before our meeting and continued as we talked.

Because headaches are often the result of problem issues just outside of awareness, I suggested that Amelia speak to the headache as if it were a Part, and ask it to come forward. It was Violet. She too had a headache. Amelia asked her what caused it: *"She feels guilt over Noelle. She does not know how to get close to her. She feels like a bad mother. She feels frustrated, worthless, hopeless."* I suggested that Amelia ask Violet to place her headache in a box so as to block it from our session: *"She is trying. But she cannot. It will not go in the box."*

I encouraged Amelia to guide Violet in getting a sense of where her headache might be coming from. *"It is the Pile of Bones."* When I asked if this Part had a headache too, Amelia laughed: *"She does not have a headache because she does not have a head* [laughing], *but she is feeling her frustration with Noelle and it makes Little Twin feel guilty. Her irritation makes Little Twin feel she cannot protect Noelle. I notice I have been trying to touch her more, hold her more, be closer to her, but there is a block there. It is not her. It is from me. It is not like my son where I feel the connection easily, with no effort."*

THE PILE OF BONES

Violet and Big Twin seemed to be continuing their competition for attention in therapy. Since Big Twin, as the Pile of Bones, appeared to be the problem Part at this point, we turned to work with her: *"She feels frustrated and irritated because of Noelle's behavior."* For example, Noelle had been uncooperative with Amelia's mothering, crying a lot, and feeling sensory discomfort with touch and with the tightness or looseness of her clothing. Amelia asked the pile of bones to search her past for early memories that might be related to her feelings toward Noelle.

The memory that surfaced was *"the lack of physical connection with my mother and grandmother. All the years I was with my grandmother, she never held me. From six to eleven. When I went back to my mother and she tried to be physically close with me, I pushed her away. Not until I was an adult would I allow her to be physically close. In my twenties I began to be okay with hugging her. It is disturbing to her because now she does not know how to do that with Noelle. Now she wishes she could have that."*

As Amelia described her experiences with her mother and grandmother and talked about how she didn't feel physically close to them, I began to wonder how we might give Big Twin something she had never felt—a close physical connection to Noelle. If she had felt a small amount of attachment energy to Noelle, we could amplify it. If she once had it, but could no longer feel it, we could find it again. But she had never felt that connection at all. We had hoped that the healing of the twins' negative emotions would spontaneously bring positive feelings toward Noelle by Big Twin. But that never happened. Her earlier irritations had come back as Noelle struggled with her own discomfort with being touched.

Looking for Mother Love

Love

How do we go about installing in a Part emotions and sensations that are missing? I recalled interventions I had used in the past in which I had helped one Part to share some of an emotion with a Part that lacked it. Because Amelia had the ability to feel close to her son, that meant she had a Part with the qualities we needed for Big Twin. We needed to find the Part that carried Amelia's connection with her son and try to transplant that ability to Big Twin.

I asked Amelia to imagine holding her son in her lap and to allow herself to feel the connection with him: *"It is a warm feeling,"* she said. I asked her to immerse herself in the warm feeling and to ask the feeling to provide an image of itself in her mind: *"It is me, dressed in white, with an angelical kind of happiness. It is very pure. She knows who I am. She is in her twenties. Her name is not Amelia. It is* Love. *She feels the purest love for her son. The most powerful I ever felt. It fills me up."*

Sharing Mother Love

"She does not know the Twins, but she is willing to share with them." I directed Amelia to visualize Love together with the Twins and to reach one hand out to each of them, and through this touch to transfer the energy of mother-love they could use to relate to Noelle. Right away, Amelia interrupted her visualization to say, *"Little Twin is upset because she feels that she should feel the connection without help."* I didn't want to stop the momentum of the intervention, so I asked Amelia to speak to Little Twin and ask her to move her **upset** into a container so that she could receive Love's energy, but that was no help: *"The Pile of Bones is receiving it more than Little Twin."* Then, after about two minutes of inward focus, Amelia smiled and said, *"The Pile of Bones is becoming a person again. The other one is not having it. She just crawls into a ball. She feels she is undeserving."* I asked Amelia to check her own body sensations: *"I feel a big ball of pressure in my chest. It is from Little Twin. She feels a lot of negative things about herself—guilt, worthless, hopeless, unworthy— stuff like that."*

Our intervention was partly successful. Big Twin could now feel mother-love for Noelle, but Little Twin needed more help. My working hypothesis was that there was another Part involved, perhaps Violet, blocking her from accepting the loving feelings for Noelle. We would have to await the New Year to test this. In the meantime, I suggested that Amelia call upon newly-reconstituted Big Twin and Love when she needed help in coping with Noelle.

Optimism for the New Year

As we prepared to part at the end of the session, Amelia summarized her current life, looking into the New Year: *"It is unbelievable how much relief I feel now that The Witch is not affecting me! She is present now as Angel and not a problem. She is dancing with Gypsy. She is young now, and does not look at all like The Witch. She does not exist in that way anymore. I feel that it was she who carried my depression. And I think she carried a lot of my PMS. And she had so much anger for my husband. And I am not angry with Michael the way I used to be. Like when I wanted to kick him to the curb. I even told him the other day I wanted us to go through life together. And that I did not want to do it by myself. I feel so much compassion for him rather than frustration with his problems. I do not think about divorce anymore. Thank you for saving my marriage!"*

We had more work to do. The problem with Little Twin needed to be fixed, perhaps by merging her with Big Twin. And there might be more work to do with Violet. We had apparently made great strides in reducing PMS symptoms and possibly brought about a remission of the more powerful diagnosis of PMDD (Premenstrual Dysphoric Disorder). But we needed more time to know for sure.

I intended to continue work on this manuscript even as I half-expected that Amelia would be pregnant when she returned to Utah in the New Year. Unfortunately, the New Year would bring new problems.

SUMMARY OF PARTS

Gypsy. She was originally Old Woman but therapy had transformed her in Chapter 5 into Gypsy. She appeared again here in Chapter 15 as the Part who carried out a fiery transformation of The Witch into Angel. Gypsy seemed to have replaced The Witch as the dominant mood-setter for Amelia.

Angel. After Gypsy burned up The Witch in a fire, Angel appeared out of the ashes. Angel no longer attacked Amelia as she had done in her previous form as The Witch.

Big Twin and **Little Twin**. The larger twin appeared again as the Part of Amelia who couldn't easily connect to her daughter Noelle. As we processed her guilt and other emotions, she immolated herself in a fire and transformed into a **Pile of Bones**—but we could still interact with her. Little Twin turned out to be stronger than we thought. She carried a lot of anger and temporarily prevented our healing of Violet.

Violet. She carried high anxiety and embarrassment, especially in regard to disappointing her parents or grandparents. School grades were important. She also felt the guilt for failing to develop a good mother-daughter bond with Noelle.

Love. She showed herself as in her twenties, and she carried the love—the maternal connection—that Amelia felt toward her son but not her daughter.

PART THREE

Resolution

Chapter 16
After the New Year

The processing of Amelia's Pennsylvania Christmas vacation and its fallout took all of one session and part of the next. It wasn't a good vacation. From the high of feeling close to Michael and planning a grand future a week before the trip, Amelia fell to a low of notable pessimism and thoughts of divorcing him.

PENNSYLVANIA CRISIS

The couple had twice allowed their angry arguments to spill over in front of Michael's family, producing great embarrassment for Amelia. She could still feel that flush on her face as she shared her experiences with me. One argument coincided with her mild PMS symptoms (frustration and irritability) at ovulation, but Amelia believed that both were largely Michael's fault: *"By the time we returned to Utah, he was worried about divorce. I told him I would not put the kids through that but I did not know how long I could resist it. He was very apologetic and very nice, as he always gets when he thinks I might divorce him."*

Travel Plans

Amelia's thoughts of divorce were only temporary, linked primarily to Michael's blow-ups in Pennsylvania. In fact, the couple was in a substantially better place than they had been a year earlier. They continued to make plans for the future. Both loved to travel and had been researching countries where they might work and visit new cultures. They had completed the application process over the previous weekend and would soon fly east to Iowa for interviews at a center for international placement: *"Yes, it is the Gypsy Part of me. I am happy and she is ready to go."*

Getting Past Pennsylvania

At our first session of the New Year, Amelia was expecting her period to begin at any moment, but she had no PMS symptoms. This, in combination with only two days of mild PMS symptoms while they were in Pennsylvania, was good evidence that the therapy was proving itself. Her period began the day after our session.

Our session coincided with Day 7 of Amelia's cycle. Unfortunately, while PMS or PMDD symptoms had been absent, the first two days of her period had been very unpleasant, alternating between numbing, heavy fatigue, irritation, and unmanageable crying. Dysmenorrhea rather than PMS struck hard:

"I exploded with emotion on Michael. I went over all the things that happened in Pennsylvania. I was more hopeless than angry. I told him, 'I do not think this is going to work and I think we are taking steps backward rather than forward.'

"We had a deep conversation about what each does that hurts or irritates the other. He said he is still afraid of me running away like I did when we were courting. I told him he has to tell me ahead of time when I frustrate him so he does not blow up. There is a Part of me that automatically plans ahead when we fight—like applying for a job, getting a divorce, going somewhere. When I tell him I am not thinking of divorce and I want to be with him forever, then he turns around and stomps on me like his blow-ups in Pennsylvania.

He is so distracted by other things. He goes to la-la land and he is not really present. I have to be almost ready to leave before he realizes he needs to make changes. When we are at his parents' house, he changes. Even my mother noticed. His teenager Part comes out."

LITTLE TWIN AND DAUGHTER NOELLE

With Amelia feeling calmer after sharing her story of the holidays, she was ready to return to the work we had left unfinished before the break. This was our work with Big Twin and Little Twin and their relationship to Amelia's daughter Noelle: *"I feel less irritated with Noelle but I am still not fully connected."*

Looking inside, Amelia found that Little Twin was still curled into a ball as we had left her. Thinking that there might be unresolved issues from the past, we asked her to remind Amelia of her earliest painful memory. She recalled the weeks after childbirth as *"being home alone with Noelle every day and not seeing anyone. There were no friends or family to talk to. She was lonely."* Amelia tried to use a wind intervention to blow away Little Twin's **loneliness** but the wind had no effect. Looking around for possible blocking Parts, Amelia found Big Twin and Love (the Part bonded with her son), but neither of them was blocking our work. Violet was there too but she said she wasn't aware of doing any blocking.

Then Amelia tried a different intervention, switching the scene to a bathtub shower and asking Violet to help by using a hand-held shower attachment with Little Twin. This intervention also failed: *"There is a blocker that I cannot see,"* Amelia concluded. *"Little Twin cannot move backward or forward. Emotionally, she is stuck."* We ended the session at this point, with plans to return to Little Twin at our next meeting.

Amelia's Joy for Life

A week later Amelia arrived with all smiles. It was Day 14 in her cycle. Her expected PMS symptoms at ovulation did not appear. She was excited about the trip she and Michael would make the next week for international job placement. Her overall good feeling was an unusual experience. Yesterday morning, she had been sad about the death to cancer of one of her patients. But by the evening she *"just felt happy without reason."*

Of her relationship with Michael, Amelia said, *"We are okay. He has been very stressed with grading. But he has not been snapping or irritable—even when I was cranky when I got a virus from my son. There is something about Michael's smell that is making me calm and happy. It is something that also happened with my son when I was in postpartum. Just smelling him would make me calm and not depressed. I told him, 'I like where we are right now. Please do not mess it up.' It is either very intense love or very intense hate."*

Looking for Love

With Amelia in such a good place, I thought it was an opportune time to return to Little Twin. When Amelia located her internally, she was no longer wrapped into a ball but standing up: *"She wants the energy from Love* [that would permit bonding with Noelle] *but she does not think she can... Yes, she does feel a positive connection to Noelle but her guilt prevents her from allowing herself to feel the love... Yes, she wants to give up the guilt."*

Amelia attempted to guide Little Twin in a wind intervention to blow the **guilt** out of her but within fifteen seconds she said, still with her eyes closed: *"It is hard. There is a blocker! I can see the wind but it is not reaching her!"* I asked her to focus on the blocking force or shield that prevented the intervention and to follow it to its source. I used the words "force" and "shield" to suggest how she might think about the blocker: *"She can feel it and a shield-type thing but cannot see the blocker."* A request of the "shield" to permit the healing gave us nothing.

Mother and Grandmother Introjects

Finally, I asked Amelia to find Gypsy (formerly Old Woman) and Angel (formerly The Witch) and remind them that they were her strongest Parts (appealing to vanity), and that she couldn't function without them. If anyone could find the blocker it would be them. After a minute of focused silence, Amelia said, *"Okay, there are two Parts. My mother and my grandmother. I cannot tell how they are dressed. I just see their faces. My grandmother is about fifty and my mother is about thirty. Yes, they know me. They say they are my mother and grandmother."*

We had found the blocking Parts. We named them by their functions, *Mother* and *Grandmother Introject,* costumed versions of parental figures from Amelia's childhood.

Not all introjects are harmful to a functioning person. For example, a nurturing and encouraging parental introject can be a valuable resource in difficult times, a positive voice *inside* when there's stress or danger *outside.* For this reason, I didn't immediately suggest that Amelia unmask them. I first wanted to see whether they would cooperate with our work.

Amelia explained, *"The Mother accepts that she is a Part of me. The Grandmother insists that she is not a Part of me."* Further, the Mother Introject gave her permission for the healing of Little Twin, while the Grandmother Introject refused permission. She insisted that Little Twin needed the pain to remind her of her faults. It was time to do an unmasking.

A guiding principle in this work is to change as little as necessary in the patient's inner world as long as we can accomplish the healing. It seemed that we didn't need to unmask the Mother Introject, but we probably did need to unmask the Grandmother Introject.

First, however, I wanted to make one more effort to convince the Grandmother Introject that she wasn't separate from Amelia but a Part of her. I used an intervention I often used with other patients when they have ordinary Parts (not introjects) that insist they aren't a Part of the patient. I asked Amelia to open her eyes while staying in touch with the Introject and to ask her if she could see me patting the top of my head with my right hand. She could. Then I asked Amelia to close her eyes and ask again if the Grandmother could see what I was doing with my right hand. She couldn't. I repeated the exercise three times, each time moving my right hand to a different part of my body. Then I asked Amelia to make the point to the Grandmother Part that because she could only see what I was doing when Amelia had her eyes open, she had to reside within Amelia. Her only view of the world was through Amelia. She wasn't a separate person.

The Grandmother Spontaneously Unmasks

Surprisingly, without an unmasking ritual, the Grandmother image spontaneously unmasked herself by transforming a much younger Amelia: *"Yes, she knows she is a Part now. It is a little girl, about nine years old. She says, 'You are not supposed to make mistakes.' She gets scared when she makes mistakes. Because then people yell at her and get mad at her."*

We wanted to heal this child Part because the energy that drove her to be perfect seemed to be the same energy that drove Little Twin to her self-punishing affliction. Amelia directed the little girl to focus upon her **fear** of making mistakes as the wind blew it away: *"She let go of her fear of making mistakes but she is still afraid of other people getting mad at her."*

I couldn't see the distinction, but what's important is my patient's perception, not mine. So I urged Amelia to help her neutralize this brand of **fear** as well. When Amelia took more time than I expected, I interrupted her concentration to explain to the little girl that her job was not to worry about other people. The adults could do that. Her job was just to have fun: *"She says her job is to make other people happy."* I asked Amelia to tell her no, that her job is to make herself happy. Beginning again with her wind intervention, Amelia soon said, *"Now she is confused."* I asked Amelia to help the little girl to focus on the **confusion** and blow that away. Finally, it worked. *"Okay. She wants to go play now."* Perfect result!

Healing Little Twin

Quickly then, we returned to Little Twin, stopping momentarily to ask permission from the Mother Introject. With her eyes closed, Amelia acknowledged the Mother's permission with an *"Mm hmm,"* and then turned the wind onto Little Twin's **guilt**: *"Mm hmm, it's working now."* Within thirty seconds Amelia exclaimed, *"She did it! She looks very different. She looks like Love. She's wearing white robes. And she is blond. She is hugging all the Parts—Big Twin, the Mother, Love, Violet, Gypsy, Angel."*

I explained to Amelia, as outlined above, that I had guided her to work on the Grandmother Introject rather than the Mother Introject because, the Grandmother wouldn't accept that she was a Part of her. The Mother, on the other hand, seemed to be cooperative while acknowledging that she was a Part of her. Amelia replied, *"Yes, I felt tenderness from the Mother Part. She wanted Little Twin to be healed."*

ANTICIPATING NEXT PARTS

Now near the end of the session and planning for the next, I asked whether Violet—the Part whose chest anxiety slowed our work with Little Twin—had any other disturbing memories: *"She does not have memories but she still has some sadness."* The healing of other Parts had lessened her distress but her sadness told us that we still had more work to do. That sadness would be connected to specific memories even if Violet wasn't aware of them.

Before we ended the session, Amelia added that she also wanted to find the Part of her *"who wants to run away when Michael gets into his anger and we get into a huge fight. It is this Part always making plans about where to go, how to leave him. It just comes over me. I do not want to be that way. Ever since we first started dating, I would run away when I got mad about him. He was clueless about dating. One time I went to his apartment and he made a sandwich for himself and ate in front of me, and did not offer me any. I got so mad at him for being so rude. I ran away then, and he did not understand why I was mad."*

Finally, Amelia added, *"I have not been angry with Noelle since we did the intervention with the Pile of Bones. I still get upset but not angry."*

We weren't quite there, but I thought we were close to finishing. We were both afraid to say so out loud. As we stood to leave, however, we laughed and smiled and agreed that we were near the completion of therapy. It had been a sort of superstitious fear that if we said it aloud, we would jinx the results.

SUMMARY OF PARTS

Little Twin. She carried the memories of loneliness during the early months following the birth of Noelle. She also experienced tremendous guilt for not being a better mother. Her healing led to her taking on a new self-image, one that resembled Love, but with blond hair.

Gypsy, **Angel**, **Violet**, **Big Twin**. These Parts appeared in the chapter only as helpers as we tried to heal Little Twin. Big Twin was just an observer.

Mother Introject, **Grandmother Introject**. The Mother introject wasn't a problem in doing the healing work. However, the Grandmother Introject refused to allow the healing to move forward and refused to acknowledge that she was a Part of Amelia. When unmasked, the Grandmother Introject revealed a nine-year-old girl who believed her job was to be perfect and to please the adults.

Chapter 17
A New Life Beckons

Amelia and Michael, with many of their issues reduced or neutralized, were now ready to begin again their commitment to life together. However, they both felt financial pressure in their Utah lives and sometimes felt a sense of desperation as they tried to move forward. They had options, such as withdrawing their children from private schools or Michael moving into school administration, but they were not attractive options. Traveling was an attractive option. The idea of traveling to other countries—something they both liked to do—led them to seek employment outside the United States. They hoped to find positions that would satisfy their wanderlust while also reducing their financial burdens.

We met again after two weeks, following their visit to Iowa to interview for international positions. The interviews went well and they were excited about the possibility of again living and working in another country. They awaited the results of their applications and interviews.

RESUMING THERAPY

Our session took place on Day 2 of Amelia's cycle. She wasn't experiencing the negative emotions that she often felt during her period. Nor did she have PMS symptoms at anytime during the week before her period. This was very good news. However, two weeks previously, just after our last session, she had a difficult couple of days at ovulation. Day 16 and Day 17 were days when she was irritable, even angry, with everyone in her family. She fought again with Michael, although not to the degree that her marriage was threatened. Daughter Noelle had asked, *"Mommy, why are you so cranky?"*

Therapeutic Progress

Despite her frustration and irritability, Amelia didn't take time off from work. And she felt no depression or self-deprecation. She had gone another month without meeting criteria for PMDD and had only mild PMS symptoms. As a result Amelia was optimistic and pleased with the therapy:

"When I came to therapy I was miserable three days every two weeks. I took time off from work to stay in bed. I have not felt any depression since The Witch changed. No 'I am a horrible mother—a worthless person' anymore. I was afraid of change. I wasn't good where I was but I was afraid to do anything else. Finding Gypsy gave me hope again. And now we are trying to work in another country. I gave up also the heavy guilt. A year ago, I would not be ready to go to another country. I would have been unsure, untrusting of Michael. I want to get rid of the Part who wants to divorce him in that time of the month. It was okay last time. I did not want to divorce. When he is patient with me, I am fine. Two weeks ago he was patient with my irritability. It is when he gets angry that is a problem for me. It is not The Witch. It is another Part." We planned to work with Violet and seek out the new angry Part in our next session.

Stable Emotions

Two weeks later, we met on Amelia's Day 16. She was in a good place. Her ovulation Days 14, 15, and 16 were usually PMS days. This time Day 16 was fine and Days 14 and 15 brought only mild fatigue and some acne. Very encouraging results. In talking about her ovulation experiences, Amelia recalled that she had a difficult time a month ago, but it was the week before she and Michael flew to Iowa for their interviews. She attributed the difficult days to the anxiety she felt about the job application process. Stressful times had always created more powerful PMS symptoms for her.

She and Michael were expecting an offer soon. Michael had done a follow-up Skype interview for one school and they had already checked his references. He would be an assistant principal if they hired him. They didn't have an opening as school psychologist or school counselor for Amelia, but she was positively anticipating housewife-time without outside work demands.

She had had no depressive feelings for a couple of months: *"It feels good not to feel depressed anymore. Without our work I do not think I would still be married."* She added that she believed we would soon be finishing the therapy. Just a few things to wrap up. One of those things was our work with Violet.

WORKING WITH VIOLET

When Amelia looked inward to find Violet she said, *"She is there with the other Parts: Gypsy, Angel, the two Twin Parts, and Love. They are on the other side of the room and Violet is by herself. She is still sad. She is lonely in being separated from the other Parts."*

Violet's earliest still-disturbing memories were of growing up without other children around: *"Just adults around and no one to play with. It was hard to get permission to visit the neighbor children. My grandmother did not like for me to play or visit other children."* The memories were disturbing to Violet at a level 6 or 7 on the 0-10 scale.

With a wind intervention, Amelia closed her eyes and visualized neutralizing Violet's **loneliness**. After ninety seconds of silence, I became nervous enough to ask what was happening with the intervention. Amelia answered, *"She is getting it out,"* but after another forty seconds, she added, *"Something is blocking her. The other Parts are not blocking. They say it is me."*

Finding a Blended Part

When other Parts identify the conscious self as the source of a processing difficulty, it means that the problem Part is blended so completely with the conscious self that other Parts can't tell the difference between them. In order to separate the blocking Part from Amelia, I suggested that she ask the group of observing Parts to appoint a speaker who would then speak to the Part blended with Amelia and ask her to step-away from Amelia. That worked: *"It is my grandmother."* Increasingly, grandmother and mother introjects seemed to be preventing the smooth process of healing painful memories.

Amelia requested permission from the new *Grandmother Introject* to allow us to continue healing Violet of her childhood loneliness: *"She is not sure,"* which seemed to me to be the same as refusal. And when Amelia asked if the Grandmother knew she was a Part of Amelia, the answer was an unequivocal *"No!"*

Unmasking a Grandmother Introject

An introject that denies it's a Part of the patient is poorly oriented to the whole person. And because its memories are not accurate memories but projections by the child of what she thinks the introject believes, we can't easily neutralize them. Generally, this sort of introject believes it has no disturbing memories of its own, and consequently, no need for healing. The introject views the problem as lying in the behavior or attitude of the child.

We moved directly to the unmasking ritual. Amelia praised the Grandmother Introject for helping her survive to adulthood, for being strong and powerful and a great actor. Then she spoke to the internal Part that wore the grandmother costume and asked her to unzip and step out of it, or pull it over her head, and just *be* the Amelia underneath. Amelia identified the young Part that appeared as *"a child, about eight years old. She is confused about wanting to be with other kids and having to obey her grandmother and stay away from them."* Amelia explained to the child Part that she could now play with anyone she wished: *"She is happy now, not upset any more. She wants to go play."*

Healing Violet

With the Grandmother Introject now out of the way, we returned to our work with Violet. Just twenty seconds were needed to complete the healing of her **loneliness**: *"She let go of that. But there is still something that bothers her but she does not know what. She feels it in her core—her chest, her stomach, her spine."* We moved forward with Amelia using a wind intervention directed at that core, while expecting that the intervention would generate the memories that underlay the problem:

"She remembers being punished for playing with other kids and exploring our sexual Parts—nothing really sexual, just showing and touching. My grandmother severely punished her. She yelled at her and made her feel like a really bad girl and that the naked body is wrong and touching anybody is wrong. There are a lot of memories about body shame. When I had my first period I was ashamed and afraid to tell my grandmother or anybody else. She had a deep sense of guilt about anything related to her body. Until seventeen or eighteen I was very guilty about my body. Having a period and getting breasts made me feel lots of guilt."

Amelia chose a waterfall intervention for Violet's healing, asking her to feel the water soak her from head to foot and let the water flow through her while dissolving and washing away her **guilt** and **shame**. She also provided psychoeducation in the form of explaining that showing her naked self to another little girl was normal childhood exploration and it didn't make her a bad girl. Within a minute Amelia had finished the intervention. She had released Violet's guilt and shame: *"Mm hmm. She is okay now. She turned younger, about seventeen or eighteen and she is naked. Other Parts are bringing her clothes and welcoming her to the group. She feels clean."*

Amelia expressed surprise to find that a Part of her had carried guilty and shameful feelings about her body. It wasn't how she lived her life and not how she related or expected to relate to her children. She was unaware of feeling guilt or shame with respect to her adult sexuality. Nevertheless, as all of our work with Violet illustrates, the Part's memories and beliefs (and those of the Grandmother Introject) made a powerful but unconscious impact on Amelia's emotional life. Those buried memories had significantly contributed to negative emotions at important moments during her menstrual cycle— at ovulation, premenstrually and menstrually.

In our next session we planned to seek out the Part that continued to be angry during and before Amelia's period.

SUMMARY OF PARTS

Violet. In this chapter Violet healed memories of loneliness and body and sexual shame. Following her healing she showed herself as a late adolescent of seventeen or eighteen.

Gypsy, Angel, Big Twin, Little Twin, Love. These Parts were present as internal bystanders and observers. They helped Amelia find the Grandmother Introject that had blocked Violet from healing.

Grandmother Introject. This Part was another introject created while Amelia lived with her grandmother. When unmasked the introject transformed into an eight-year-old child, needing only permission to play with other kids.

Chapter 18
The Last Angry Part

We met again a week later on Day 23 of Amelia's cycle, five days before she expected her period. We were now at the end of February, 18 months after beginning therapy. Amelia was experiencing mild PMS symptoms: bloating, acne, light headache, and mild fatigue. All of these were physiological symptoms rather than emotional ones. Emotionally, the only thing Amelia noticed was some impatience with her children. So far, things looked good, but there were still five more days of suspense before we would know if she was free of more serious symptoms.

FINDING BIG BERTHA

We had planned to seek out what we hoped was the last remaining angry Part who regularly presented herself during Amelia's PMS or her period. Unfortunately, because she couldn't muster any irritation or anger in her life at the moment, Amelia couldn't easily find the angry one. I suggested that Amelia consult again with the group of Parts that had observed and helped us in our previous work. She found them easily. They were the Twins, Gypsy, Angel, Love, and Violet. She asked them for help in locating the angry one.

Amelia then remembered that there had once been a Part near The Witch in her hammock that we hadn't returned to. She could visualize her: *"She does not look like me. She is in her early twenties. She seems disoriented, lost. Her clothes are mismatched, like she doesn't know what goes with what. Her hair is crazy—not washed or combed."*

Twenty-Something

She wasn't the angry Part we sought, but we took the time to try to get acquainted anyway. When Amelia asked questions of her, she learned that the Part claimed to know her, but didn't know who she herself was. She then corrected herself to say she didn't really know Amelia either, but *"had seen her around."*

She didn't know Amelia's husband, mother, grandmother, or children. Nor did she know her own age. She didn't know any of the Parts who had helped to bring her out. She knew The Witch and also noticed that The Witch wasn't around anymore. She didn't know that The Witch had transformed into Angel. She indicated that she was unsure of her earliest memory, and in fact she said she didn't have any memories at all. When Amelia tried to do a wind intervention for her **confusion**, no memories were triggered. The only change that Amelia noticed was that the Part's hair was now combed. She continued to feel lost and confused.

There seemed to be nothing we could do with this young adult Part. She appears again in our narrative three sessions later, when she takes a more important role. I began to call her *Twenty-Something* at that time.

Did Twenty-Something Have a Purpose?

Because functioning Parts always appear as the result of a person's life experiences, and therefore always have memories—and she claimed no memories—I suspected this Part was merely a pawn of the angry one we were searching for—sent out because the angry one didn't want to talk to us. Still, we made one more try to learn more about her history by asking her to focus on her feeling of **being lost** as Amelia brought the wind to her. Immediately, Amelia said, *"It is hard; something is blocking her."* With the help of her group of healthy Parts, Amelia located the blocking Part. Disappointingly, it was *"a man with white hair and a white beard, wearing a hospital gown and acting like he has Alzheimer's. He is confused and does not know where he is."*

Rather than attempt to interview the confused old-man Part as Amelia did with Twenty-Something, I suggested we cut through the procedure and bring the two confused Parts together and ask them for their boss. (I didn't know if they had a boss, but the question had worked with other patients to bring out a hidden manager.) Amelia described their response: *"They both got scared and said they do not know where she is."* I thought I'd made a good guess in viewing them as momentary creations of the angry manager. We would later realize that my guess was wrong, but at the time I thought they were just a screen to hide the angry Part.

Big Bertha Shows Herself

Amelia called upon her group of helpful Parts once more, and asked them to bridge from the two Parts' fear to its source (their "boss"). This time Amelia could visualize the angry one we had been seeking: *"She is a large, obese woman, forty or fifty. She could be a prison guard. She is wearing a uniform, kind of green, like a military uniform."* Initially she claimed not to know Amelia. She didn't have a name but said we could call her *tough lady* because she was tough when it was hard to be tough. When I jokingly said she might want to be called *Hercules,* she said she liked that name but didn't want a man's name. She agreed that *Big Bertha* was a good name for her. In her mind, Big Bertha was the female equivalent of the powerful Hercules of Greek mythology.

Big Bertha

She was emphatic in her belief that she wasn't a Part of Amelia. I used the same exercise I had used earlier—of showing the Part that she could only observe the outside world through Amelia's eyes and therefore must also be Amelia: *"Of course!"* said Big Bertha, when I asked if she could see me waving my hand when Amelia looked at me. And she acknowledged that she couldn't see my hand when Amelia's eyes were closed. But she refused to admit that she was a Part of Amelia. Finally, after three repetitions of this proof, Big Bertha snapped at Amelia: *"Enough game playing! So what! I'm still gonna do what I want!"*

Big Bertha's Job

Further interviewing brought Big Bertha to acknowledge that she knew what a period was: *"She knows because that is why she has to work so hard to keep everybody in check—by making orders, by telling people what to do—people in my family, like Michael especially. She tries to make me survive by going to work and taking care of the home stuff. She does not like my mother or Michael. And she does not like my children either. They are a pain in the ass! She does not know any other Parts, just the two confused ones. She likes to scare them. She has them make me confused and tired so I will stop irritating her... Yes, she yells at Michael. She thinks he is a child and has to be told what to do all the time... Yes, she remembers the postpartum depression after my last child. She says Michael does not do what he is supposed to do—take care of the car, do stuff in the house. She has to remind him what to do because otherwise he does not do anything. He is like a child."*

Big Bertha's earliest memories dated to the age of nine or ten: *"Having to do things for other people when they are not capable of doing their jobs. Like when I had to do things for my dad when he was drunk, guiding him upstairs or to the bathroom when he was too drunk to go on his own. Maybe pulling off his shoes so he could get into bed. Having to do things for herself when she was not old enough. Like ironing my best dress by myself or taking care of her little sister when she was just a child herself. I had to do it and be tough about it; no whining. She despises my dad a lot for times he was too drunk to take care of himself. She was a child and she had to take care of* him *when* he *should have been taking care of* her."

As we closed the session, Amelia and I talked about our hopes that Big Bertha would be the last of the angry Parts we had to heal. We hoped the healing would tame her anger with Michael. It seemed that Big Bertha was triggered mostly *during* Amelia's period rather than before it. We expected that we would clarify this as we neutralized Big Bertha's "being-tough" memories.

POSITIVE DAYS

We met again on Day 2 of Amelia's cycle. During these first two days of her period, Amelia was just a bit tired and felt none of her usual menstrual symptoms. She had no bloating, no cramping and no acne. Further, on Days 27 and 28, the last two days before her period, she had no negative symptoms at all, neither emotional nor physical.

Interestingly, from Day 24, the day after our previous session, through Day 26, she felt a host of symptoms that she at first thought of as PMS. She felt *fatigue, irritability, tearful, and snappy with Michael*. But then she went to a nearby Quick Care and found she had a urinary tract infection. Once the antibiotics had taken effect she was fine for the last two premenstrual days. It was a good reminder for us to avoid over-interpreting symptoms as PMS.

Getting the Job Offer

We would soon talk about healing Big Bertha's painful experiences, but Amelia first had good news to share. They had been offered and accepted the international position for which Michael had interviewed. They didn't yet have an opening for Amelia but promised one in the future. Amelia was all smiles as she talked about how much they had to do to get ready for the move. It was now early March and they were to be at their destination by the middle of July.

Michael would be an assistant principal with a salary that was close to what he currently made. However, all of their housing and school expenses would be paid, and they would pay no income taxes. The position was ideal. They both loved to travel and experience new cultures and languages. Amelia wouldn't initially work and would get a break from pursuing her own professional career. Just caring for the children and taking care of other household duties would be plenty for her. She had never had a chance to try out full-time housewife work and looked forward to it. The timing was also good for our psychotherapy. We both felt we were very close to completing the work.

HEALING BIG BERTHA

We returned to Big Bertha. She was still upset by the memories of having to take care of her father's and others' chores when she was the one who needed care. For some reason—perhaps just because we had listened to her—those experiences had spontaneously reduced in intensity to a SUD level of 7 from their previous 9 or 10 in the previous week.

Big Bertha talked about taking care of her drunken father—helping him up the stairs, guiding him to the bathroom, taking off his shoes so he could get into bed: *"No, she did not like it but it was better than nothing at all. She liked helping her dad because it was a way of being close to him. She wishes he would be close to her at other times. He would say, 'I love you,' when he was drunk. That was when he was emotionally available."*

Amelia 14 Appears

But those experiences also made her sad and frustrated. Amelia guided Big Bertha in a wind intervention to heal her **sadness**. It took ninety seconds to complete it. Then, surprised, Amelia said, *"She changed! She looks like me now, younger. She feels like she is fourteen, and she is wearing a white dress.*

She does not want the name Big Bertha. *She is kind of confused. She does not recognize herself. I cannot focus her image well. She is restless, looking around... Yes, she is the one who took care of my dad when he was drunk... No, she is not sad about acting as a responsible child—Now I see Big Bertha again! She did not know the fourteen-year-old was inside of her!"*

Parenthetically, when the fourteen-year-old temporarily replaced Big Bertha during the intervention, we saw clearly that Parts have separate identities and have their own sense of how they should be known or perceived. The fourteen-year-old said she didn't like the Big Bertha name, although Big Bertha still thought it was fine. The fourteen-year-old was a skinny teenager and found it uncomfortable to be labeled as a heavyset grown-up.

What seems to have happened during the replacement, is just one of those interesting surprises that go with working with the world of inner Parts. Amelia 14 seems to be a subpart of Big Bertha, much like the many subparts of The Witch—all of them Stuck-in-Time Parts—who we had met in healing her. Unlike the case with The Witch, where we actively sought out the Stuck-in-Time Parts who had actually experienced the memories upon which we worked, I didn't originally try to work with Big Bertha's Stuck-in-Time Parts. Instead, we tried to do the healing by working just with Big Bertha. But Amelia 14 was too substantial for indirect healing through Big Bertha. She broke through and presented herself during Big Bertha's processing. Now we could work with the fourteen-year-old subpart directly.

Faking Being Tough

Amelia 14's next painful memory—it was also Big Bertha's memory—was of being tough during the divorce. Dealing with the divorce was disturbing for her at a level 6: *"Everybody was saying what a good job she was doing in coping with it. So she had to be tough."* Amelia kept Amelia 14 and Big Bertha together while bringing the wind to blow away the **distress** of their parents' divorce. After thirty seconds, Amelia shared that lots of memories were popping up during the processing: *"Memories of being around family and they were saying how tough and mature I was. I did not know what I was doing well but I wanted them to keep saying it. I had to continue to be strong and acting like nothing bothered me. I did not show it because I had to be strong and well put-together. So when I got bad grades people did not know it had anything to do with the divorce. I had to be strong when my mom cried and when she had her miscarriage, strong for her and my little sister. And I had to be strong when my dad disappointed me by not coming to pick me up when he said he would after the divorce."*

When I checked with Amelia regarding how the two Parts felt now about those experiences, she said they were still upset *"a little bit."* That was because of *"the fact that those people did not take the time to really ask how she was doing. They just told her how well she was doing. She did not know what she was doing well but tried to keep on doing it. She felt lonely in that process."* Amelia easily neutralized the remnant of **lonely** feeling with a short blast of wind.

Big Bertha in College

Big Bertha's next disturbing memory dated to her first year of college. It disturbed her only to a SUD level of 4: *"She did not fit in with the others at first. They were middle class and wealthy students. At first it was difficult to handle those kids who made fun of her clothes and were even kind of bullying. She was **intimidated**. Eventually she made friends and it got better.*

"Big Bertha's job was to be tough and pretend she did not care about not having clothes or not going to eat with others because she had no money. They were sophisticated girls who

talked about boys and other stuff she knew nothing *about— college-like things. But they said she was too young for them. She was more like a high school girl. I stayed with those girls and took it until I made other friends later. They were eighteen and nineteen and I was just sixteen because I skipped a grade.*

"One time a teacher saw what they were doing and stood up for me and told those girls that when I finished college I would be younger than they are now. I felt good that he stood up for me that first semester." Amelia neutralized Big Bertha's **intimidation** in her first semester of college with thirty seconds of wind.

As we ended the session and planned for additional work with Big Bertha, Amelia said, *"I did not remember that Part of college until now, that first semester."* This is a good illustration of the function of subpersonalities in dissociating painful memories outside of consciousness. Dissociating memories permits the physical person to move forward in her life without a conscious awareness of her emotional baggage.

BEING IN A CALMER PLACE

Our next two sessions were pleasant. At the first of those meetings, Amelia was in Day 9 of her cycle—always a good time for her. She was in the midst of planning for the family's new life overseas, taking care of business and personal taxes, car repairs, helping her patients find therapists for continuing work after her departure, and more. Much of our discussion dealt with which of my interns were the best fits for continuing therapy with her patients in the future; i.e., best fits in the sense that they would be with therapists who understood working with inner Parts.

Amelia acknowledged that she had screamed at Michael on one occasion—after she had spent *"ten consecutive hours"* doing their taxes and he had failed to supply her with the information she needed to complete the work. But unlike previous blowups, their breech of peace was short-lived: *"It was soon over and we talked later in the day. All was calm."* Perhaps we too might be forgiven if we do taxes for ten hours but don't get the promised support from our spouses.

Amelia was especially pleased with her relationship with Noelle. Since our work with Big Twin and Little Twin, she and Noelle had been doing well: *"I am doing great with my daughter. We are closer. Now I get equally irritable with both of my children. We are rebuilding our relationship. I invite her to sit with me. Before, she did not look for opportunities to be with me and now she does. I was not aware of that before."*

We met again on Day 16 of Amelia's cycle, a day when she would usually be experiencing the PMS that came with her ovulation. This time she wasn't even aware of ovulating. She was surprised to realize that she had made no notes of negative emotions over the last three days. Previously, PMS symptoms at this time of her cycle were typically worse than the symptoms directly premenstrual.

As Amelia described her relative calm, I felt optimistic about being able to say we had healed her PMS and PMDD. While it was too early to know for sure, I looked forward to Amelia's reports for her premenstrual Days 23 through 28. I felt myself smiling inside. And I wondered what emotions she would find during her period, and would Big Bertha show up? My optimism should have been more restrained because we ran into new problems in our next session.

Amelia's Plans

The remainder of our current session went well and was primarily a summary of positive changes in Amelia's life. She reiterated that life with daughter Noelle was good. And her relationship with Michael was solid. He had made changes too: *"He knows now that if I get frustrated it is not only about him. It is just about the stress I am feeling, like doing taxes. He is better about not reacting to me. He might say, 'Oh boy, you are really hormonal today,' and that makes me aware of it and I can check myself. I am not depressed anymore, even during hormonal changes. I have not been depressed since we healed The Witch.*

"I made the decision to do surgery so there will be no more kids. I am almost thirty-seven and it would be really difficult to have a baby at the beginning in a new country. I have not felt any problems from the Part who wanted another child. I think it was Big Twin and Little Twin who wanted that, because they felt so guilty about Noelle. So they wanted to do it again and do it better.

"It is so peaceful now not to think there is something wrong with me. I never felt before that there was not anything wrong with me. It is a very serene type of emotion I have now. This therapy has changed my life so much for the better. I would not be going now to another country without this work. I would be going back to Costa Rica, divorced. It is so nice to be free of The Witch. My depression—I cannot remember when I did not feel some depression.

"In Costa Rica, my first attraction to Michael was because he had traveled so much—Europe, England—and he liked to visit the indigenous cultures of my country and try out their foods. He was always open to traveling to other cultures. Plus, I was always attracted to smart men. Since we got together we always talked about going to work in other countries, other cultures. We were talking this week about how this was our dream from the beginning."

If everything continued in the way it was now, we would have a resounding success. Amelia's marriage, her therapy for PMS and PMDD, their plans for the future were all in a very good place. Our next two sessions would be crucial for our final assessment. We would check Amelia's PMS symptoms and also look for Big Bertha to assess whether she needed more work.

SUMMARY OF PARTS

Big Bertha. She's an angry Part who drives herself and others to keep going and get things done, especially during Amelia's period.

Twenty-Something. She's a confused Part without apparent purpose and without recall of any of her life.

Amelia 14. She's a Stuck-in-Time subpart of Big Bertha. She took care of her father when he was drunk but still married to her mother, and she pretended to be tough when her parents divorced and her father distanced himself from her.

Chapter 19
Trouble with Big Bertha

We had hoped to continue patting ourselves on the back. Instead, we were slapped in the face. When I asked Amelia how she was doing, she looked down at her feet, frowned, and said, *"Not so good."* It was Day 23 of her cycle and her PMS/PMDD hormones were dominant. Big Bertha was out with a vengeance.

BIG BERTHA'S INFLUENCE

"Yesterday I was craving sugar all day and in the evening I was tired. I got very angry with Michael about things I had to remind him to do—things he had to do for his job, like paperwork. Bertha thinks she has to tell people what they should do. Why should I have to remind him when it is his job!

"Afterwards we were laughing and joking. He said, 'Boy! You are really hormonal tonight.' I said, 'Yes, Bertha really came out.' He said, 'Who is Bertha?' and I explained she is the one who has to tell people what they need to do. He said, 'Oh yes! I have known her for many years.' I laughed about it too, but I was still upset because he does not get it. It took him only a half-hour to get the paperwork done. But I have to get angry to get him to do things. Otherwise he does not do them. Even my mother noticed this about him."

Amelia Heals Big Bertha

"I was still upset when I went to bed and I tried to do a couple of interventions with Bertha. She showed me all these images of my dad not being there for me, and him playing soccer or drinking rather than being there for me. She is angry about having to take care of adult things rather than just being the child. Why cannot he take care of her?

"She threw the **pain** *of the memories into the fire. She kept doing it and eventually she got tired and felt sorrow and not anger and she kept throwing* **sorrow** *into the fire. And then she threw her Big Bertha costume into the fire and became an eight-year-old.*

"There was another Part standing around, the confused Twenty-Something Part from before, when you thought she was just a distraction. And the eight-year-old was bawling and crying, and one of the Twins came over, the one who was guilty about my daughter, and Love [who embodied maternal attachment] *came to help too. That is when the angry one, the confused one* [Twenty-Something], *came forward. She seemed to be angry at the pain of the eight-year-old.*

"Little Twin and Love put the eight-year-old on a couch to sleep after she became too weak to do more work. It took maybe twenty minutes to do the neutralizing. Then I was too exhausted to continue. By then it was midnight."

STRESSING AT EIGHT YEARS OLD

Being eight years old was difficult for Amelia. Much earlier in Amelia's story (Chapter 5) we saw that the child beneath a Father Introject costume was also eight years old. She carried the pain of missed good times—because of her father's absence or his quarrels with her mother. In Chapter 17 we discovered that the child Part wearing the Grandmother Introject costume was also eight; she played a different role. Her job was to handle all the rules she had to follow to please her grandmother and other adults. The next eight-year-old, who wore the Big Bertha costume, had the job of driving Amelia (and sometimes others) to do the responsible adult things that needed doing when no one else was stepping up.

Eight years old was the age when Amelia's parents' marital difficulties overflowed into the lives of her grandparents and other relatives. Her grandparents, her uncles, and her aunts became publicly involved in their quarrels. Actually, their fights occurred as early as age seven, but age eight was the time when their quarrels became so disruptive that the extended family felt called upon to intervene. One of Amelia's memories places her head-banging episodes at age eight (although another placed her at age nine). At age eight—Amelia's fourth grade because she had skipped a grade—she shared with her teacher the distress she felt over her parents' screaming fights. The teacher called a meeting with her parents, causing Amelia to fear possible punishment for revealing her parents' problems.

It isn't surprising that this age spawned the creation of many new Parts. Parts form when there's a need for them, and Amelia needed help in coping with multiple sources of anxiety and stress. Soon we would discover yet more Parts created when Amelia was eight.

The internal work that Amelia had accomplished alone with Big Bertha was exceptional. She was able to take what she learned in therapy with me and do her own therapy outside of my office. Few patients are brave enough to attempt their own interventions, but the few who do are generally successful. She had accomplished a major internal change in helping the militaristic and demanding Big Bertha give up that role and just be the distressed child who needed help. It had become clear in our work with Big Bertha that she had taken on the major adult responsibilities of managing others when she was young. Now we learned that she was only eight, trying to do an adult's job.

THE TWENTY-SOMETHING PART

Twenty-Something

The Twenty-Something angry one had originally appeared as a confused, lost, poorly dressed woman with messy hair, who seemed to me to be a pawn of either The Witch or another manager. I thought that she and another Part—a white-haired old man in a hospital gown—were just temporary creations, and likely to be of no further consequence. I was wrong. We had found Big Bertha by asking to see the two confused Parts' boss. Now Twenty-Something reappeared and seemed important, having taken the mantle of PMS anger from The Witch and Big Bertha. We would need to do more work with her. The other confused Part, who we would eventually call *Old Man*, dropped below my awareness at this point, but we would see him again in the final stage of therapy.

We were approaching the end of our session but I hoped we could still do deep healing before Amelia left to see her own patients. I asked her to return to the Big-Bertha eight-year-old and ask about her earliest memories. The memories were unsurprisingly those of *"her dad not being there for her, not putting her first."* The memories were troubling to the child at a level 9 on the SUD scale. She felt very sad. Amelia asked her to focus on her **sadness** as a great wind broke it up and blew it away:

"She lets the wind get some of it off of her but it is hard getting it all. I think there is a blocker—It is the angry one. She does not want to give her permission to heal the eight-year-old. She wants her to remember not to trust men. She will get hurt again. They cannot be relied upon. They always come short of what they are supposed to do—so many man haters I have! She is angry with my father and my grandfather. He was how my dad learned to be irresponsible. But my grandfather was a very sweet man, never angry, but very irresponsible. A lot of drinking, a lot of women."

I asked Amelia to speak to angry Twenty-Something and explain that healing the eight-year-old wouldn't make her vulnerable, but just the opposite. Healing would mean that she would actually hurt less when a man again let her down. And she would keep all of the knowledge that came from the memories: *"She says okay."* Within a few seconds of beginning a wind intervention, Amelia said, *"She is fine now. She is going off with Little Twin. But now Twenty-Something is crying. It is somehow like she is a protector of the eight-year-old. Her anger is like a fear kind of anger. Now she feels alone and abandoned by the eight-year-old because she went off with Little Twin."*

More drama! This was an unusual response. Twenty-Something's relationship with the eight-year-old was more complex than at first appeared. The sense of abandonment was a surprise, but it showed us that we had more work to do with these Parts. We would soon discover the underlying dynamics, but we were at the end of the session and would have to await our next meeting. Amelia visualized placing Twenty-Something in a Sleeping Beauty Bed until then. Before our next meeting, unfortunately, Amelia was overcome with allergies and a throat infection. She had to cancel.

Twenty-Something's Influence

We met again two weeks later. It was Day 10 of Amelia's cycle, usually a calm and peaceful time. However, Amelia had been noticeably irritable for the last three days. The source was easy to locate. It had nothing to do with her cycle and everything to do with our unfinished processing: *"I think I have been irritable since our last session. That Part we were working with is full of many emotions. She is the one making me irritable... Yes, she is still in the Sleeping Beauty Bed. She feels abandoned by the eight-year-old who went off with the other Parts. She did not know the eight-year-old was under Bertha's costume, but she knew she was somewhere nearby. She does not know why she is connected to that eight-year-old but she was always looking for her. There was a connection there between them."*

The irritability was just one of the emotions Twenty-Something amplified through Amelia. She was also quite anxious because of her separation from the eight-year-old. She had defeated the purpose of the Sleeping Beauty Bed, which was to keep her calm while *not* amplifying her emotions through Amelia.

Twenty-Something and the Eight-Year-Old

During the remainder of the session, Amelia and I worked on understanding the dynamics between Twenty-Something and the eight-year-old: *"They connected around the time when my dad did not show up at her events, like First Communion or school performances. I think he was more interested in his career than in me. I remember being aware of his drinking and seeing him drunk. But I liked that because that was when he was nice to me.*

"Bertha became the one who had to handle things. [Thus she presented with a self-image of a militaristic, disciplined, get-things-done attitude.] *Bertha was the take-action Part. The other one* [Twenty-Something] *was the thinking Part who watched and tried to act like an adult by acting like she was not confused."*

But Twenty-Something *was* confused. That was evident in the self-image she presented when we first encountered her, when I thought she was just Big Bertha's pawn and of little importance. It became clear that, as an eight-year-old, Amelia's mind created both of these two distinct but connected Parts to help her deal with the stress in her life. Both initially presented themselves as adults and both would eventually reveal themselves to be about eight years old.

One of them became the task-oriented Big Bertha and the other became the reservoir for the confusion and uncertainty of the time. The source of the confusion became clearer when Amelia asked Twenty-Something for her earliest disturbing memory, a memory we had visited recently.

Earliest Memories

"When I was in the fourth grade [at eight years old], *I started to notice my parents were having problems and I got scared. I told my teacher about them and she called them for a private conference. I was very afraid of what would happen to*

me but they never said anything. They didn't ever tell me any-
thing about it. I was very confused about it. Was I going to
get punished? Were they going to talk to me? But they never
said anything after that and I never said anything.

"*I just observed them and I felt confused. They never ex-*
plained anything about what was happening to me. Like
what was it like for me to hear them fighting or to observe all
the things like at Christmas when they had a big fight and all
the family and my grandmother and uncles and aunts and
everybody got involved. I did not know if my dad had another
woman or what was going to happen. So I just learned to ob-
serve and keep quiet with my confusion.

"*One Christmas he came with presents for all my cousins,*
but when he came to me he said, 'Oh, you are too old for pre-
sents.' I was only thirteen. So I had to pretend it did not both-
er me and pretend I was an adult when all my cousins were
there getting presents."

Rushing to Heal

We were almost out of time and hadn't yet done any deep work
in the session. I rushed to guide Amelia in healing the **confu-**
sion and **fear** that followed when her teacher called a conference with her parents. Amelia began a wind intervention but
shortly said: "*It is hard. Nothing is happening with Twenty-*
Something's feelings."

Because this Part had felt abandoned by the eight-year-old
when she went off with other Parts, I thought it might help just
to bring her back. Amelia did so. Twenty-Something felt "*a lit-*
tle better." With no time left, I suggested Amelia urge the Part
to place her remaining negative emotion into a container for
storage until our next visit. Twenty-Something filled the container by vomiting into it. The action again illustrated a subpersonality's partial autonomy. Amelia hadn't instructed her to
use vomit to put away her emotion.

HEALING TWENTY-SOMETHING

Our next meeting, took place on Day 17 of Amelia's cycle, a time that had recently been peaceful, but prior to therapy was usually difficult. Now there was trouble again: *"That Part is driving me crazy. It was not a good week. I am explosive again with Noelle. Very irritable. Those feelings like, 'I am a bad mother,' are back again. I cannot relax and just enjoy life. On Tuesday I went to work, and then I cancelled my clients on Wednesday because my son was sick at home. I did not enjoy work, which is unusual. I usually enjoy doing my work with clients. On Saturday and Sunday* [Days 12 and 13], *I was impatient, irritable, feeling an overall drag. On Day 14, I just felt physically tired."*

In this case, Amelia's emotional upheaval, while exacerbated by ovulation, also preceded ovulation. Her emotional volatility was partly because of Twenty-Something's continued distress. This Part had deeper issues than we had known. Amelia returned to the internal Sleeping Beauty Bed where she had left Twenty-Something. The eight-year-old was with her. So were all the other Parts that we had previously healed. They seemed to be fixtures now in the forefront of Amelia's mind.

Memories from Five

Amelia said of the problem Part: *"She is on edge. Something is not right."* She asked Twenty-Something to examine herself and tell us what was wrong: *"She thinks she is broken. She thinks something was broken when she was born."* I wondered if she meant when she first appeared in Amelia's life—I thought that might have been at eight—or when Amelia was born. But I was wrong to think her first appearance was at eight, because Amelia soon reported that the Part remembered even earlier events.

Her earliest memories dated to about age five when she (as Amelia) was yelled at often by different adults: her mother, grandmother, uncles, and aunts. She remembered *"always be-ing corrected; how to eat properly; how to sit properly; how to be self-contained; not allowed free range; how to play with toys and Crayons; not to make messes; color between the lines—Otherwise she would be corrected. My guilt is I do the same things to Noelle."*

The age of five was also the age when Amelia lost the daily nurturing of her mother, the time when she was forced to live with her grandmother during the week so that her mother could return to work. Losing her mother for most of every week had a profound effect on her feelings for her mother. Not until she was an adult would Amelia allow herself to feel comfortable with her mother's physical touch.

Amelia began with a wind intervention to heal the **frustration** of learning and obeying the adult rules. But she could make no progress: *"Little Twin—the twin with the guilt—is blocking her. She is hesitant. She wants me to remember so I do not forget and do these things with my daughter."* This was a complaint similar to those from other blockers we had met. As with them, Amelia explained that the factual memories would be retained and that only the painful emotions would be carried away. Little Twin was almost ready to relent and permit the healing, but she first had one other angry complaint: *"These Parts* [i.e., Twenty-Something and the five-year-old] *are making her make mistakes with Noelle again because it makes her irritable and not enough patience."* After Amelia explained that this result was precisely why Little Twin shouldn't block the healing, only forty-five seconds of wind was necessary until Amelia could say, *"Okay, she* [the five-year-old] *is healed now."*

Memories from School

Twenty-Something's next disturbing set of memories were of *"being passed over in many things at school. Either because I was afraid or because of the teachers. One time I practiced a lot with a flute and I wanted to be picked to play in a concert in front of the school. The teacher said I was not good enough but did not tell me what I did wrong. I was so disappointed. The teacher told me as consolation I could stand in front of others and hold the music so they could read the notes. I got angry and threw my flute on the floor and I was punished and could not go to the concert. I was in fifth grade.*

"*By sixth grade, I stopped trying to get awards or parts in performances. After the fifth grade, I was invited to try out for the swimming team because I was a good swimmer out-side the school. But I did not try out because I was so **afraid of failing**.*" With wind interventions, it took just twenty seconds and thirty seconds respectively to neutralize the flute and swimming-team memories.

Then, because I didn't think we needed every detail of her school-age disappointments, I suggested that Twenty-Something wrap all of her remaining memories of this type into a single package and heal them all at once. Amelia did that in less than two minutes.

After those two minutes, Amelia added, "*Twenty-Something is a child now, like a twin of the other eight-year-old. She is very tired.*" As had happened with so many problem Parts during the therapy, Twenty-Something had transformed into a more pleasant image through her healing. Like Big Bertha before her, Twenty-Something transformed into an eight-year-old child Part. The connection between them was now clear. They had developed at the same time in Amelia's life, and perhaps might be understood as branches of the same tree. Each branch had different functions.

Gypsy Helped Out

I had noticed that Amelia had a small smile on her face much of the time as she did the work with Twenty-Something. When I asked about this she said, "*Something funny was happening all along. It was Gypsy. She was using a vacuum cleaner to vacuum out the negative emotions because it was hard to clean them out. At the same time, she was using it on Little Twin, the one with* **guilt** *about my daughter. Because when we were working on my memories, Little Twin was feeling guilt because what happened to me reminds her of what I was doing with Noelle."*

We had previously seen that subpersonalities sometimes acted spontaneously without direction from Amelia during the healing. Gypsy's use of the vacuum cleaner was one of those spontaneous actions by an internal Part.

CHECKING OUR PROGRESS

We had made significant progress with Amelia's issues since we began therapy. Early on we had healed her postpartum depression. Her PMS/PMDD improved, worsened, and improved again. Overall there was good progress. We both thought that we might heal the premenstrual problems completely. We had only a little more work to do to be sure. And Amelia was now emphatic that her marriage was a good one. She looked forward to a long life with Michael.

Interestingly, Amelia's improvement seemed to have left an emotional vacuum in the way she and Michael interacted. Michael had begun to display the same sort of negative self-talk that had dominated Amelia for so long: *"Michael was having a hard time all the time since I saw you last time, and I told him he should be working with you every week. For the first time, he was the one who said, 'You are right. I am a failure and always have been.' And for the first time, he talked about leaving. It was always me who did that before. He said he should go to his new job alone and I should stay with the kids. 'I am a failure and I do not give you the kind of life I should.'"*

This was just a temporary aberration. After my session with him the following week he was centered again. That was fortunate, because the family was preparing to leave the country in the approaching summer and there wasn't enough time to do the more elaborate program with him that I had done with Amelia.

Our next session would have fallen on Amelia's Day 1, the first day of her period. But she cancelled because of two sick kids at home. Still, she texted me that she had no PMS symptoms in the days immediately before her period. Excellent news!

Near-Tragedy Averted

Unfortunately, Amelia had to cancel five of our next six appointments. Noelle had contracted a serious staph infection that ultimately led to surgery and a five-day stay in the hospital. It was the first of June, six weeks later, before we could continue with Amelia's therapy. There was now a real sense of urgency for both of us. She would be leaving for her life in a new country in July, and traveling to another state for pre-employment family training at the end of June.

Healing Noelle's Trauma

When we met again, we discussed the health trauma Noelle had experienced, and made plans to meet again the next day for me to work with Noelle. She had been mildly traumatized by the hospital experience—by the absence of the familiar comfort of home—but more seriously traumatized by the open wound (kept open until they were sure the infection was cured).

With a little girl's modesty, Noelle didn't want me to see her wound. It was low in her side near her hip. But she was more concerned with what she believed would be an ugly scar there when the wound healed. Amelia explained, *"She is afraid that she will never be normal again. Her scar will disfigure her forever, and people will think she is ugly."* These issues, plus the coming departure of the family for a new country, together with the anticipated loss of things to be left behind—

including school friends and the family dog—left her in a state of extreme **anxiety**. Nightmares punctuated her sleep.

I've found that children respond much more quickly than do adults to trauma work, probably because they have so few memories in their young lives. She responded quickly and completely to our healing interventions. I worked with her twice—with Amelia's assistance—and she was soon a happy six-year-old again.

Minimal PMS

When Amelia and I finally met again it was the week after her ovulation. She felt no symptoms. She and Michael hadn't fought, and she was only mildly irritated when she couldn't hold his attention. She accepted that this would happen when she lived with an ADD husband. He was busy on his cell phone checking what his students were saying about him on the eve of departure. Amelia told him that *"his teenager Part needed to take a break."*

Amelia was unable to conclude much from her PMS notes over the last six weeks: *"I could not tell what was due to the crisis with Noelle or what was PMS. Before my last period, I had just one day of feeling tired and sad, but I was not depressed."* Overall then, our work seemed to have been successful. Minimal days of distress; no divorce; going to work except when she had to care for her daughter. Because she could live life normally, without disruption by her remaining mild PMS symptoms, she no longer fit the diagnosis of PMDD.

We had no time to connect with the work we were doing before Noelle's health problems appeared. But Amelia said that the two eight-year-olds (the previous Big Bertha and Twenty-Something) were still in their Sleeping Beauty Beds: *"Something is keeping them there. I tried to get them to go play but they could not. Little Twin is also in a Sleeping Beauty Bed."*

We planned to return to these Parts and give them our full attention at our next meeting. This was especially important because Amelia and Michael would be training for their new country in just four weeks. That training was in another city. We had little time left to complete our work.

LITTLE TWIN AND NEW MOTHER

We returned to our often-interrupted work with Little Twin, who reported that she was still nervous when she thought of Amelia's difficulties in giving birth to Noelle more than six years ago. Amelia quickly neutralized Little Twin's **nervous feeling** with wind.

She then asked Little Twin if she could visualize Amelia in the memory of having just given birth to Noelle. Yes, she could see the *New Mother* in the hospital bed. She was twenty-nine years old. The Part acknowledged that she was in **physical pain**. Amelia guided her in releasing the pain to the wind: *"Okay, but there is still a little bit. It is not completely gone. Her body is very weak because of the loss of blood."*

Problems in Healing

I thought we could be creative with New Mother, and suggested to Amelia that she visualize herself providing an arm-to-arm transfusion of blood to the Part. It was a bad idea. *"This is weird. The blood is coming out of her. She has holes everywhere."* Rather than relief, the intervention brought a dramatic worsening of the Part's condition. As noted elsewhere, this symbolism tells us that there's likely a blocking Part nearby. Looking around the scene, Amelia's first candidate was an image of Michael: *"He is the same as now but young, just a young face. He is wearing a T-shirt. He seems angry. When I ask why, he does not talk."*

While I couldn't fathom why there would be a husband introject here, his image was the only one visible to Amelia, so we followed the unmasking protocol to reveal the Part beneath the costume. But there was nothing there. Still, Amelia tried the transfusion intervention once more: *"Now the blood is coming out of the wound in my private parts."* In vain we looked for another blocker: *"No, I cannot see anyone."*

Unresolved Memories

We turned to the other possibility that could explain the failure of an intervention: the amplification of negative emotions linked to earlier, unresolved memories. When Amelia asked New Mother about her earliest painful memories, she recalled that: *"She dated three guys who were very rough with her. So aggressive. She feels disgusted and used. It bothers her at a 6 or 7."*

Amelia brought a wind intervention to heal the feelings of **disgust** and **being used**. She worked directly with the twenty-three-year-old who carried New Mother's early memories. The intervention was helpful but Amelia had more to say: *"There were three guys in the same part of the country. My work had transferred me there. They did not ask permission for anything. They just did what they wanted.*

"I was feeling lonely and wanted to be with somebody. They all acted the same—even one who was a friend before. When I consented to sex he was like the others. She feels she put herself in that position by being lonely and obviously longing for companionship or love or a relationship, and they took advantage of that.

"I did not meet Michael for another seven months. These men were a little older, in their early thirties, and I later learned that men in that region have a reputation for being rough and uncaring. She feels stupid for letting it happen three times before she stopped."

Amelia guided the twenty-three-year-old in releasing her **self-anger** and for **feeling stupid**: *"Okay, she let it all go. She is becoming diffuse now. I cannot see her clearly."* This is an unusual response to the healing protocol, but it sometimes happens when a Part has only a few memories from a tightly circumscribed period of time.

We returned then to New Mother. We expected that our work with the twenty-three-year-old would have released most of New Mother's pain. But it had no effect: *"It is weird. As the wind comes to take away her negative emotions, she keeps bleeding and bleeding and bleeding. Those memories are still there for her, at about a level 6, and she just keeps bleeding. I never saw the bleeding when I had Noelle. The nurses took care of that. There was so much blood the nurses were worried and called the doctor back."*

We were at the end of the session and needed to reach temporary closure. Amelia imagined New Mother wrapped up tightly to staunch the bleeding and told her to sleep until we could return. We were both disappointed that we hadn't managed to heal her. There had to be a blocking Part or an amplifying memory that prevented us from healing New Mother. We just hadn't found it. Amelia looked around the crowd of observing Parts that were now always present in our sessions, hoping to find the blocker: *"It is Little Twin. She says New Mother deserves that punishment because of those things she did with those men in the past."* We had found the blocking Part and would work with her soon.

PMS Absence

We were rushing to finish our work. We met on June 1, June 4, and June 9. Amelia was now on Day 24 of her cycle, and symptom-free. In the previous month, she had experienced a 24-day cycle and if the continued stress in her life produced another 24-day cycle, her period ought to begin tonight. Or, if she had her normal 28-day cycle, she should be having PMS symptoms now. In either case, we were looking good.

BLOCKING BY LITTLE TWIN

We returned to the pursuit of that material by locating Little Twin, along with the cast of characters who now always showed up to observe our continued work. Little Twin admitted blocking our work with the images of a bleeding New Mother: *"She says my Parts deserve to suffer for allowing the men to do those things to her."* Her position was that Amelia was weak, not strong like she should be. She should be punished so that she would avoid punishment in the future by being strong.

Because Little Twin refused to permit us to move forward with the healing, we focused our work on her own early memories with the expectation that as we healed them, she would become flexible and eventually lift her blocking force.

Being Submissive

Amelia described Little Twin's disturbing memories as *"having to please people, having to be submissive. She could not speak her mind or she would be punished. She became passive. She never learned to stand up for herself. That put her in harm's way. She did not know how to stand up to those guys."* Little Twin rated this constellation of complaints at a SUD level of 9, for her **sadness** and her **anger**.

Focusing first on the **sadness**, Amelia tried a wind intervention, but soon reported, *"It is not working. She is still afraid to let go. She feels stuck. She has all these negative emotions about herself and knows she was not trained to stand up for herself. So she could not resist. She does not know if she can let go of these things and be different."*

When Amelia asked Little Twin to focus on her **fear** of letting go and tried another wind intervention, the result was the same: *"It is still not working. I think it has something to do with the two Parts who are stuck in bed."* Amelia was talking about the two eight-year-olds who had originally presented as Big Bertha and the confused Twenty-Something. They seemed to be comatose where we had left them. I thought their condition was more likely the result of our problem with Little Twin rather than the cause of it. Consequently, I guided us in continuing the work to heal Little Twin's memories of being passive.

Passive at Grandma's House

We had so far tried to neutralize Little Twin's memories by working directly with her. Now we decided to work with her subparts, the Stuck-in-Time Parts who acted out the remembered events. When asked, Amelia could visualize the passive little girl whose memories were affecting Little Twin. She was at her grandmother's house. She was seven years old, and she knew Amelia was the grownup version of her: *"She knows she has to be perfect and be quiet. She is afraid of being yelled at. She does not want to disappoint her family if she does not do something right. She feels scared and nervous that she will not do it right."* She responded quickly to Amelia's wind intervention and fully neutralized her SUD level of 6 for **scared** and **nervous**.

Hopeful now that this healing would make Little Twin more flexible, we returned to her. Amelia attempted to guide her in releasing her **fear** of being different to the wind: *"The wind is not clearing it up. She is throwing up black, oily stuff into a hole in the floor. She just knows she feels sick and she keeps throwing it up."*

This sort of imagery of painful processing tells us that there is still significant interference to the healing of Little Twin. Because she was herself a blocker in our work with the bleeding New Mother, I chose to look for earlier memories rather than another Part who might be blocking the blocker.

THE TWELVE-YEAR-OLD

Bridging from Little Twin's body sensation of "feeling sick," Amelia asked her to follow the sensation back in time to her earliest still painful memory. What came up first was an image of a Part rather than a memory. We called her the *Twelve-Year-Old*. She was a special kind of Stuck-in-Time Part that wasn't stuck in a particular memory but, instead, held a range of memories in her memory bank.

My guess is that she was probably once co-conscious with an adolescent Amelia, like the current Parts Love, Gypsy, and others were now co-conscious with adult Amelia. Her earliest memories were about her elementary school experiences: *"She had to be good at school, had to be successful. She has lots of memories about similar things. Like sometimes she would have liked to be more outgoing but she was afraid of making a fool of herself. So she carried that anxiety with her."*

Amelia tried to bring wind to heal the Twelve-Year-Old's **anxiety** but she soon found the intervention was having no effect.

A Bully Steals Lunch

There were still earlier memories impacting her anxiety: *"There are various, similar memories. Most of them are unclear, but in the third grade an older girl in the fifth grade would come and take her lunch. So for weeks she didn't eat any lunch. I was afraid to tell anyone until finally she told her grandmother who told her mother, and she went to the school and talked with the principal. Before that she felt stuck and couldn't tell anybody. For weeks or a month, she was constantly afraid of the fifth grader who would take her food. The principal had her identify the girl. She did and they punished her and she did not bother her after that."*

Following this narrative Amelia easily healed the third grader's **fear** with a wind intervention. Then she returned to the previous work with twelve-year-old Amelia.

The Twelve-Year-Old was no longer anxious about making a fool of herself, making clear to us that healing the bully memory was effective for healing later memories as well. It also validated my theory about the source of blocking—that it came from amplification of earlier memories. The Part had still other memories she wanted to heal.

A Friend Dominates Her

"But there is one thing she wants to talk about. She had been afraid from then throughout high school. She took a diminished role. She had a friend. She was not a bad friend; she just took control of their friendship. She decided what they would do together and I just accepted it. And boys would pay attention to her friend first and not her. She felt she was in the shadow of her friend. She changed after a big fight in the eleventh grade, and they were not friends anymore. She felt sad and angry that she let her friend dominate her."

She had felt inhibited from being her own person. The Twelve-Year-Old responded quickly to the imagery of letting the wind take away her **self-anger** and **feeling inhibited**: *"Okay, she did it. She went off to be with her other friend."*

A Side Note

Notice here that we worked with the Twelve-Year-Old to heal connected memories that lasted from third grade, when she was seven, to eleventh grade when she was fifteen. The age for which a Part shows an image of herself doesn't limit her from being present for experiences at later ages. The age she presents is a marker for significant memories, but not just memories limited to that age. Like other aspects of Parts, age of presentation is partially symbolic. It's common for a Part's apparent age to remain unchanged over two or three years of later memories. But it's also common for Parts' images to grow in age as we move to later memories for processing. There's no constant rule Parts follow in presenting images of themselves.

THE CHOIR DIRECTOR

Without prompting, after healing the Twelve-Year-Old, Amelia went on to talk about other memories that troubled Little Twin: *"In college, the choir director humiliated me several times. Apparently, I was not a good enough singer. She would make fun of me in front of my friends. I took it because I liked to sing and I wanted to be a part of the group. She humiliated me for four years."*

College Self

Amelia visualized this *College Self* as nineteen or twenty years old, wearing *"tight beige pants, a tan and green sweater, and long hair. She is sad and angry with the choir director. When I won a singing contest at the university she congratulated me but it was clear that she did not like it that I won. She was not one of the judges that year. Probably I would not have won if she was a judge. She never believed that I was a good singer. I took that punishment for all those years because I wanted to sing and be with my friends. She would do things like give me a solo to do and then take it away a few days later because she did not like how I was doing it. She would give the solo to somebody else."*

Amelia attempted to guide College Self in healing her **humiliation** with another wind intervention, but the Part, with a will of her own, chose a different means: *"She threw up her pain right in the face of the director! That is funny! Now I see the connection between these memories: being around highly critical, toxic people but I chose to stay there because I got some kind of secondary gain. But I never stood up to any of them.* [Laughing] *That's a Part that Michael does not know— the submissive one."*

I added that the theme of the memories was broader than that. All of them involved stronger, dominant persons who held a power position over her, from her grandmother and her uncles and aunts to her teachers, a schoolyard bully, a choir director, and then sexually demanding, dominant males. She had been trained into submissiveness from an early age, but had managed to find a stronger subpersonality within herself by the time she met Michael.

We had journeyed far from bleeding New Mother in order to neutralize earlier memories that were preventing her healing. We had neutralized anxiety and fear from school-age memories and later ones of disrespect and humiliation from college years. We still had to return to unfinished work with New Mother and other Parts in temporary stasis. We would do so in the final chapter of Amelia's narrative.

SUMMARY OF PARTS

Big Bertha/Eight-Year-Old. In this chapter, Amelia heals Big Bertha on her own. She transforms into an eight-year-old girl distressed that she had to take over adult responsibilities.

Twenty-Something/Eight-Year-Old. As with Big Bertha, the healing of Twenty-Something transforms her into an eight-year-old, but a different one. She too is concerned with her childhood hurts, especially those from her father, because of his absence at important events in her life.

Little Twin. She makes an important appearance in this chapter as a blocker in the healing of Twenty-Something, asserting that she and other Parts should suffer for the way they had lived their lives. Getting her permission to heal Twenty-Something and the Stuck-in-Time Parts in her memories required that we heal previously unknown memories carried by Little Twin.

New Mother. This Stuck-in-Time Part was important for the dramatic images she presented of unstoppable bleeding following the birth of Amelia's daughter Noelle. Before we could heal her, we had to heal the early memories of Big Twin.

College Self. She's another Stuck-in-Time Part who carried the pain of disrespect and humiliation she felt from her choir director. She was triggered unconsciously whenever events in the present involved disrespect by a person in authority.

Twelve-Year-Old. This Part carried fears from early school years through late adolescence. She was a Stuck-in-Time Part, but was probably once a conscious player in Amelia's adolescent life.

Chapter 20
Putting It All Together

Amelia had made great strides in overcoming the depression, anger, and fatigue she usually experienced during ovulation and just before her period. She no longer met diagnostic criteria for Premenstrual Dysphoric Disorder (PMDD), the condition that had prevented her from going to work several days a month and that had often threatened her marriage. Nor did she meet criteria for the less severe PMS (Premenstrual Syndrome). If her monthly cycle continued in the same way over time, we could say we had healed both.

We had already healed her postpartum depression, her failure to bond as a mother with Noelle, and the serious breach in her marriage. Despite the crisis of a seriously ill child, the couple were still together and still working to achieve the next step in their wonderful adventure.

It was now the middle of June. Amelia's family would leave in just one week for pre-departure training in the culture and conditions of everyday life in their new country. They would return to Utah briefly before making a farewell trip to Michael's family in Pennsylvania. They would then spend another ten days in Utah making final arrangements before departure for their new home.

A MARATHON SESSION

We had only one weekly-scheduled appointment left. But we both believed that more than that would be required to finish our work. We decided to meet on a Sunday. That session lasted for three hours. At the end of our meeting, Amelia was exhausted. Ordinary talk therapy would have also been tiring, but Parts and Memory Therapy is especially demanding of emotional energy.

For our marathon session, Amelia dressed casually for the first time. She wore a grey, collarless, sports shirt with khaki capris and matching tan sandals. From her shoulder hung a multicolored cloth purse. She came directly from the two-day garage sale they had held to help rid them of everything that wasn't indispensable for their new posting.

Family Harmony

Amelia first talked about the couple's much improved marital relationship: *"Michael is managing his anger much better. He has his moments but it is not the way it was before. He is better, too, at not blowing up when we get in an argument. And he comes back quickly. He still throws back at me critical things from our past but not as much. As a couple, we're closer. We do not have the big blowups we used to have. But I think he resents the time I spend with my mother. It used to be just us but now my mother is here and so he gets less attention from me. He does not say anything but I think he feels abandoned sometimes. I try to be sure I give him his own attention.*

"Noelle is doing great. The only thing she cries about is leaving our dog. She has not talked about the wound at all. She hasn't mentioned anything about the hospital or the surgery or anything about that. No more nightmares. And she has been helping with the garage sale and showing the children the toys we are selling. And she is not angry with her brother the way she was."

Work in Progress

When we reconnected to our work-in-progress, Amelia said it was Day 29 in her cycle and she expected her period to begin at any time. She felt no symptoms of PMS.

We had left Amelia's inner world in an unsettled state. There were now a number of fully functioning, healed Parts who appeared each time Amelia looked inside. Mostly they stayed in the background but they volunteered to help us whenever called upon.

There were also several Parts stuck between unhappy places and full healing. The two eight-year-olds who had previously appeared in the form of Big Bertha and Twenty-Something, lay paralyzed in a Sleeping Beauty Bed. New Mother, who gave birth to Noelle, was still stuck in a hospital bed, wrapped in bandages to staunch her bleeding.

And there was Little Twin, who seemed somehow the key to it all, unhappy, guilty, and sad. We had been working at making her more flexible by healing earlier memories from Amelia's past. My hypothesis was that it was these memories that caused her to block the healing we had tried to do with the bleeding New Mother.

Little Twin and New Mother

We returned to Little Twin: *"She is sitting on a Sleeping Beauty Bed. She still has some sadness but does not feel continually out of control like she was."* She couldn't connect to any other disturbing memories. That seemed positive for the therapy, but the sadness she continued to feel told us that something still wasn't quite right. She gave us permission to finish our healing work with New Mother:

"She is at the hospital, in bed, bundled up like we left her. She feels weak because of all the blood she lost." Amelia began a wind intervention to break up New Mother's feeling of **weakness** into particles of dust and blow them away. Simultaneous-

ly, she suggested to New Mother that the wind also brought healing energy that would multiply her blood supply. After thirty seconds, Amelia opened her eyes to say, *"She actually crawled more into a fetal position. Something is blocking her."*

Old Man

Old Man

I suggested that Amelia ask New Mother to focus on the feeling of being blocked, and try to trace it to its source: *"She thinks it is the eight-year-olds. And do you remember the Old Man Part who was there with Twenty-Something? He is there now, wearing a nursing robe and pajamas like in a nursing home. He is in his eighties. His hair is white but bald on the top of his head. He is a little bit hunchback, and he has a cane.*

He was there all along but I never mentioned him because you thought he was unimportant. He is linked to the two eight-year-olds somehow."

In fact, I did remember the Old Man. He had appeared at the same time as the confused young woman we had called Twenty-Something. Now he showed us that he was indeed important:

"Yes, he knows me. 'Amelia.' ...No, he doesn't know how he is connected to me. But he knows he is connected to the eight-year-olds, but not why. He is connected to the old Big Bertha and misses her because she is not around anymore. She used to take care of him." Amelia explained to the Old Man that he was a Part of her and lived within her: *"He says, 'Okay.'"* When Amelia asked about his earliest painful memory, she relayed his response as: *"He just remembers being alone, but does not remember when. Just a feeling of loneliness."*

Another Eight-Year-Old

Following our usual approach to Parts' emotions that lack attached visual memories, Amelia brought a wind intervention to blow away the **loneliness**, expecting this to trigger visual memories. To our surprise, however, we got an unmasking: *"The wind took away the costume of the Old Man and showed another little girl. She is the third eight-year-old. They look alike. The three of them are connected somehow. She is still sad and lonely."*

Then, by refocusing her wind intervention from the Old Man onto the third eight-year-old, Amelia brought out the memories she had been looking for: *"A lot of pictures of being alone. Playing by herself. Watching TV by herself. Not having a playmate and doing everything on her own. Yes, there were adults around but they were all doing their own stuff. She had nobody to share with in doing kids' stuff. She enjoyed it somewhat because she learned to do stuff on her own, but it contributed to her isolation."*

Loneliness and Isolation

Amelia then directed the wind at the child Part's **feeling of isolation**. After just ten seconds, Amelia said, *"She feels better now but she is worried about the other two eight-year-olds. They look sick and are in the bed."*

Giving her attention now to the girls in the bed, Amelia soon elicited additional memories: *"Being sick many times and not having my mother next to her. It was my grandmother who took care of her. She was well taken care of but my grandmother did not nurture her like my mother would."* Amelia focused her wind upon the two little girls' **sadness** for their mother's absence. Amelia said that the wind was a mixture of wind and light now because she had added light when trying to help New Mother to increase her blood supply. After forty-five seconds of eyes-closed focus, Amelia opened them again to say, *"All right. They feel fine now. They are all together on top of the bed. They want to go play.*

"Little Twin feels better too. She is better with them gone— Oh! I see the association now. I see the connection! Little Twin was feeling guilt from the eight-year-olds when they felt abandoned by my mother, and this made her feel guilt for all she wasn't doing for Noelle as a mother. I think she is still some bothered by the one in the hospital."

HEALING NEW MOTHER

We returned to New Mother, still stuck in the hospital. Following Amelia's observation that the Part was still weak, we moved directly to a new intervention, hoping that all of the related work with other Parts had loosened up the resistance to healing. This time the process went smoothly. Amelia again used her new intervention of wind intertwined with light to conduct the healing. Within fifteen seconds Amelia laughed and said, *"She is levitating from the hospital bed as the wind is cleaning her."* After another minute she added, *"All right!*

She is back in the hospital bed and has Noelle in her arms and she is breastfeeding her. And Michael is there and they are both looking with love at Noelle, and Michael is petting her hair, being tender with her. It is exactly what she would have liked for it to happen from the beginning—instead of being in pain and so weak that she could not hold her."

Amelia had spontaneously created a loving scene to replace the original one for New Mother, who had been stuck in the time of Noelle's birth. It was a harmless fantasy and left us with an easy exit from the complex work we had done to neutralize the original crisis surrounding that birth.

HEALING LITTLE TWIN

We checked then with Little Twin to see how she was responding to our healing of New Mother: *"She is feeling a little sadness that that was not what really happened. It is a little bit of a lie that it did not happen, but she wishes that it had happened too. So she feels some sorrow that it did not really happen."* Amelia immediately brought Little Twin into a wind and light intervention to carry away her **sorrow**. As I watched her conduct the intervention with her eyes closed, I saw her smile and thought the process was going well. But after ninety seconds, she opened her eyes to say, *"It is hard! At first, she was letting it go. But then it came back."*

Baby Parts

Amelia asked Little Twin to follow the force of the push-back of sorrow to its source in earlier memories: *"It is a very deep sorrow. I am feeling it in my chest too. It is a very young child, like two or three years old."* This was a surprise. In nearly two years of therapy we had never seen any Parts younger than five: *"She is crying because she is in pain. She is like a two-year-old, maybe younger. She is feeling alone and lost and she is crying a lot.*

"Little Twin is holding her in her lap but she does not know what to do." I advised that Little Twin should tell the child that she will care for her now and that the child will never be alone again.

Amelia refocused her wind and light on the **sorrow** that emanated from the child. After twenty seconds with her eyes closed, Amelia sighed and opened them again to say, *"The baby fell asleep in her arms."* The healing seemed to be successful.

But then Amelia added, *"I still feel pressure in my chest."* Looking inside again, Amelia found another source of the continuing pressure: *"It is a big desire to cry, that is what I feel. It is another baby, a smaller one. I do not know what she is feeling, probably feeling alone too. She does not answer to what she is feeling. She cannot talk. She is just a baby. Angel* [formerly, The Witch] *is holding her."* After one more wind and light intervention Amelia opened her eyes, nodded, and said, *"She is sleeping. And Little Twin is fine. She is happy to have a child in her arms. Angel has the other one. They are sitting in rocking chairs side by side."*

Memories without Pictures

We had been at the work for nearly two hours, and we had successfully healed the eight-year-olds, the Old Man, New Mother, Little Twin, and two infant or toddler Parts. All of the blocking we had earlier encountered now seemed cleared away and I thought the therapy might finally be finished. I asked Amelia, "Are we finished?" She answered, *"I think so."* I felt a tentative but very warm feeling of accomplishment come over me.

She went on to comment on our work with the babies: *"That was very strange. I wonder what was wrong with them. They just had very strong feelings but no* [explicit] *memories. I wonder if it was when I spilled very hot water on my legs and I had to go to the hospital. I do not remember it but my mother told me about it. And the first little girl was in physical pain. And I think there was some abandonment there because once somebody picked them up they calmed down."*

Amelia's musings were consistent with what neuroscience tells us about memory. Before the age of eighteen months or two years, the hippocampus, the organ that processes explicit memory, isn't yet mature. Consequently, explicit, visual, factual memory isn't saved. However, the primary organ of emotional memory, the amygdala, is mature at birth, and is capable of saving emotional memories. A painful burn and hospital visit and a sense of abandonment from being left alone, could be stored and conceivably retrieved in the kind of deep work we do in Parts and Memory Therapy. The two apparently preverbal baby and toddler Parts could retain emotional but not explicit memories.

A LITTLE BIT MORE

We had accomplished a lot on this long Sunday session, and I was preparing to bring it to a close. But Amelia said she felt a small amount of discomfort: *"There is still a little bit of sadness deep inside."* Somewhat dismayed that there might be more to do, I suggested that Amelia just sit with the feeling and fully explore it, doing no more than being aware of it. Then I suggested she ask for a picture of the Part that felt the sadness.

A Hyperactive Three-Year-Old

"It is a three-year-old girl but she is playing." Evidently, there were more Parts from the previously silent spaces in the years before Amelia lived with her grandmother. After Amelia spoke inwardly with the new little-girl Part, she said, *"She says 'Hi' back to me. There is no sadness. She is more hyper. She cannot be still. She is running around everywhere."* Amelia tried her wind intervention to heal the child's apparent **anxiety** but soon said, *"She cannot be still for the wind."* I suggested a rain intervention, with the raincloud broader than the little girl

could escape with her hyperactivity. However, Amelia soon said, *"It is not neutralizing her."*

Switching our approach, Amelia asked for the *Three-Year-Old*'s earliest disturbing memory, but *"She cannot think."* Amelia then asked the previously-healed Gypsy Part (formerly, Old Woman) to help with the little girl. *"She is holding her hand but she is running around and around Gypsy."* With little success in getting through the hyperactivity, I suggested something new. I asked Amelia to ask Gypsy to look inside the three-year-old's mind and locate her earliest disturbing memory. I'm not sure if I had previously asked one Part to locate a second's Part's earliest memory, but it worked! *"She is lost. She is feeling lost. She cannot find her mommy. She is scared and lost."*

To help calm the little girl I coached Amelia to tell her that her mommy was nearby and then to use her wind intervention to neutralize her **fear**: *"It is not working... Yes, there is a blocker. I asked Gypsy and she said it is me."*

Seven-Months-A-Mother

When one Part identifies a strong emotion as residing within the patient, it means that a second Part is so completely blended with the conscious self that the first Part can't distinguish the second Part from the conscious self. Amelia asked Gypsy to speak to the hidden Part within Amelia and ask her to "step away." This would normally allow Amelia to see the Part, but there was no response:

"I can feel it inside of me," Amelia said, as she clutched at the center of her chest. *"It is very strong. This Part does not want to detach from me, to unblend from me. It is an adult, unclear. I just asked her to detach from me and she says no. She feels fear of not being good enough for her family and failing again. She means Noelle and Nathan* [Amelia's son] *and Michael. She says she is thirty. I can see her back. Now I can see her face. She looks like me with shorter hair, and she*

is wearing a striped T-shirt and jeans. She is afraid of hurting them and failing them.

We called this Part *Seven-Months-A-Mother*: *"She remembers being with Noelle when she was at around seven months old* [Amelia sobs], *feeling sadness and aloneness and feeling she was failing. She was not joyful like she should be as a mother. So she thought something was wrong with her."*

Amelia's comments here make clear that she had experienced postpartum depression with her first child too. Apparently, it was less debilitating than the depression that followed her second baby, and that might be why the Seven-Months-A-Mother Part played a lesser role in Amelia's life than did Postpartum Me, who we worked with early on in the narrative.

An Irritated Part

Amelia tried to help Seven-Months-A-Mother release her **sadness** with a wind intervention. To do so, she closed her eyes—head bent, chin resting on her hand—and allowed her hair to fall forward to cover her face. After a full minute of concentration, she lifted her head and opened her eyes with a mirthless smile and said, *"It is not working. An irritated Part came up and said, 'Be done with it! We should be done. Stop the drama! You are being dramatic.'"* Of this new Part, Amelia said, *"It is just me, when I get irritated. I just see her face, an impatient face. She doesn't want to wait anymore. She is impatient, frustrated. Probably me when I have one of those days and I just want everyone to go away from my side. I do not like these Parts. They are trouble."*

Amelia was making an indirect reference to our earlier sense that we had finished the therapy. Now new Parts were showing up and demanding attention while we were trying to reach closure on our work before Amelia left the country.

After nearly three hours of intense work, we had to put everybody away for the day. Amelia now had a headache that she attributed to the irritated one: *"I am negotiating with her.*

I asked her to step back and now she is putting her irritation in a suitcase. She is going to watch movies."

Reducing Chest Pressure

"But I still feel pain in my chest. I think it is the Part who prevented the healing of the Seven-Months-A-Mother Part. *It is an introject of my mother."* It's unclear whether this was a different *Mother Introject* from those we had seen earlier in the therapy, but Amelia moved her to a Sleeping Beauty Bed so we could go home. That helped the pressure, but there was still more.

Speaking to the pressure, Amelia asked the Part for a picture of itself: *"It does not want to show itself. It is female, an adult, and she does not know how to show herself. She wants me to know that things are not perfect yet."* Amelia explained to this *Perfectionist Part* that she got the message, and we would return to talk to her in our next session: *"She says 'Okay' and she stepped back."*

JUST TWO SESSIONS LEFT

We planned two more sessions for the coming week—before Amelia and her family left for training. The first of these was two days later, on a Tuesday. It was Day 31 in Amelia's cycle. As we had done a few months previously, we talked about the possibility that she might be pregnant. She said, *"Michael is already picking out girls' names because he wants a second daughter. He wants me to buy a pregnancy test today. But I remember I was five days late before and I was not pregnant."* Amelia planned to go to the drugstore after our session and buy a test. She would tell me the results when we met for our final session in two more days.

Perfectionist Parts

We wanted to find the Part who was blocking our work with Seven-Months-A-Mother. We turned first to the Mother Introject in the Sleeping Beauty Bed: *"She is a perfectionist in a different way. She is a little bit OCD about it. It is about house work, homemaking. She never stops cleaning and organizing. But she is not a perfectionist like the one we talked to last time. She says she was not blocking the mother or the three-year-old. But she knows the perfectionist blocker."* Amelia asked her to connect her with the blocker.

"She is an adult female. I cannot see her clearly. Now I see! It is me, with long hair in my twenties, wearing a green sweater and jeans... No, she does not remember any previous conversation with us... Yes, she was blocking Seven-Months-A-Mother, but not the three-year-old. She says those two are related somehow.

"She is upset with Seven-Months-A-Mother. She feels she is weak. She is kind of irritated with her... Yes, she knows me, and says I am the host of all the Parts. Her job is to make sure I do things perfectly. She feels that when I get emotional, I do not do things well."

Amelia explained that getting control of her emotionality was what we were working on: *"In that case—because she did not know that—she gives her permission to heal the Seven-Months-A-Mother."* We called this blocking Part the *Twenty-Year-Old.*

Healing Seven-Months-A-Mother

Amelia immediately brought the wind to blow away Seven-Months-A-Mother's **sadness** in the scene with Noelle at seven months of age. But she still couldn't do the healing: *"I think it is her doing the blocking because the sadness starts to come out and then it goes back. Oh! It is the Three-Year-old. She is with the Mother Introject now. This calms her down. She is not running around and around now. She is happy with the mother, smiling."* With this change, Amelia quickly healed the **fear** that the little girl had felt when she was lost.

Returning to Seven-Months-A-Mother, one minute of visualization was enough to neutralize the **sad** and **lonely** feelings she had when she reached seven months of motherhood: *"Okay, she is better, but she is holding a deep sorrow she has always had. She doesn't know where it came from. She wants to get rid of it but cannot. It is more of a thought that she will never be good enough. She was born that way. The Twenty-Year-Old feels the same way."*

Perfectionism at Two or Three

Asked about Seven-Months-A-Mother's earliest memory, Amelia said, *"She was very young. It was mostly from her mom, who was gentle and did it in a subtle way. Like she could be mean and yell but always correcting her. Like starting kindergarten and she had to make her letters and if they were not perfect, her mother would erase it and have her do it again and again. She was always doing things like that.*

"One time she got into her mom's makeup and put it on herself so she could be like her mom, but she made a mess and got punished.

"She treated her differently than her grandmother did. She was always correcting her. Her reading could be better; correct that. The margins could be better; do it over. Always trying to get her to be perfect. That was from about two or three years old until about the time her mom went back to work. However, on weekends I had to do homework and she would make her do it over and redo it. It was the amount of time that she was always correcting her. She needed the nurturing from her mother but there was always the correcting that made her feel she could never do anything right."

We had nearly concluded the session, and I wondered aloud whether this new material might be somehow less important than the material we had previously worked with. Amelia agreed saying, *"Yes, I think this is really leftover stuff. I think it is because my mom is with us now and it triggers the memories from my childhood with my mother. She gets frustrated because she cannot tell the kids how to do homework* [in English].

I *have to tell her it is okay. But this work is different now. On Sunday, when we finished with Little Twin, I felt calmer. Like we had finished something."*

PREGNANT!

We met for our last session two days later. When she came into my office she was all smiles: *"Guess what!"* she said. "No! Really?" I responded. *"Yes! I am pregnant! We are so happy. I think whoever was blocking my conception finally let go. I think my body and my mind finally came to a place where it is now the right time. I can just relax and have fun and be pregnant. It is perfect timing now. Michael and Noelle want it to be a girl and my son wants a little brother. I told my mother it is a good ending for the book, for my story.*

"And it is going to be a more relaxing pregnancy. I am not working and all I have to do is study for my [marriage and family therapy] *licensing exam. I can do that from there* [in the destination country]. *And my mother will be there to help me. It will be a good pregnancy. If it is not, I will call you on Skype. We can do therapy long distance."*

AMELIA HEALS HERSELF

Amelia had much more to share. After she left my office, she drove back to Utah to take a different exam-for her permanent license as a school counselor. She was already licensed provisionally, but for her permanent license she needed to pass a test on the Utah and U.S. constitutions, and on education law. (She passed all the tests.) It was a ninety-minute drive. During the drive she continued to work with her Parts.

Seven-Months-A-Mother and the Twenty-Year-Old

"After last session, the Parts were very activated. I kept doing some work. I did more interventions with Seven-Months-A-Mother and she neutralized all the corrections my mother did to

me. Then she joined the Three-Year-Old and the Mother Intro-ject to hang out with them.

"Then I worked with the Twenty-Year-Old who felt all the perfectionism pressure. She felt restricted and could not be her-self because she always had to be perfect and meet others' standards. So I neutralized those **feelings**. *In that process she turned into an eight-year-old ballerina. I remember that at eight I liked to pretend being a ballerina because that's the one time she felt free."*

The Irritated Part and the Hippie

The Hippie

"I worked also on the irritated Part. [This was the Part who showed herself briefly at the end of our marathon session the previous weekend.] *She had trouble being flexible, like in col-lege when friends asked why she had to be perfect. She didn't know she was that rigid and when she realized that, she got*

*angry with herself. I neutralized her rigidity and her sense of frustration at finding out that she was rigid. She preferred to be a hippie. There were lots of college memories of being rigid and hard times adjusting to being in college and being flexible. When things did not work out the way they were supposed to, she freaked out, and she had to learn to be flexible. My classmates asked me why I was like that. She released all that **rigidity** and the difficulty adjusting and people making comments about her perfectionism. And when we were done with the neutralizing, she became a hippie.*

"Before, when she was the irritated me, all I saw was her face, probably my current age. She became a seventeen- or eighteen- or a nineteen-year-old, dressed like a Hippie. Baggy clothes, more colorful, a bandanna around her forehead. A more relaxed type of attire, hair to her waist, hand-made type of bracelets. She just wanted to relax and read a book.

"The last thing my Parts were doing when I got to my test was having a party. Different people having lemonade and wine. I remember there was music and dancing. They were celebrating that all the Parts are doing well. That was the last thing I saw before I got to the testing."

WHAT ABOUT PMS AND PMDD?

The big question I had for Amelia as we spent our last few therapy minutes together was whether we had done the job we set out to do. Did we fix her rage, her marriage, her postpartum depression, her relationship with her daughter, and her PMS, PMDD?

Her answer to all of these questions was a firm *"Yes!"* I asked again whether we had regulated her PMS or PMDD: *"I think so. The last few times I hardly felt anything. And before I came here I would have to take off two or three days of work. I think I will be like a normal woman and just get cranky when my period comes. It made a big difference to heal all of that guilt for Noelle. I think there are a lot of Parts* who felt like they could not be who they wanted to be. They felt they had to be what others wanted them to be. For so long I felt broken. Like you said, growing up with adults shaped me and I couldn't be a child.

"The therapy definitely organized my internal world and made a lot of sense and it made me understanding of Michael's internal world as well. It helped me understand why I was so reactive to him. Knowing how my father abandoned me made me understand how I reacted to him and how I would run away, and how I would threaten to divorce him when he ignored me or argued with me.

"I do not feel broken anymore. It is just how life happens. It was not something I did or that I was born broken. It was just the environment I was in. My mother had to go back to work and I had to live with my grandmother. It is just what it was. It was not my fault. They did not know they were affecting me. I do not experience my childhood with pain anymore."

SUMMARY OF PARTS

Eight-Year-Olds. Several eight-year-olds make an appearance in this chapter. There are the two who transformed from Big Bertha and Twenty-Something during the healing process. They begin the chapter paralyzed and lying in a Sleeping-Beauty Bed. Two others appear when the Old Man and the Twenty-Year-Old are healed.

New Mother. She's the Stuck-in-Time Part in the hospital recovering from a difficult childbirth. Little Twin prevents her healing until several other Parts and their memories are also healed.

Old Man. He first pictured himself as an eighty-year-old, confused and weak, barely-functioning Old Man. He transformed into another eight-year-old Part when we began to work with him.

Seven-Months-A-Mother. She's a Stuck-in-Time Part who experienced Amelia's milder postpartum depression following the birth of her daughter Noelle.

Irritated Amelia/The Hippie. The Hippie was the final Part to show herself. She developed out of the healing we did with Amelia's disembodied, irritated, current-time face. Her therapy changed her from rigid to flexible.

Mother Introject. The last of several Mother Introjects appears in this chapter. She's the Part who drives Amelia's perfectionism at home, as a homemaker.

Three-Year-Old. She was a hyperactive, preschool Amelia who learned from her mother that she had to be perfect and to do her homework exactly right.

Five Eight-Year-Olds

POSTSCRIPT

Amelia finished her therapy in the summer, two and a half years ago. It's now the middle of January, and cold in Las Vegas. Amelia and her family are in a different country pursuing their dream of traveling to new places and experiencing new cultures. I do not share the name of the country in order to maintain the confidentiality I guaranteed her when we agreed to do the book.

She has three children now. The baby is almost two years old and walking. The family is doing well in their new posting, although Michael has taken some lumps as he adapts to his new role as an administrator rather than a teacher.

Postpartum Depression No More

Amelia didn't—as The Witch and other Parts feared— experience postpartum depression following the birth of her new daughter. It seems that with the great bulk of Amelia's painful memories neutralized, there is no longer an emotional foundation for depression.

PMDD in Remission

Amelia no longer fits criteria for the diagnosis of PMDD (Premenstrual Dysphoric Disorder), the extreme form of PMS. She had achieved this remission prior to becoming pregnant and has maintained her gains following pregnancy and childbirth.

Rage Absent

She no longer rages at Michael or her children, although she can express appropriate anger. She doesn't threaten divorce or separation, and her relationship with all three of her children is equally loving. The baby gets the greatest attention, but Amelia and Noelle now have a normal mother-daughter bond.

PMS Minor

Amelia isn't one hundred percent free of minor PMS symptoms. Previously she was emotionally distressed at ovulation, a few days before her period, and throughout menstruation. Her ovulation distress was once so great that she often stayed in bed a few days each month rather than go to work. She no longer experiences emotional distress at ovulation. And she's like most women now in that her emotional symptoms rapidly decrease at the beginning of her period.

Her remaining PMS symptoms are minor. Sometimes she has no symptoms at all. Here is what she says about her new normal:

> *"I am experiencing some PMS but now it is normal, just before my period, and it gets better as my period passes. Also, it is not every month. Some months are harder than others but nothing compared to what it used to be. I get frustrated or irritable, sometimes sad, but it passes in a day or two, I would say it is only mild."*

CONCLUSION

I'm pleased that Amelia's PMDD diagnosis is no longer applicable. And I'm happy as well that she experiences no distress at all during some months. I'm disappointed that she continues to have even mild premenstrual symptoms sometimes. Based upon the results of my therapy with other women since Amelia left, I believe we could reduce her remaining symptoms to zero or near zero.

Overall, though, we made great progress. It's clear that Parts and Memory Therapy can greatly reduce PMS/PMDD symptoms and even cure PMDD. Work with other patients (see Appendix 2) corroborates these findings.

Amelia's story of psychotherapy is a kind of adventure that few patients have the opportunity to enjoy. *Parts and Memory*

Therapy (formerly *Parts Psychology*) is not well known. The recognition of memory reconsolidation, the most powerful tool we have for healing traumatic and other painful memories is slowly gaining recognition.

Doing psychotherapy with Parts of the self (also called ego states, subpersonalities, voices, and a few other things) has been adopted by a much larger body of therapists than even a decade ago. The recognition by mainstream psychology and psychotherapy of the natural multiplicity of the mind is near. These two factors—the normal multiplicity of the whole personality and the power of memory reconsolidation in healing implicit emotional memories—are poised to bring about a paradigm change in psychotherapy specifically, and in psychology's understanding of the mind more generally.

Appendix 1
Resources

If you're looking for a therapist to help you with PMS, PMDD, or postpartum depression, look beyond the traditional "talk-therapy" approaches. They won't heal you because, while well-intentioned, they unwittingly discourage you from exploring the source of your present-time distress in the history of your past. That source, although made worse by present-time stress, probably has its foundation in your childhood and adolescence, during your home and school years, in the ways you were treated by mom, dad, siblings, peers, teachers, and sweethearts.

A SELF-HELP TECHNIQUE

Most of the deep work in *Healing Amelia* is not something you can do for yourself right away. But here are a couple of things you can do that don't require a thorough knowledge of Parts and Memory Therapy. You don't even have to "believe" in the therapy to find it helpful.

Step-Back

The *step-back* technique permits you to calm and center yourself when you're feeling anxious, agitated, sad, or some other troubling emotion. Or maybe you can't name the emotion but you simply have an uncomfortable body sensation in your chest, head, shoulders, or stomach. You can give yourself some relief.

You should focus on the sensation of anxiety, for example, that you feel in your chest, and then speak to that sensation, aloud or silently, and say, "Step back, please. Don't go away; just step back." If the sensation lessens, you could say, "Thank you, that helps. Please take another step back." Keep repeating the request for as long as the request leads to a lessening of the body sensation.

If you get no response to your request, try bargaining with the anxious Part of you. For example: "Okay, I'm paying attention to you, and I've got your message, so please step back now. Thank you for letting me know. Please step back." You could repeat a variation of that, or you add, "Please step back for just sixty seconds (or thirty seconds). Nothing bad will happen in just sixty seconds. Please step back." If you get a positive response to these requests, use the "Thank you; please take another step back" technique, above.

If you get no response at all, you may be one of the few people who do not respond to the technique. But just to be sure, try again on another day or try again with different emotions or body sensations.

Systematic Step-Back

You can also use the step-back technique in a systematic way in order to achieve longer-lasting calm with respect to all negative emotions or sensations. For the systematic approach, you intentionally bring about temporary distress by thinking about someone or some situation that causes you disturbing emotions. For example, think about your most recent fight with your spouse, and permit yourself to be angry all over again. Then use the step-back technique to calm yourself.

When the anger has stepped back you might feel sadness or anxiety. Do the step-back exercise until that emotion has dissipated. If you still feel a negative emotion, perhaps anxiety, re-peat the exercise. Once you are completely calm, bring to your mind again the original person or situation that caused the an-ger. Repeat the exercise. Keep repeating until you can think about the original image while getting no emotional arousal.

Now think about some other person or situation that brings on negative emotions. Repeat the exercise that you used for the first image. When you have reached a place where thoughts of the new image or situation doesn't cause you dis-tress, think about another one. Repeat as needed. When you complete the systematic step-back procedure you will feel calm and centered.

Your state of calm may last for a short time or for hours. If you do the exercise frequently, you will find yourself feeling calm and centered for entire days. The more often you repeat the exercise, the more quickly you will reach the calm state.

The Rescue

The *rescue* intervention that you've seen a number of times in this book is also something you might be able to use on your own. It requires, however, that you be able to accept the reality of Stuck-in-Time Parts attached to painful memories. If you are careful in the way you approach a given painful memory, and you've activated the memory enough so that you feel some of the distress of the Part still captured in the pain of the memory, then all you have to do is to imagine reaching out your hand to that version of yourself in the memory, step out of the memory and guide the Part to a safe place. That place can be a place from your past, perhaps your childhood room, your present, perhaps your present home or Disneyland, or an imaginary place, such as floating on a cloud. For the Stuck-in-Time Part the rescue will be real and you will feel immediate relief from the disturbing memory.

Neutralizing on the Run

Sometimes errant memories pop into your head when you are busy doing other things. You may be able to neutralize such irritating intrusions with a quick visualization. For example, you are out shopping and something triggers a memory of being out with your mother when you were nine, when she created a scene that embarrassed you. You don't have the time to work on the issue but you can access the memory, find yourself in the memory, and put your stuck-in-time self into a waterfall and wash away the embarrassment. Sometimes this will actually fully neutralize the disturbing memory in just a few seconds. More likely it will only partially do so, but you will find some relief

TRAUMA-BASED THERAPY

For permanent, deep healing—necessary for PMS, PMDD and postpartum depression—your best source of help is with a therapist with a lot of years of experience in the treatment of traumas, large and small. Such a therapist should be comfortable working with emotional issues, including past and present, and willing to seek out your disturbing memories from the years of growing up.

But here's a cautionary note. "Trauma therapy" has become a buzzword among psychotherapists, with many therapists offering treatment but with little experience and without an adequate treatment plan for healing trauma and trauma-like memories. It's not enough to access traumatic memories. Once you've done so, you still need to have specialized techniques for healing the memories you've accessed. Otherwise you risk re-traumatizing yourself.

I'm aware, for example, of a local treatment facility that encourages the sharing of "your most painful memories" in a group setting. Once a given patient shares his/her story, the therapist asks for the next patient's tale of pain. That's a formula for re-traumatization. They bare their souls and then are left alone with that raw, emotional pain as the next patient shares his/her story. Just telling the story won't heal the patient. Your therapist must have techniques to help you once you have allowed yourself to face the pain of the memory.

Parts and Memory Therapy

My first recommendation is to do therapy with someone trained in Parts and Memory Therapy, the approach I developed and shared throughout this book. Unfortunately, these therapists are relatively few in number, and most practice in the state of Nevada. You can find them listed on my website at PartsandMemoryTherapy.com. I write a blog about mental health issues that can also be found there.

For more information about Parts and Memory Therapy, you might want to take a look at my earlier books. I published the first one in 2011: *Parts Psychology: A Trauma-Based, Self-State Therapy for Emotional Healing.* "Parts Psychology" is the original name I used for the Parts and Memory Therapy model. The book contains twelve case studies (each one of them much shorter than *Healing Amelia*) of patients with a variety of ailments, including jealousy, rage, low sexual desire, depression, lost love, bulimia, binge eating, and porn addiction.

My second book on Parts and Memory Therapy appeared in 2014: *For Women Only: Healing Childbirth PTSD and Postpartum Depression with Parts Psychology.* This little book describes the rapid healing of one woman's PTSD and postpartum depression in just six sessions. Her thirty-seven hours of very painful labor caused her to believe she was going to die—leading to her PTSD. The rapidity with which she healed her postpartum depression is remarkable. She had been miserable for the eight months since the delivery of her son and before she began therapy with the Parts and Memory Therapy approach.

OTHER HELPFUL THERAPIES

In seeking therapists, you are unlikely to find PMS or PMDD listed among the problems they treat. Finding a therapist to heal postpartum depression can also be problematic. Most therapists, like most of the general public, don't view PMS or PMDD as mental health issues. So you may have to specify that the therapist you find be willing to treat your PMS with a trauma-based therapy, one that aims to heal the painful memories that underlie the problem. True also for efficient treatment of postpartum depression. The best time for your therapist to help you find the memories that fuel the PMS is during the PMS phase of your cycle.

EMDR

This trauma-based approach, *Eye Movement Desensitization and Reprocessing* (EMDR), is powerful and directly focused on painful memories (see Shapiro, 2001). It's especially effective when coupled with Parts—called "ego states" in this model. Its developer, Francine Shapiro, took the position that nearly all adult mental health problems were the result of the large and small traumas of childhood. I've taken this position as my own.

EMDR is now available in every-mid-size or larger city in the United States (and probably the world). Just type in EMDR and your location in your search engine, and you'll find therapists trained in this work. I recommend calling and asking if they combine ego state work with their EMDR. If they work with ego states, they should be familiar with a little book by Robin Shapiro, *Easy Ego State Interventions* (2016). As with most therapists, you'll likely have to alert them to the news that their approach can significantly reduce or bring about remission of PMS, PMDD.

Internal Family Systems

The closest approximation to Parts and Memory Therapy is Richard C. Schwartz's *Internal Family Systems* [IFS] *Therapy* (1995). I learned a lot from this model as I developed my own way of working with Parts. There are significant differences in the ways our models are conceptualized, but you can still gain a lot from working with this approach. One IFS therapist, Jay Early, has written a self-help book, *Self-Therapy*, for work with Parts.

Ego State Therapy

Another approach, recognized internationally, is *Ego State Therapy*, developed by John and Helen Watkins (1997). I learned a lot from their work as well. Their model makes use of therapeutic hypnosis and works through direct communication between therapists and Parts, which they call "ego states." Once their patient is in a hypnotic trance, they ask that Parts relevant to the problem at hand speak with them.

Helen Watkins developed what she called the "silent abreaction" for reducing the intensity of ego states' negative emotions. This intervention appears to be the forerunner of the process Richard C. Schwartz calls "unburdening" and what I call "neutralizing."

Coherence Therapy

Another therapy with great promise for healing emotional issues is *Coherence Therapy,* described in *Unlocking the Emotional Brain*, by Bruce Ecker, Robin Ticic, and Laurel Hulley (2012). This is the book that brings the concept of "memory reconsolidation" to psychotherapy from neuroscience. Because this book is dense reading, I recommend individual chapters by Bruce Ecker in *The Neuropsychotherapist* Special Issue: *Memory Reconsolidation in Psychotherapy*, edited by Mathew Dahlitz and Geoff Hall (2015).

These authors don't mention Parts or subpersonalities, but I use their description of the process of memory reconsolidation to explain why the fantasy interventions we use in Parts and Memory Therapy work.

REFERENCES CITED

Abraham, G. E. (1980). Premenstrual tension. In M. Levanthal, Ed., *Current problems in obstetrics and gynecology* (pp. 1-48). Chicago: Year Book Medical Publishers.

American Psychiatric Association (2013). *Diagnostic and statistical manual of mental disorders* (5th ed.). Arlington, VA: American Psychiatric Association.

Dahlitz, M. & Hall, G. (Eds.). (2015). *Memory reconsolidation in psychotherapy*. Queensland, Australia: *The Neuropsychotherapists* Special Issue.

Earley, J. (2009). *Self-therapy* (2nd ed,). Larkspur, CA: Pattern System Books.

Ecker, B. (2015). Using NLP for memory reconsolidation. A glimpse of integrating the panoply of psychotherapies. In M. Dahlitz & G. Hall, (Eds.), *Memory reconsolidation in psychotherapy*. Queensland, Australia: *The Neuropsychotherapist* Special Issue.

Ecker, B., Ticic, R., & Hulley, L. (2012). *Unlocking the emotional brain: Eliminating symptoms at their roots using memory reconsolidation*. New York & London: Routledge.

Kosslyn, S. M. (2005). Mental images and the brain. *Cognitive Neuropsychology, 22,* 333-347.

Kreiman, G., Koch, C. & Fried, I. (2000). Imagery neurons in the human brain. *Nature, 408,* 357-361.

McCormick, K. (2003). PMS: From puberty to menopause. *Women's Health Connection* [Newsletter]. Madison, WI: Women's International Pharmacy.

Noricks, J. (2011). *Parts psychology: A trauma-based, self-state therapy for emotional healing*. Los Angeles, CA: New University Press LLC.

Noricks, J. (2014). *For women only, book 1: Healing childbirth PTSD and postpartum depression with parts psychology*. Los Angeles, CA: New University Press LLC.

Schwartz, R. C. (1995). *Internal family systems therapy*. New York, NY: Guilford Press.

Shapiro, F. (2001). *Eye movement desensitization and reprocessing: Basic principles, protocols and procedures* (2nd ed.). New York, NY: Guilford Press.

Shapiro, R. (2016). *Easy ego state interventions: Strategies for working with parts*. New York, NY: W.W. Norton.

Watkins, H. H. (1980). The silent abreaction. *International Journal of Clinical and Experimental Hypnosis, XXVIII*, 101-113.

Watkins, J. G. & Watkins, H. H. (1997). *Ego states: Theory and therapy*. New York, NY: W.W. Norton.

Wolpe, Joseph (1969). *The practice of behavior therapy*. New York, NY: Pergamon Press.

Appendix 2
The Healing of PMS and PMDD

Healing Amelia describes twenty months of psychotherapy. But it would be inaccurate to say it took twenty months to heal Amelia's PMS or PMDD. We used Amelia's progress with her PMS as a measure of overall progress, but that emphasis was the result of concerns with her other issues. We began our work with the problem of Amelia's anger toward her husband and a lingering postpartum depression. We ended our therapy working on issues of parental bonding and Amelia's stored anger for having to take on an early adult role because of an under-functioning, alcoholic father.

As we worked through the many problems linked to her childhood and young-adult experiences, the painful emotions that waxed and waned with her menstrual cycle became a means by which we could assess the therapy. But the healing of PMS or PMDD was a byproduct of the therapy, never the primary purpose of the therapy.

Discovering that Parts and Memory Therapy could heal PMS and PMDD was serendipitous. And because these cyclic emotional issues significantly impacted the mental health of millions of women—including my own daughter—it seemed to me important enough to include in a book about the healing of women's issues.

As Amelia and I worked with the emotional problems linked to her menstrual cycle, I soon became sensitive to my other psychotherapy patients who experienced similar distress. Offering emotional relief for menstrual cycle issues became a standard part of my intake protocol. I include below the results of work with five other patients.

CANDACE

The first, Candace, was a forty-two-year-old mother of three in a professional career that permitted her to work from home. Her husband also worked from home but in a different profession. Candace came to therapy in a state of high anxiety. She was overwhelmed with fear at the thought of separating from her husband, even for a few days. Yet her job would soon require her to leave him while attending a professional conference in another state.

We did not specifically target her PMS/PMDD symptoms in our interventions, but a clear connection emerged between those symptoms and her fear of separation. Further, the rage she experienced during her premenstrual phase threatened her marriage. The intensity of her symptoms and the threat to her marriage combined to make clear that Candace met criteria for PMDD (Premenstrual Dysphoric Disorder).

We met for just five sessions over three weeks. Candace successfully attended her conference and gave up her fear of separation from her husband. She was pleased with her success in therapy but chose not to continue with other issues that sometimes caused her problems—especially a powerful need to control her husband and any part of her environment that yielded to control.

Over our three weeks together, we neutralized ten painful memories. Most of them related to physical abuse by her mother as a child. The other memories had to do with more recent adult experiences of feeling excluded from recognition by her in-laws at significant family events such as wedding receptions and reunions.

CANDACE'S PMS SYMPTOMS*						CANDACE'S PMS SYMPTOMS*					
Pre-Treatment Questionnaire						**Post-Treatment Questionnaire**					
PMS – 1 (Cognitive / Emotional)						**PMS – 1 (Cognitive / Emotional)**					
		0	1	2	3			0	1	2	3
Angry/Irritable				x		Angry/Irritable			x		
Anxious					x	Anxious			x		
Mood Swings			x			Mood Swings			x		
Nervous Tension				x		Nervous Tension			x		
Overwhelmed				x		Overwhelmed			x		
Suspicious				x		Suspicious			x		
PMS – 2 (Cognitive / Emotional)						**PMS – 2 (Cognitive / Emotional)**					
Crying					x	Crying					x
Confused		x				Confused			x		
Depressed					x	Depressed			x		
Forgetful				x		Forgetful			x		
Insomnia/Hypersomnia					x	Insomnia/Hypersomnia			x		
Less Interest Usual Activities				x		Less Interest Usual Activities			x		
PMS – 3 (Physiological)						**PMS – 3 (Physiological)**					
Dizzy/Fainting		x				Dizzy/Fainting			x		
Fatigue			x			Fatigue			x		
Food Cravings			x			Food Cravings			x		
Headache			x			Headache			x		
Palpitations		x				Palpitations			x		
PMS – 4 (Water Retention, Swelling)						**PMS – 4 (Water Retention, Swelling)**					
Abdominal Bloating					x	Abdominal Bloating			x		
Breast Tenderness					x	Breast Tenderness				x	
Fluid Retention					x	Fluid Retention				x	
Swollen Hands/Feet		x				Swollen Hands/Feet			x		
Weight Gain					x	Weight Gain			x		
PMS – 5 (Other Symptoms)						**PMS – 5 (Other Symptoms)**					
Acne				x		Acne			x		
Backache					x	Backache				x	
Constipation		x				Constipation			x		
Diarrhea		x				Diarrhea			x		
Hives		x				Hives			x		
Oily Skin					x	Oily Skin				x	
Radiation Down Thighs		x				Radiation Down Thighs			x		

I had given Candace my PMS questionnaire at her first meeting and collected a follow up questionnaire five months later when her husband came to therapy for his own issues.

The comparison between the two questionnaires shows stark differences. The tables contain simple check-offs for Candace's self-report of level-of-distress, using a 0-3 scale for each of the twenty-nine PMS symptoms. Candace scored a 28 on her intake questionnaire for the cognitive/emotional items and a 24 on the physiological/other items, for a total of 52 points. Five months later, her scores were 1 and 4, respectively for a total of 5 points. She no longer fitted criteria for either PMS or PMDD.

The difference in before-therapy and after-therapy scores were dramatic. Even the physiological scores were greatly improved. Intuitively, I would have expected less improvement in the physiological scores. The cognitive/emotional scores were nearly a perfect zero.

ADRIENNE

My second patient was a forty-three-year-old mother of four children, aged seven to nineteen. Adrienne was a full-time homemaker. She came to therapy to work on her previously-diagnosed panic disorder. She also met criteria for clinical depression.

We met in twenty-one sessions for just over five months. Adrienne left therapy feeling that she had accomplished her goals. The major painful memories we neutralized involved childhood abandonment through her parents' divorce and years-long harassment of her mother by Adrienne's violent father. Following marriage at age seventeen, Adrienne struggled with social isolation from her closest relatives, condemnation for not being good enough by her in-laws, and feeling like she raised her kids as a single mother because of the work-absence of her husband for three out of every four weeks. On her original PMS questionnaire, taken two weeks after beginning therapy, Adrienne scored 33 for the cognitive or emotional symptoms and 23 for the physiological/other symptoms. On her last PMS questionnaire, five months later, she scored only 3 on the cognitive/emotional scale and 18 on the physiological/other scale. While she continued to fit PMS criteria because of her physiological scores, she no longer met criteria for PMDD.

ADRIENNE'S PMS SYMPTOMS*

Pre-Treatment Questionnaire

PMS – 1 (Cognitive / Emotional)

	0	1	2	3
Angry/Irritable				x
Anxious				x
Mood Swings				x
Nervous Tension				x
Overwhelmed				x
Suspicious				x

PMS – 2 (Cognitive / Emotional)

	0	1	2	3
Crying	x			
Confused			x	
Depressed			x	
Forgetful			x	
Insomnia/Hypersomnia			x	
Less Interest Usual Activities			x	

PMS – 3 (Physiological)

	0	1	2	3
Dizzy/Fainting	x			
Fatigue			x	
Food Cravings			x	
Headache	x			
Palpitations			x	

PMS – 4 (Water Retention, Swelling)

	0	1	2	3
Abdominal Bloating			x	
Breast Tenderness			x	
Fluid Retention	x			
Swollen Hands/Feet	x			
Weight Gain	x			

PMS – 5 (Other Symptoms)

	0	1	2	3
Acne		x		
Backache			x	
Constipation		x		
Diarrhea			x	
Hives	x			
Oily Skin		x		
Radiation Down Thighs		x		

Post-Treatment Questionnaire

PMS – 1 (Cognitive / Emotional)

	0	1	2	3
Angry/Irritable	x			
Anxious	x			
Mood Swings	x			
Nervous Tension	x			
Overwhelmed	x			
Suspicious	x			

PMS – 2 (Cognitive / Emotional)

	0	1	2	3
Crying	x			
Confused		x		
Depressed			x	
Forgetful		x		
Insomnia/Hypersomnia			x	
Less Interest Usual Activities		x		

PMS – 3 (Physiological)

	0	1	2	3
Dizzy/Fainting	x			
Fatigue			x	
Food Cravings			x	
Headache	x			
Palpitations				x

PMS – 4 (Water Retention, Swelling)

	0	1	2	3
Abdominal Bloating			x	
Breast Tenderness				x
Fluid Retention	x			
Swollen Hands/Feet	x			
Weight Gain	x			

PMS – 5 (Other Symptoms)

	0	1	2	3
Acne		x		
Backache			x	
Constipation			x	
Diarrhea	x			
Hives	x			
Oily Skin	x			
Radiation Down Thighs	x			

Adrienne's improvement in cognitive/emotional symptoms was as dramatic as Candace's. Unfortunately, she didn't match Candace on the physiological/other items, which were largely unchanged. But she has maintained her gains for more than two years.

Seven months ago, as I worked on the final draft of this book, I decided to increase the sample size of women who had used Parts and Memory Therapy to reduce their PMS or PMDD symptoms. I invited therapists who attended my P&MT workshop to volunteer to take part in a study of how well the P&MT model would do in reducing their PMS symptoms. I would only take volunteers who had severe PMS symptoms and met criteria for PMDD. Four therapists quickly volunteered. A former patient of mine was the fifth participant.

For this study of five women, I would see each of them at no cost for up to five times during the troublesome premenstrual phases of their cycles. Ideally, I would see each of them once in five consecutive months.

Of the five volunteers, one dropped out because of emergency surgery and one dropped out because she could not distinguish her PMS/PMDD symptoms from those she experienced throughout her cycle. I describe below the results for the remaining three volunteers.

KIM

Kim was twenty-eight-years old, the head of her own small company, and had recently married when we began the trial. She actually took only three sessions to eliminate almost all of her PMS symptoms and to bring full remission to her diagnosis of PMDD. However, before she began the three-session trial with me, she had completed five sessions in which we treated painful childhood experiences, the details of which she chose not to publicly share. One indication of the seriousness of her symptoms was her monthly rage-filled fights with her husband, in which she demanded a divorce and ordered him out of the house.

KIM'S PMS SYMPTOMS*

Pre-Treatment Questionnaire

PMS – 1 (Cognitive / Emotional)	0	1	2	3
Angry/Irritable				x
Anxious				x
Mood Swings				x
Nervous Tension				x
Overwhelmed				x
Suspicious				x

PMS – 2 (Cognitive / Emotional)	0	1	2	3
Crying				x
Confused				x
Depressed				x
Forgetful				x
Insomnia/Hypersomnia				x
Less Interest Usual Activities				x

PMS – 3 (Physiological)	0	1	2	3
Dizzy/Fainting	x			
Fatigue		x		
Food Cravings			x	
Headache		x		
Palpitations		x		

PMS – 4 (Water Retention, Swelling)	0	1	2	3
Abdominal Bloating				x
Breast Tenderness				x
Fluid Retention				x
Swollen Hands/Feet		x		
Weight Gain				x

PMS – 5 (Other Symptoms)	0	1	2	3
Acne			x	
Backache		x		
Constipation		x		
Diarrhea		x		
Hives	x			
Oily Skin		x		
Radiation Down Thighs	x			

Post-Treatment Questionnaire

PMS – 1 (Cognitive / Emotional)	0	1	2	3
Angry/Irritable	x			
Anxious	x			
Mood Swings	x			
Nervous Tension	x			
Overwhelmed	x			
Suspicious	x			

PMS – 2 (Cognitive / Emotional)	0	1	2	3
Crying	x			
Confused	x			
Depressed	x			
Forgetful	x			
Insomnia/Hypersomnia	x			
Less Interest Usual Activities	x			

PMS – 3 (Physiological)	0	1	2	3
Dizzy/Fainting	x			
Fatigue	x			
Food Cravings	x			
Headache	x			
Palpitations	x			

PMS – 4 (Water Retention, Swelling)	0	1	2	3
Abdominal Bloating			x	
Breast Tenderness	x			
Fluid Retention	x			
Swollen Hands/Feet	x			
Weight Gain				x

PMS – 5 (Other Symptoms)	0	1	2	3
Acne	x			
Backache	x			
Constipation	x			
Diarrhea	x			
Hives	x			
Oily Skin	x			
Radiation Down Thighs	x			

As the table shows, the three sessions directed at PMS-linked memories led to nearly 100% remission. She had a score of 65 prior to our last three therapy sessions and a score of only 3 after those sessions. The post-treatment questionnaire showed only mild physiological distress—in water retention symptoms.

NADINE

Nadine's PMS Symptoms*

Pre-Treatment Questionnaire

PMS – 1 (Cognitive / Emotional)

	0	1	2	3
Angry/Irritable			x	
Anxious			x	
Mood Swings			x	
Nervous Tension			x	
Overwhelmed			x	
Suspicious			x	

PMS – 2 (Cognitive / Emotional)

	0	1	2	3
Crying				x
Confused				x
Depressed			x	
Forgetful		x		
Insomnia/Hypersomnia				x
Less Interest in Usual Activities			x	

PMS – 3 (Physiological)

	0	1	2	3
Dizzy/Fainting		x		
Fatigue		x		
Food Cravings		x		
Headache		x		
Palpitations		x		

PMS – 4 (Water Retention, Swelling)

	0	1	2	3
Abdominal Bloating		x		
Breast Tenderness		x		
Fluid Retention		x		
Swollen Hands/Feet		x		
Weight Gain		x		

PMS – 5 (Other Symptoms)

	0	1	2	3
Acne				x
Backache		x		
Constipation			x	
Diarrhea	x			
Hives	x			
Oily Skin			x	
Radiation Down Thighs	x			

Post-Treatment Questionnaire

PMS – 1 (Cognitive / Emotional)

	0	1	2	3
Angry/Irritable	x			
Anxious			x	
Mood Swings		x		
Nervous Tension			x	
Overwhelmed			x	
Suspicious	x			

PMS – 2 (Cognitive / Emotional)

	0	1	2	3
Crying				x
Confused			x	
Depressed			x	
Forgetful		x		
Insomnia/Hypersomnia		x		
Less Interest in Usual Activities			x	

PMS – 3 (Physiological)

	0	1	2	3
Dizzy/Fainting		x		
Fatigue		x		
Food Cravings		x		
Headache		x		
Palpitations			x	

PMS – 4 (Water Retention, Swelling)

	0	1	2	3
Abdominal Bloating		x		
Breast Tenderness		x		
Fluid Retention		x		
Swollen Hands/Feet		x		
Weight Gain		x		

PMS – 5 (Other Symptoms)

	0	1	2	3
Acne		x		
Backache		x		
Constipation		x		
Diarrhea		x		
Hives		x		
Oily Skin		x		
Radiation Down Thighs	x			

The second volunteer was Nadine, a twenty-seven-year-old, single therapist who regularly broke up with her fiancé during her PMS phase and who had lost close friends—including her best friend—during PMS /PMDD episodes. She shared one aspect of Amelia's atypical PMS pattern in that it occurred during her ovulation. But unlike Amelia, she did not experience PMS symptoms directly before her period.

After just two sessions Nadine was surprised to find that for the first time she could remember, she went two months without significant symptoms. In the fifth month her symptoms returned but coincided with a cold and upper-respiratory infection. Then, in the sixth month she once again experienced no symptoms. In the seventh month, just before this book went to press, the symptoms shown in her table returned.

In the previous six months we had managed to meet for only two therapy sessions. Only in the seventh month did we finally manage to synchronize our schedules so that we could have a third session. The after scores in the table below were taken before this third session.

Before any therapy sessions, her total PMS score was 37. The important cognitive/emotional scores totaled 23. Seven months later the return of some symptoms showed a total score of 14, all of which related to the cognitive/emotional issues. From my perspective, this score is on the borderline of qualifying for a PMS designation. Some would say yes, others no. But with the absence of the rage that previously caused disruptions in her social life, she no longer fits the PMDD diagnosis.

JULIE

Married with one child, Julie is a thirty-six-year-old African American therapist who quickly volunteered when I announced this study. She had the highest beginning PMS score of any of my patients, a 75, but measured only a 3 after three therapy sessions that focused upon the childhood memories linked to her PMS symptoms. She easily fitted criteria for the diagnosis of PMDD because of her need to cancel sessions with her patients and take off a few days when her symptoms were at their worst.

JULIE'S PMS SYMPTOMS*

Pre-Treatment Questionnaire

PMS – 1 (Cognitive / Emotional)

	0	1	2	3
Angry/Irritable			x	
Anxious			x	
Mood Swings			x	
Nervous Tension			x	
Overwhelmed			x	
Suspicious			x	

PMS – 2 (Cognitive / Emotional)

	0	1	2	3
Crying			x	
Confused			x	
Depressed		x		
Forgetful			x	
Insomnia/Hypersomnia			x	
Less Interest Usual Activities		x		

PMS – 3 (Physiological)

	0	1	2	3
Dizzy/Fainting		x		
Fatigue			x	
Food Cravings	x			
Headache			x	
Palpitations		x		

PMS – 4 (Water Retention, Swelling)

	0	1	2	3
Abdominal Bloating				x
Breast Tenderness		x		
Fluid Retention			x	
Swollen Hands/Feet			x	
Weight Gain		x		

PMS – 5 (Other Symptoms)

	0	1	2	3
Acne			x	
Backache			x	
Constipation			x	
Diarrhea		x		
Hives		x		
Oily Skin			x	
Radiation Down Thighs		x		

Post-Treatment Questionnaire

PMS – 1 (Cognitive / Emotional)

	0	1	2	3
Angry/Irritable	x			
Anxious	x			
Mood Swings			x	
Nervous Tension	x			
Overwhelmed	x			
Suspicious	x			

PMS – 2 (Cognitive / Emotional)

	0	1	2	3
Crying			x	
Confused		x		
Depressed		x		
Forgetful		x		
Insomnia/Hypersomnia		x		
Less Interest Usual Activities		x		

PMS – 3 (Physiological)

	0	1	2	3
Dizzy/Fainting		x		
Fatigue			x	
Food Cravings		x		
Headache		x		
Palpitations		x		

PMS – 4 (Water Retention, Swelling)

	0	1	2	3
Abdominal Bloating		x		
Breast Tenderness		x		
Fluid Retention		x		
Swollen Hands/Feet		x		
Weight Gain		x		

PMS – 5 (Other Symptoms)

	0	1	2	3
Acne		x		
Backache		x		
Constipation		x		
Diarrhea		x		
Hives		x		
Oily Skin		x		
Radiation Down Thighs	x			

In addition to these three sessions in which we focused upon neutralizing PMS symptoms, we met for one other session—between our first and third PMS sessions—to treat the trauma of a hit-and-run automobile accident. The accident left her temporarily in a high state of anxiety with fear of another accident while driving.

For her PMS-linked symptoms, we neutralized childhood witnessing of domestic abuse and the crisis of her mother's major illness. In her teen years Julie witnessed police drawing guns to confront her younger brother and friends playing games with water pistols as her mother and neighbors pleaded with the police not to shoot their children. As of this writing Julie has been free of PMS or PMDD issues for eight months.

A PROTOCOL FOR THERAPISTS

Short-Cut Protocol for Healing PMS and PMDD

1. Meet with your patient on a day when she is actively experiencing PMS symptoms.

2. Use the PMS Questionnaire found in this book to rate each item on a 0 to 3 scale.

3. Ask the patient to choose a significantly disturbing PMS symptom for specific work.

4. Ask her to focus on the emotion or body sensation of the symptom chosen.

5. Ask her to stay connected to the emotion or body sensation as she lets her mind float back in time to the earliest disturbing memory of any kind.

6. Ask the patient if she can visualize her younger self (her memory self) in the memory.

7. Instruct the patient to share with the image of her younger self that she is her, older, and that she has come to help.

8. Guide the patient in using wind, water, fire, toilet flush, or some other symbolically powerful action to release the memory self's disturbing emotion or body sensation.

9. Repeat with other memories linked to the first symptom chosen.

10. Repeat the process with the next significantly disturbing symptom.

11. Follow the protocol for three to five consecutive months.

I believe we have enough evidence now to say that we have a cure for PMDD and a cure for at least the cognitive and emotional symptoms of PMS.

The broader model of Parts and Memory Therapy (including the framework for understanding Parts of the self and the role of memories in the development of mental disorders) is probably too radically different from traditional psychotherapy models to be readily accepted by most psychotherapists today—who primarily practice Cognitive Behavior Therapy, Solution-Focused Therapy, or a variety of Psychoanalysis.

A true paradigm shift in the scientific understanding of mental illness—and its foundation in traumatic or other disturbing experiences of growing up—will be necessary for that to happen. But I provide a simplified protocol above that will permit the healing of PMS and PMDD even when the therapist is uncomfortable with the Parts and Memory Therapy model.

For contact with the author or for therapists who would like further information about how to adapt my findings to their models, please see PartsandMemoryTherapy.com.

35269904R00231

Made in the USA
Middletown, DE
04 February 2019